Science for Every Teacher
Volume 1: Physics

Science for Every Teacher
Volume 1: Physics

John D. Mays

NOVARE
SCIENCE & MATH

Austin, Texas
2013

Front cover art created by Andrew Cherry, andrewcherryart.com.

Published by
Novare Science & Math
P. O. Box 92934
Austin, Texas 78709-2934

novarescienceandmath.com

Printed in the United States of America

ISBN   978-0-9883228-1-3 (hardcover)
        978-0-9883228-4-4 (softcover)

Other titles by John D. Mays, published by Novare Science & Math:

- *NSM Physical Science*
  A Mastery-Oriented Curriculum
- *Introductory Physics*
  A Mastery-Oriented Curriculum
- *Accelerated Studies in Physics and Chemistry*
  A Mastery-Oriented Introductory Curriculum
- *Teaching Science so that Students Learn Science*
  A Paradigm for Christian Schools
- *The Student Lab Report Handbook*
  A Guide to Content, Style and Formatting for Effective Science Lab Reports
- *Favorite Experiments for Physics and Physical Science*

These may all be acquired at novarescienceandmath.com.

To Anne Kelly, with whom the idea for this project began.

Acknowledgements

I would like to thank Anne Kelly, Nancy Lockett, and Rob Williams for their generous willingness to read this manuscript and give me their comments. These experienced and very busy teachers had a lot of other things they could have been doing over their holiday break.

Thanks to faithful editor Rebekah Mays, whose ongoing input is invaluable. Thanks, as always, to Dr. Chris Mack, who continues to read and advise me on every book, and who still hasn't given out. Thanks to Jeffrey, brother, companion and fellow laborer.

Finally, thanks to my wife Neda, for her faithfulness, encouragement and constant support.

Contents

Preface

Some time ago I was approached by a fifth-grade teacher with science on her mind. She told me she feels at home with all of the different subjects she teaches to her students except one—science. When it came to lessons about atoms or light or electricity, she didn't feel like her background in science was adequate for teaching these topics. She felt her lack of understanding was limiting the quality of her lessons, and she also knew that students sometimes asked questions during science lessons that she did not feel equipped to answer.

Since that first encounter I have talked to a number of other elementary school teachers, and some engaged parents as well, who have expressed exactly the same concern. It is apparent that there is a need for new science resources for dedicated teachers and parents like these.

A review of the available literature revealed books that are very curriculum specific, with scripted lesson plans and demonstrations. These might be helpful in designing specific lessons in a specific curriculum environment, but do not provide the general background one expects from a primer. They do not, for example, give a fourth-grade teacher any deeper understanding about electricity than is contained in the fourth-grade lesson itself. There are also more general treatments that claim to be written at an introductory level, but our reviews suggest these books cannot be read easily without prior scientific training.

Thus was born the *Science for Every Teacher* project. My goal is admittedly ambitious: to provide clear explanations in a broad spectrum of science topics that can be read by virtually anyone, without any significant prior background in science.

Please note this important aspect of the *Science for Every Teacher* series:

My treatment of the standard topics in science will go well beyond what teachers will actually teach to most elementary students in the classroom.

But this is exactly the point: not to explain only what the students need to learn, but to equip teachers with a deeper understanding of the topics they teach, so they can provide a rich and scientifically accurate learning experience for their students.

The books in the *Science for Every Teacher* series are primers, not texts. There are no sets of exercises or labs to perform (although the Chemistry volume will contain some fascinating chemical reactions to explore). Accessibility is our goal.

Ready to learn some physics? I invite you to settle into your favorite chair, favorite beverage at your side, and turn the page.

Goals for Chapter 1

1. Explain the particular characteristics of scientific knowledge.
2. Describe the "Cycle of Scientific Enterprise," including the relationships between facts, theories, hypotheses, and experiments.
3. Explain what a theory is and describe the two main characteristics of a theory.
4. Explain what is meant by the statement, "a theory is a model."
5. Explain the role and importance of theories in scientific research.
6. Describe the possible implications of a negative experimental result. In other words, if the hypothesis is not confirmed, explain what this might imply about the experiment, the hypothesis or the theory itself.

About This Chapter

One cannot understand science, or make sense of scientific claims, without knowing about the *kind* of claims scientists make. In other words, to have an accurate understanding of what scientists mean when discussing a particular fact or theory, we need to understand the *nature* of scientific knowledge. So this is where we must begin.

Chapter 1
The Nature of Scientific Knowledge

To understand science correctly one needs to understand what we mean by scientific knowledge. Unfortunately, there is much confusion among non-scientists about the nature of scientific knowledge, and this confusion often leads to misunderstandings when we talk about scientific findings and scientific claims. This is nothing new. Misconceptions about scientific claims have plagued public discourse for thousands of years, and continue to do so to this day. This confusion is a severe problem, much written about within the scientific community in recent years.

Clearing up such misunderstandings is obviously an important issue in science education, for teachers and students alike. One of my hopes is that by helping to equip school teachers and parents with correct ways of talking about science, books like this one can help us begin to raise up generations of students who can avoid getting tangled up in the misunderstandings of past centuries, as well as the confusions that haunt us today. For this reason, each of the volumes in the *Science for Every Teacher* series begins with this same chapter.

To clear the air on this issue it is necessary to examine what we mean by the term *truth*, as well as the different ways we discover truth. Then we must discuss the specific characteristics of scientific knowledge, including the key scientific terms *fact*, *theory*, and *hypothesis*.

Whether you teach sixth grade or third grade or first grade, I would like you to stick with me for the next dozen-plus pages. Though it may look like we are about to jump into a college-level philosophical discussion, we aren't. We will keep it simple. But for reasons that should become clear as we go along, we need to begin our scientific study with a short lesson in *epistemology*. So we will begin by defining this term.

What is Truth and How Do We Know It?

Epistemology, one of the major branches of philosophy, is the study of what we can know and how we know it. Both philosophers and theologians claim to have important insights on the issue of knowing truth, and because of the roles science and religion have played in our culture over the centuries, we will need to look at what both philosophers and theologians have to say. The issue we need to treat briefly here is captured in this question: What is truth and how do we know it? In other words, what do we mean when we say something is *true*? And if we can agree on a definition for truth, how can we *know* whether or not something is true?

These are really complex questions, questions philosophers and theologians have been working on for thousands of years. But a few simple principles will be adequate for our purposes.

As for what truth is, my simple but practical definition is this:

Truth may be defined as *the way things really are.*

Whatever reality is like, that is the truth. If there *really* is life on other planets, then it is true to say, "There is life on other planets."

The harder question is that of how we can know the truth. Here the philosophical schools differ (no surprise there). But a mainstream approach that I find helpful claims there are two ways that we can know truth, and these involve either our senses or our use of reason. First, truths that are obvious to us just by looking around are said to be *evident*. It is evident that birds can fly. No proof is needed. So the proposition, "Birds can fly," conveys truth. Similarly, it is evident that humans can read books and that birds cannot. Naturally, when we speak of people knowing truth this way we are referring to people whose perceptive faculties are functioning normally.

The second way of knowing truth is through the valid use of logic. Logical conclusions are typically derived from a sequence of logical statements called a *syllogism*, in which two or more premises lead to a conclusion. For example, if we begin with the premises, "All dogs have four legs," and, "Buster is a dog," then it is a valid conclusion to state, "Buster has four legs." The truth of the conclusion of a logical syllogism clearly depends on the truth of the premises. The truth of the conclusion also depends on the syllogism having a valid structure. Some logical structures are not logically valid. (These invalid structures are called *logical fallacies*.) If the premises are true and the structure is valid, then the conclusion must be true.

So the philosophers provide us with two ways of knowing truth that most people agree upon—truths can be evident (according to our senses) or they can be proved (by valid use of reason from true premises).

> Philosophy gives us two ways of knowing truth, by the direct testimony of our senses and by logical deduction from true premises.

The theologians in some faith traditions argue for an important third possibility for knowing truth, which is by revelation from supernatural agents such as God or angels. As obvious examples, Christians, Jews and Muslims believe that God has spoken to humans through prophets, and continues to speak to humans through the Bible, the Torah or the Koran. However, it is also obvious that not everyone accepts the possibility of knowing truth by revelation. Specifically, those who do not believe in God do not accept the possibility of revelations from God. Additionally, there are some who accept the existence of a transcendent power or being, but do

Theology argues that a third way of knowing truth is by revelation from God.

not accept the possibility of revelations of truth from that power. So this third way of knowing truth is embraced by many people, but certainly not by everyone.

Few people would deny that knowing truth is important. This is why we started our study by briefly exploring what truth is. But this is a book about science, and we need to move now to addressing a different question: What does *science* have to do with truth? The question is not as simple as it seems, as evidenced by the continuous disputes between religious and scientific communities stretching back over the past 700 years. To get at the relationship between science and truth, we will first look at the relationship between propositions and truth claims.

Propositions and Truth Claims

Not all that passes as valid knowledge can be regarded as *true*, which I defined in the previous section as "the way things really are." In many circumstances we do not actually *know* the way things really are. People do, of course, often use propositions or statements with the intention of conveying truth. But with other kinds of statements people intend to convey something else.

We will unpack this with a few example statements. Consider the following several propositions:

1. I have two arms.
2. My wife and I have three children.
3. I worked out at the gym last week.
4. My car is at the repair shop.
5. Texas gained its independence from Mexico in 1836.
6. Atoms are composed of three fundamental particles—protons, neutrons and electrons.
7. God made the world.

Among these seven statements are actually three different types of claims. From the discussion in the previous section you may already be able to spot two of them. But some of these statements do not fit into any of the categories we explored in our discussion of truth. We will discover some important aspects about these claims if we look at them one by one. So suppose for a moment that I, the writer, am the person asserting each of these statements as we examine the nature of the claim in each case.

I have two arms. This is true. I do have two arms, as is evident to everyone who sees me.

My wife and I have three children. This is true. To me it is just as evident as my two arms. I might also point out that it is true whether or not other people believe me when I say it. (Of course, someone could claim that I am delusional, but let's just keep it simple here and assume I am in normal possession of my faculties.) This bit about the statement being true regardless of others' acceptance of it comes up because of a slight difference here between the statement about children and the statement about arms. Anyone who looks at me will accept the truth that I have two arms. It will be evident, that is, obvious, to them. But the truth about my children is only really evident to a few people (my wife and I, and perhaps a few doctors and close family members). Nevertheless, the statement is true.

I worked out at the gym last week. This is also true; I did work out last week. The statement is evident to me, because I clearly remember going there. Of course, people besides myself must depend on me to know it, because they cannot know it directly for themselves unless they saw me there. Note that I cannot prove it is true. I can produce evidence, if needed, but the statement cannot be proved without appealing to premises that may or may not be true. Still, the statement is true.

My car is at the repair shop. Here is a statement that we cannot regard as a truth claim. It is merely a statement about where I understand my car to be at present, based on where I left it this morning and what the people at the shop told me they were going to do with it. For all I know, they may have taken my car joy riding, and it may presently be flying along the back roads of the Texas hill country. I *can* say that the statement is correct as far as I know.

Texas gained its independence from Mexico in 1836. We Texans were all taught this in school, and we believe it to be correct, but as with the previous statement we must stop short of calling this a truth claim. It is certainly a historical fact, based on a lot of historical evidence. The statement is correct as far as we know. But it is possible there is more to that story than we know at present (or will ever know).

Atoms are composed of three fundamental particles—protons, neutrons and electrons. This statement is, of course, a scientific fact. But like the previous two statements, this statement is not—surprise!—a truth claim. We simply do not know the truth about atoms. The truth about atoms is clearly not evident to our senses. We cannot guarantee the truth of any premises we might use to construct a logical proof about the insides of atoms, so proof will not be able to lead us to the truth. And as far as I know there are no supernatural agents who have revealed to us anything about atoms. So we have no access to knowing how atoms really are. What we do have are the data from many experiments, which may or may not tell the whole story. Atoms may have other components we don't know about yet. The best we can say about this statement is that it is correct as far as we know (that is, as far as the scientific community knows).

God made the world. This statement clearly is a truth claim, but people disagree on whether the statement is true or not. Many faith traditions assert that God did make the world, and many people accept this as the truth. Others do not. I include this example here because we will see soon what happens when scientific claims and religious truth claims get confused. Whether you teach in a public school, or a faith-based school, or a non-religious independent school, the issue is important. We all need to learn to speak correctly about the different claims people make.

To summarize this section, some statements we make are evidently or obviously true. But for many statements we must recognize that we don't know if they are actually *true* or not. The best we can say about these kinds of statements—and scientific facts are like this—is that they are correct as far as we know. Finally, there are metaphysical or religious statements about which people disagree; some claim they are true, some deny the same, and some say there is no way to know.

> With some statements we communicate truth. With other statements we communicate knowledge that is *correct as far as we know*. Scientific facts are of the second type.

Truth and Scientific Claims

Let's think a bit further about the truth of reality, both natural and supernatural. I think most people agree that regardless of what different people think about God and nature, there is some actual truth or *reality* about nature and the supernatural. Regarding nature, there is some full reality about the way, say, atoms are structured, whether we currently understand that structure correctly or not. As far as we know, this reality does not shift or change from day to day, at least not since the early history of the universe. So the reality about atoms—the truth about atoms—does not change.

And regarding the supernatural, there is some reality about the supernatural realm, whether anyone knows what that is or not. Whatever these realities are, they are *truths*, and these truths do not change, either.

Now, I have observed over the years that careful scientists do not refer to scientific claims as truth claims. They do not profess to knowing the ultimate truth about how nature *really* is. Instead, scientific claims are understood to be statements about *our best understanding* of the way things are. Most scientists believe that over time our scientific theories get closer and closer to the truth of the way things really are. But when they are speaking carefully scientists do not claim that our present understanding of this or that is the truth about this or that.

> Scientific claims are statements about our best understanding of the way things are. Hopefully, our understanding gets closer to the truth over time.

Truth vs. Facts

Whatever the truth is about the way things are, that truth is presumably absolute and unchanging. If there is a God, then that's the way it is, period. And if matter is made of atoms as we think it is, then that is the truth about matter and it is always the truth. But what we call scientific facts, by their very nature, are not like this. Facts can change, and sometimes do, as new information comes to light through ongoing scientific research. Our definitions for truth and for scientific facts need to take this difference into account. As we have seen, truth is the way things really are. By contrast, here is a definition for *scientific facts*:

> A scientific fact is a proposition that is supported by a great deal of evidence.
>
> Scientific facts are discovered by observation and experiment, and by making inferences from what we observe or from the results of our experiments.
>
> A scientific fact is *correct as far as we know*, but can change as new information becomes known.

So facts can change. Scientists do not put them forward as truth claims, but as propositions that are correct as far as we know. In other words, scientific facts are *provisional*. They are always subject to revision in the future. As scientists make new scientific discoveries, they must sometimes revise facts that were formerly

> Scientific facts are provisional.

considered to be correct. The truth about reality, whatever it is, may be regarded as absolute and unchanging.

The distinction between truth and scientific facts is crucial for a correct understanding of the nature of scientific knowledge. Facts can change; truth does not.

Science

Having established some basic principles about the distinction between scientific facts and truth, we are now finally ready to define science itself and examine what science is and how it works. Here is a definition:

> Science is the process of using experiment, observation and logical thinking to build "mental models" of the natural world. These mental models are called *theories*.

We do not and cannot know the natural world perfectly or completely, so we construct models of how it works, and we explain these to one another with descriptions, diagrams and mathematics. These models are our scientific theories.

Theories never explain the world to us perfectly. To know the world perfectly we would have to know the absolute truth about reality, which we do not know. So theories always have their limits, but we hope they get better and better and more complete over time, accounting for more and more physical phenomena (facts), and helping us to understand the natural world as a coherent whole.

Scientific knowledge is continuously changing and advancing through a cyclic process that I call the *Cycle of Scientific Enterprise*, represented in Figure 1-1. In the next few sections we will examine this cycle in detail.

Theories

Theories are the grandest thing in science. In fact, it is fair to say that theories are the *glory* of science, and developing good theories is what science is all about. Electromagnetic field theory, atomic theory, quantum theory, the general

Figure 1-1. The Cycle of Scientific Enterprise.

Theories are the *glory* of science.

theory of relativity—these are all theories in physics that have had a profound effect on scientific progress and on the way we all live. Now, even though many people do not realize it, *all scientific knowledge is theoretically based.* To explain this statement we need a definition for theories, so here is mine:

A *theory* is a mental model or explanatory system that explains and relates together most or all of the facts (the data) in a certain sphere of knowledge.

A theory is not a hunch or a guess or a wild idea, even though theories are often regarded this way by the lay public. Theories are the mental structures we use to make sense of the data we have. We cannot understand any scientific data without a theory to organize it and explain it. This is why I wrote that all scientific knowledge is theoretically based.

All scientific knowledge is theoretically based.

It is inappropriate and scientifically incorrect to scorn these explanatory systems as "merely a theory" or "just a theory." It is popular in some circles to speak dismissively of certain scientific theories, or even to mock them, as if they represented some kind of untested speculation. It is simply incorrect—and very unhelpful—to speak this way. Theories are explanations that account for and connect together a lot of different facts. If a theory has stood the test of time, this means it is strongly supported by scientific evidence, it has been successful in stimulating further research, and as a result has wide support within the scientific community.

The failure to refer to theories correctly, and to understand the distinction between a theory and a truth claim, has caused a lot of confusion. To some extent, the ongoing faith vs. science debate in America is being fueled by this misunderstanding. So our public discourse could take a big step forward if the nature of scientific theories were more widely understood. For this reason, it is very important for elementary school teachers to have a

Examples of Famous Theories

There are many famous theories in modern science. Here are two examples in the field of physics:

Einstein's general theory of relativity, published in 1915, is one of the most important theories in modern physics. Einstein's theory represents our best current understanding of how gravity works.

Another famous theory we will discuss later is the Kinetic Theory of Gases, our present understanding of how molecules of gas too small to see are able to create pressure inside a container.

solid understanding of what theories are and of the critical role they play in the Cycle of Scientific Enterprise. It is also critical that elementary school teachers find ways of helping their students understand these things, too.

Let's move on now and dig a bit further into how theories work.

Characteristics of Theories

All useful scientific theories must possess several characteristics. The two most important ones are:

- The theory accounts for and explains most or all of the related scientific facts.

- The theory enables new hypotheses to be formed and tested.

Theories take decades or even centuries to form. If a theory gets replaced by a new, better theory, this also usually takes decades or even centuries to happen. No theory is ever "proved" or "disproved" and, once again, scientists do not speak this way when they are being careful. We teachers should not speak of them in this way either. We also do not speak of theories as being "true," because, as we have already seen, we do not use the term "truth" when referring to scientific knowledge. Instead we speak of facts being correct as far as we know, or of current theories as representing our best understanding, or of theories being successful (i.e., useful) models that lead to accurate predictions.

When experimental outcomes turn out the way scientists expect them to, based on their current theoretical understanding, the results are said to *support* the theory. After such an experiment the theory is stronger, but it is not proved. If a hypothesis is not confirmed by an experiment, the theory might be weakened, but it is not disproved. Scientists require a great deal of experimental evidence before a new theory can be established as the best explanation for a body of data. This is why it takes so long for theories to develop. And since no theory ever explains every-thing perfectly, there are always phenomena we know about that our best theories do not adequately explain. Of course, scientists continue their work in a certain field hoping eventually to have a theory that does explain all of the facts. But since no theory explains everything perfectly, it is impossible for one experimental failure to bring down a theory. Just as it takes a lot of evidence to establish a theory, so it would take a large and growing body of conflicting evidence before scientists would abandon an established theory.

> We do not speak of theories as being proved or disproved. Instead, we speak of them as being strengthened or weakened by new experimental results.

I have described theories as "mental models." This statement needs a bit more explanation. A model is a representation of something, and models are designed for a purpose. Consider the popular models of the organs in the human body often seen in science classrooms or textbooks. A model like this is a physical model, and its purpose is to help people understand how the human body is put together. By contrast, a mental model is not physical; it is an intellectual understanding, although we often use illustrations or physical models to help communicate to one another our mental ideas.

As in the example of the model of the human body, a theory is also a model. That is, a theory is a representation of how part of the world works. Frequently our models take the form of mathematical equations that allow us to make numerical predictions and calculate the results of experiments. The more accurately a theory represents the way the world works, which we judge by forming new hypotheses and testing them with experiments, the better and more successful the theory is. A solid track record of successful, accurate predictions is what makes a theory strong and leads to widespread acceptance in the scientific community.

For a scientist to subscribe to a theory means that in the view of that scientist the theory represents our best explanation for known facts in a specific area of research. As we have seen, theories evolve over time, sometimes being replaced as better or more comprehensive explanatory frameworks are conceived of and developed. This means that as with scientific facts, theories too are provisional. They represent the best understanding we have at present, and we expect them to evolve further in the future.

To summarize, a good theory represents the natural world accurately. This means the model will be useful, because if a theory is an accurate representation, then it will lead to accurate predictions about nature. When a theory repeatedly leads to predictions that are confirmed in scientific experiments, it is a good theory.

Finally, when learning about scientific facts and theories as we are here, people often ask how scientific *laws* fit in to this picture. The simplest way to think about this in a scientific context is that the term law is simply an obsolete term for a theory. All of the laws we will encounter later in this book, such as the law of conservation of energy or Newton's Laws of Motion, are simply theories. We continue using the historical names for these theories even though the term law is no longer used in scientific discourse. Isaac Newton's law of universal gravitation and Albert Einstein's theory of general relativity are both about gravity. But the statement, "Einstein's general *theory* of relativity is more accurate than Newton's *law* of universal gravitation" poses no dilemma for the scientist.

> The term *law* is simply an obsolete term for a theory.

These key points about theories are summarized in Figure 1-2.

Hypotheses

After facts and theories, the next stage in the Cycle of Scientific Enterprise is the hypothesis stage. As we saw in the previous section, good theories continue to

Key Points About Theories

- A theory is a way of modeling nature, enabling us to explain why things happen in the natural world from a scientific point of view.

- A theory attempts to account for and explain the known facts that relate to it.

- Theories must enable us to make new predictions about the natural world so we can learn new facts through experimentation.

- Successful theories are the glory and goal of scientific research.

- A theory becomes stronger by producing successful predictions that are confirmed by experiment. A theory will be gradually weakened if new experimental results repeatedly turn out to be inconsistent with the theory.

- It is incorrect to speak dismissively of successful theories, because theories are not just guesses or hunches.

- We do not speak of theories as being proved or disproved. Instead we speak of them in terms of how successful they have been at making predictions and how accurate the predictions have been.

Figure 1-2. *Key points about theories.*

lead to new hypotheses, enabling scientific research to continue moving forward. I prefer the following definition for *hypotheses*[1]:

A hypothesis is a positively stated, informed prediction about what will happen in certain circumstances.

We say a hypothesis is an *informed* prediction because when we form hypotheses we are not just speculating out of the blue. Every scientific hypothesis is based upon a particular theory. We are applying a certain theoretical understanding of the subject to the new situation before us and predicting what will happen or what we expect to find in the new situation based on the theory the hypothesis is coming from. Or put another way, a new hypothesis guides future research by pointing scientists in new experimental directions. As with the example

> Every hypothesis is based on a particular theory.

---

1   These days people tend to say "a hypothesis." Fifty years ago it was considered correct to say "an hypothesis," and some people still consider this to be the most correct form. The plural is hypotheses.

Examples of Famous Hypotheses

Einstein used his general theory of relativity to make an incredible prediction in 1917: that gravity causes light to bend as it travels through space. In a later chapter we will look at the stunning result that occurred when this hypothesis was put to the test.

The year 2012 was an important year for the standard theory of subatomic physics, known as the Standard Model. This theory leads to the prediction that there are weird particles in nature called Higgs Bosons, first predicted by Peter Higgs in 1964. For fifty years scientists anticipated the day when the Higgs Boson might be experimentally observed. An enormous machine that can detect these particles, called the Large Hadron Collider, was built in Switzerland and completed in 2008. Then after several years of collecting enormous quantities of data, scientists announced on July 4, 2012 that the Higgs Boson had been detected at last, a major victory for the Standard Model. Of course, the fact of the Higgs Boson's existence is provisional, and scientists continue to collect data to support it.

hypotheses in the box above, the hypothesis is suggested by the theory itself, and leads scientists immediately to begin thinking about ways the hypothesis might be subjected to experimental verification. If Higgs Bosons do exist as the Standard Model seems to predict, how might we go about detecting them?

Often hypotheses are worded as IF-THEN statements, such as, "If various forces are applied to a pickup truck, then the truck will accelerate at a rate that is in direct proportion to the net force." (As we will see later, this hypothesis is based on the theoretical framework known as Newton's Laws of Motion.) Every scientific hypothesis is based on a theory, and it is the hypothesis that is directly tested by an experiment. If the experiment turns out the way the hypothesis predicts, the hypothesis has been confirmed, and the theory it came from is strengthened. Of course, the hypothesis may not be confirmed by the experiment. We will see how scientists respond to that situation in the next section.

The terms *theory* and *hypothesis* are often used interchangeably in common speech, but in science they mean very different things. Successful theories allow scientists to form new hypotheses that can be tested experimentally.

This raises another important point about hypotheses. A hypothesis that cannot be tested is not a scientific hypothesis. For

In science the terms theory and hypothesis mean very different things.

example, horoscopes purport to predict the future with statements such as, "You will meet someone important to your career in the coming weeks." Statements like this are so vague they are untestable, and do not qualify as scientific hypotheses.

The key points made in this section about hypotheses are summarized in Figure 1-3.

Key Points About Hypotheses

- A hypothesis is an informed prediction about what will happen in certain circumstances.
- Every hypothesis is based on a particular theory.
- Scientific hypotheses must be testable, which is what scientific experiments are designed to do.

Figure 1-3. Key points about hypotheses.

Experiments

The final step in the main circuit of the Cycle of Scientific Enterprise is to conduct experiments, which we can define as follows:

A scientific experiment is a physical arrangement for collecting data which can be used to confirm or disconfirm a particular hypothesis.

Two hundred years ago, scientists often used fairly simple experiments performed in a spare room or workshop to make important scientific advancements. But in our day, effective *experiments* are very complex and difficult to perform. Thus, for any experimental outcome to become regarded as a scientific fact it must be replicated by several different experimental teams, often working in different labs around the world.

Once confirmed, the result of an experiment gives rise to new facts. This is the case regardless of whether the hypothesis is confirmed or not. But if the outcome of an experiment does not confirm the hypothesis we have to consider all of the possibilities for why this happened. Why didn't our theory, which is our best model of the natural world, enable us to form a correct prediction? There are a number of possibilities.

- The experiment may have been flawed. Scientists will double check everything about the experiment, making sure all equipment is working properly, going over the calculations, looking for unanticipated factors that may have inadvertently influenced the outcome, verifying that the measurement instruments are accurate enough and precise enough to do the job, and so on. They will also wait for other experimental teams to try the experiment to see if they get the same results or different results, and then compare. (Although, naturally, every scientific team would like to be the first one to complete an important new experiment.)

- The hypothesis may not have been based on a correct understanding of the theory. Maybe the experimenters did not understand the theory well enough, and maybe the hypothesis is not a correct statement of what the theory says will happen.

- The input values used in the calculation of the hypothesis' predictions may not have been accurate or precise enough, throwing off the hypothesis' predictions. Or maybe the experimental results were not precise or accurate enough to allow for comparison to the predictions.

- Finally, if all else fails, and the hypothesis still cannot be confirmed by experiment, it is time to look again at the theory. Maybe the theory can be altered to account for this new fact. If the theory simply cannot account for the new fact, then the theory has a weakness, namely, that there are facts it doesn't account for adequately. If enough of these weaknesses accumulate, then over a long period of time (typically decades) the theory might eventually need to be replaced with a different theory, that is, another, better theory that does a better job of explaining all the facts we know. Of course, for this to happen someone would have to conceive of a new theory, which usually takes a great deal of scientific insight. A new theory has to account for all of the facts as well as the old theory did, and the new facts as well. This is a tall order!

Ideas for Your Classroom

1. In third grade children should begin learning how to describe facts as "correct as far as we know," and as distinct from knowledge we would call truth. Consider activities using sample statements such as those on pages 3-5. Students could first learn to distinguish statements that are true (or not true) from those that are correct as far as we know. Later students can try forming their own statements of each type.

2. In fourth grade students can begin learning in detail about what theories are and their important characteristics. Use activities in which students develop theories to explain known information, and then use their theories to predict new information. This process is the essence of the game Battleship.

3. One example of an activity that simulates the theory-hypothesis-experiment process is called *What's Your Theory?* In this activity the teacher has a hidden set of colored tiles in a predictable, geometric arrangement. The colors and locations of several tiles are divulged to the students as known data or facts. Students work in teams to construct theories regarding the unknown arrangement of tiles, and then take turns forming hypotheses and testing them out. Each negative experimental result is taken back to the theory and the theory is revised to accommodate all of the new information. For information about this activity visit the free resources page at novarescienceandmath.com.

Goals for Chapter 2

1. State and describe the steps of the "scientific method."

2. Define explanatory, response and lurking variables in the context of an experiment.

3. Explain why an experiment must be designed to test only one explanatory variable at a time.

4. Explain the purpose of the control group in an experiment.

5. Explain the benefits of a double-blind experiment.

About This Chapter

This is a short chapter on the general topic of scientific research methods. It won't take long to read, and may clarify some things we often hear about in the news.

Chapter 2
Scientific Methods

Just as with Chapter 1, this brief second chapter contains general information about the process of scientific inquiry that applies to all of the scientific disciplines. So as before, this chapter is included in all of the volumes in the *Science for Every Teacher* series.

The Scientific Method

Students usually begin studying the so-called *scientific method* somewhere around fourth grade. But it is not really accurate to say that there is a single "scientific method." In fact, there are many different methods scientists use in their research. What we call the "scientific method" is really just a way of conducting reliable experiments. As we saw in Chapter 1, experiments are an important part of the Cycle of Scientific Enterprise. Most science textbooks list the steps in the scientific method similarly to the list in Table 2-1.

> The scientific method is simply a way of conducting reliable experiments.

Steps in the Scientific Method	
1. State the problem.	5. Collect data.
2. Research the problem.	6. Analyze the data.
3. Form a hypothesis.	7. Form a conclusion.
4. Conduct an experiment.	8. Repeat the work.

Table 2-1. Steps in the scientific method.

As you can see, these steps pertain directly to experiments themselves, and link the experiment to the hypothesis being tested. Experiments are only one part of the overall Cycle of Scientific Enterprise, so think of the steps in the scientific method as being the details describing how that part of the overall Cycle is performed.

The steps in the scientific method are fairly self-explanatory, but a few remarks are in order here. First, in some scientific experiments the researchers have a question they are trying to answer. Articulating this question is the first step in the scientific method. Often, this is some kind of question about the way one physical quantity affects another one. So the researchers design an experiment in which one quantity can be manipulated (that is, deliberately varied in a controlled fashion) while the value of another quantity is monitored. More on this below.

Step 3 says to "form a hypothesis." As we saw in two examples in the previous chapter, the hypothesis can sometimes emerge directly from studying the theory, in which case Step 1 of the scientific method never really comes up. The experimental process is initiated by the forming of the hypothesis, rather than by identifying some unanswered question or problem. The research of Step 2 may be thought of as the study of the theory that led to the new hypothesis.

Step 7 says to "form a conclusion." This conclusion is about the hypothesis tested by the experiment. If the experimental results are definitive, then the conclusion will either be "the hypothesis was confirmed" or "the hypothesis was not confirmed." It is also possible that the experimental results will not be definitive, in which case the experiment cannot be regarded as a success and a new experimental approach must be considered.

The last step in the scientific method is always written "repeat the work." What may not be obvious is how this typically happens. This doesn't simply mean for the same scientists to do the experiment over again (although they certainly might do so to confirm their results). Before a scientific result can be published in a scientific journal, the article must be vetted through a peer review process to make sure that the experimental approach was sound, and that the approach and the results are described in enough detail so that other scientific teams around the world can attempt to replicate the experiment and see if similar results are achieved. This is where the most important part of "repeat the work" actually happens. Experimental replication is a crucial part of the process, because if the results cannot be replicated, then as far as the scientific community is concerned they aren't valid.

> Scientific results that cannot be replicated are not considered valid by the scientific community.

Experimental Variables

Nearly all experiments make use of certain factors scientists try to manipulate or measure. These factors are called *variables*. Here is a definition:

> Experimental variables are factors that scientists manipulate, measure or observe in the course of an experiment, or that influence experimental results without the scientists' knowledge.

Taking a simple example of an experiment from everyday life, consider a student who wants to vary the amount of time spent each week studying for her math class in order to see what effect the time she spends studying has on the grades she earns. If the student reduces the time spent, will her grades go down? If the time is increased, will her grades go up? A precise answer depends on a lot of things, of course, including the person involved, but in general we would all agree that if a student varies the study time enough we would expect to see the grades vary as well. And in particular, we would expect more study time to result in higher grades. This is the hypothesis.

Now let us consider this same concept in the context of scientific experiments. An experiment typically involves some kind of complex system that the scientists are modeling. The system could be virtually anything in the natural world—a galaxy, an atom, chemical compound, a tomato or a badger. The variables in the scientists' mathematical models of the system correspond to the physical quantities that can be manipulated or measured in the system.

Figure 2-1 depicts three kinds of variables involved in a typical experiment. When performing an experiment the variable that is deliberately manipulated by the researchers is called the *explanatory variable*. As the explanatory variable is manipulated, the researchers monitor the effect this variation has on the *response variable*. In the example of study time versus math grade, the study time is the explanatory variable and the grade earned is the response variable.

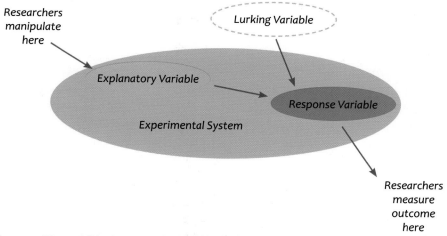

Figure 2-1. The variables in an experimental system.

Usually, a good experimental design will allow only one explanatory variable to be manipulated at a time so that the researchers can tell definitively what its effect is on the response variable. If more than one explanatory variable were changing during the course of the experiment, researchers may not be able to tell which one was causing the effect on the response variable.

A third type of variable that plays a role in experiments is *lurking variables*. A lurking variable is some factor that is affecting the response variable without the researchers' awareness. This is bad, of course, because the researchers will not be able to make a correct conclusion about the effect of the known explanatory variables on the response variable under study. So researchers have to study their experimental projects very carefully to minimize the possibility of lurking variables affecting their results.

In our example about study time and math grades, there could be a number of lurking variables affecting the results of the experiment. Possible lurking variables include changes in the difficulty of the material from one chapter to the next, or variations in the student's ability to concentrate due to fatigue from seasonal sports activities.

Experimental Controls

The development of new medical treatments is one of the most publicized goals of experimental research in the twenty-first century. Many experiments in the field of medical research are designed to test some new kind of treatment by comparing the results of the new treatment to those obtained using a conventional treatment or no treatment at all. This is the situation in medical research all the time for experiments testing new therapies, medications, or procedures. In an experiment like this the subjects under study will be randomly divided into two groups, the *control group* and the *experimental group*. These may be defined as follows:

> In an experiment to test a new treatment, the *control group* receives no treatment or some kind of standard treatment. The *experimental group* receives the new treatment being tested. The results of the experimental group are assessed by comparing them to those of the control group.

Another example will help to clarify all of these terms, and connect them to the Cycle of Scientific Enterprise presented in Chapter 1. A depiction of the terms and relationships in this example is shown in Figure 2-2.

Let's say researchers have identified a gene that relates to a plant's ability to resist drought. According to the researchers' *theoretical understanding* of how genes work in the biological systems of the plant, they *hypothesize* that if they modify the gene in a certain way the plant will be able to bear higher quality fruit during drought conditions. To test this hypothesis by *experiment*, the scientists develop a group of the plants with the modified gene. Then they place the plants in a test plot, along with other plants that do not have the modified gene, and see how they perform. The plants with the modification are the *experimental group*, and the plants without the modified gene are the *control group*.

The *response variable* is the quality of the plant's fruit, as represented by measurements of variables such as sugar content, texture and flavor. Researchers expect that under drought conditions the fruit of the modified plants will be higher in quality than the fruit of the plants that have not been modified. The *explanatory variable* is the presence or absence of the modified gene. The plants are exposed to drought conditions in the experiment. If the modified plants produce higher quality fruit than the control group, then the hypothesis is confirmed, and the theory that led to the hypothesis has gained credibility through this success.

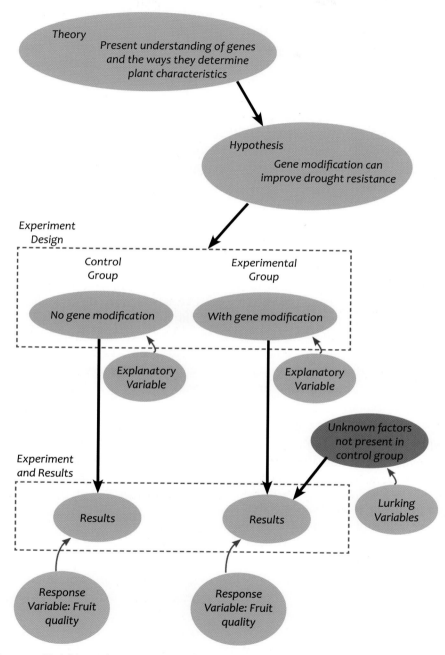

Figure 2-2. Variables and controls in experimental design.

One can imagine many different *lurking variables* that could affect the outcome of this experiment without the scientists' awareness. For example, the modified plants could be planted in locations that receive different amounts of moisture or sun than the locations where the control group plants are. In a good experimental design researchers seek to identify such factors and take measures to assure that they do not affect the outcome of the experiment.

Another very important type of experimental control is the use of blind or double-blind experiments, especially in research involving human subjects. These are easiest to understand in the context of another example, so consider a research project to test a new medication. The researchers are hopeful that the new medication will outperform the current standard medication in several ways. Participants in the study are randomly assigned to either the control group or the experimental group. As before, the control group will be the people who receive the standard medication or no medication. The experimental group will be the people receiving the new medication.

A *blind experiment* is one in which the human research subjects do not know which group they are in. If researchers wish to test the medication against a control group receiving no medication at all, the subjects in the control group are given *placebos*, which are sugar pills or some other treatment that will have no direct effect. If placebos are used, then none of the research subjects will know whether they have been given a placebo or the real medication.

Blind experiments and placebos are used because of the powerful effect the human mind can have over the response of the body. If a person thinks he is getting the real medication, he may show a positive physical response just because he feels optimistic about receiving the new medication. The blind experiment assures that the research subjects cannot influence the outcome of the research just because they know which group they were in.

But research subjects aren't the only ones who can influence experimental results—the researchers can, too! Researchers can influence the results in all kinds of very subtle ways, such as the body language they present and the tone of voice they use when interviewing patients. If the researchers know that a certain person has received the new medication, they may be subconsciously inclined to act more positively toward that person, and the research subject can subconsciously pick up on these subtle positive cues. The only way to avoid lurking variables such as these is to set up the experiment so neither the researchers nor the subjects know which groups the subjects are in. This is the double-blind experiment.

> In a blind experiment research subjects do not know whether or not they received the experimental treatment.
>
> In a double-blind experiment the researchers don't know either.

A double-blind experiment requires some intermediaries—nurses, technicians or other doctors—who will administer the medication and keep track of which subjects received the medication, and which received the placebo. The researchers will conduct their tests and perform their interviews without knowing which group any particular research subject is in. After the experimental results have been tabulated, the test results are matched up with the medication records. In this way the subject's response to the medication will be affected neither by their own knowledge nor by the researchers' knowledge. Randomized, double-blind experiments are the gold standard in medical research.

Ideas for Your Classroom

1. Students usually begin learning about the scientific method by memorizing the steps in fourth grade. This is appropriate. The topic should be revisited every year or two so students remember the steps and engage with them in more sophisticated ways.

2. Grades 2-6 are perfect occasions to perform simple experiments using plant subjects in control groups and experimental groups.[1] In an activity such as growing bean vines, place two or three plants in a group receiving only water and sunlight. Place two or three others in an experimental group where the plants receive regular small amounts of organic fertilizer. Simple experiments may be performed in the classroom by a window. If an outdoor garden plot is available students will enjoy time with the experiment even more.

3. In other experiments take the opportunity to vary one feature of the set-up among the student groups, using the opportunity to revisit the idea of manipulating one explanatory variable at a time. For example, it is common for elementary students to grow sugar crystals on a string from a hot saturated solution of sugar and water. Try initiating the crystal growth simultaneously in several separate glasses. Vary the sugar content in each glass while keeping all other factors (water volume, starting temperature, etc.) equal. Sugar content can be varied from low enough so no crystals grow, up to a high enough level so that additional sugar seems to have no effect. In activities like this where one of the set-ups is expected to fail, do the activity as a class instead of in groups so that some students do not feel singled out for disappointment.

Note: Every failed experiment is an opportunity to "repeat the work." Never fear experiments that go wrong. They are always learning opportunities for everyone!

---

1   For obvious reasons, avoid experimenting with animal subjects. Enjoy the animals in your classroom without putting them at risk.

Goals for Chapter 3

1. Define and distinguish between velocity and acceleration.

2. Explain the difference between accuracy and precision.

3. Describe the key features of the Ptolemaic model of the heavens, including all of the spheres and regions in the model.

4. State several additional features of the medieval model of the heavens and relate them to the theological views of the medieval Church.

5. Briefly describe the roles and major scientific models or discoveries of Copernicus, Tycho, Kepler, and Galileo in the Copernican Revolution. Also, describe the significant later contributions of Isaac Newton and Albert Einstein to our theories of motion and gravity.

6. Describe the theoretical shift that occurred in the Copernican Revolution.

7. Describe Kepler's Laws of Planetary Motion.

8. Describe how the gravitational theories of Kepler, Newton and Einstein illustrate the way the Cycle of Scientific Enterprise works.

About This Chapter

In addition to the physics of motion, in this chapter we are also going to review some of the history of views about the motion of the planets. There are two main reasons for integrating this material here. First, the study of motion has historically gone hand-in-hand with scientists' attempts to model the motion of the planets. So the study of motion is the perfect occasion for looking at the fascinating saga of the Copernican Revolution.

The second reason relates to one of the major topics in Chapter 1, the Cycle of Scientific Enterprise. The best way to gain a firm understanding of how this cycle continuously operates in scientific work is to see how the cycle plays out in particular historical episodes.

Chapter 3
Motion on Earth and In the Heavens

About the Mathematics

If you are apprehensive about this book because of concerns about the math, *set your mind at ease*. Yes, physics is a highly mathematical subject. As one of my favorite movies puts it, "You can't do physics without mathematics, really, can you?"

But we can, in fact, do a lot of physics without letting the math get in our way, and this will be our plan. This book is primarily a resource for teachers, and I assume that some of the teachers reading this book would like to stick to the conceptual descriptions; others may wish to see some sample calculations.

In the main body of the text I limit the mathematics to merely presenting the basic equations, variables and units of measure one might encounter in a high school freshman-level introductory physics course, without actually working through any computations. For those interested, I include a few relatively simple example problems in separate boxes. With two or three exceptions, following the solutions to these problems requires only basic skills in introductory algebra.

Also, for those interested, I have included several appendices treating mathematical topics such as unit conversions, significant digits, scientific notation, and measurement.

$$A+B$$

$$\ell^2 + \left(\sqrt{r_0^2 - \tfrac{1}{4}} \; \overline{=} \tfrac{1}{2} \right)$$

$$\tfrac{1}{2} \cdot 2 \sqrt{r_0^2 - \tfrac{1}{4}} + \tfrac{y}{4} = (A+B)$$

$$= (A+B)^2$$

$$r_0^2 - \tfrac{1}{4}$$

$$) \; r_0^2 - \tfrac{1}{2} r_0^2 + \tfrac{1}{16} + \tfrac{1}{4}(A+B)^2$$

$$) \, r_0^2 + \left(\tfrac{1}{2}(A+B)^2 + (A+B) \right.$$

$$c$$

$$\frac{s^2 - 4 \cdot 4 \cdot c}{3} = \frac{2+}{}$$

$$B)^2 + \tfrac{1}{8} \sqrt{ \left(2 + 4(A+B)^2 \right) }$$

$$+B)^2 + \tfrac{1}{8} \sqrt{ 8(A+B)^2 - 1 }$$

$$\frac{25 + 10\sqrt{5} + 5}{+ 8\sqrt{5} + 20)(5 - 2\sqrt{5})} = \frac{!}{2}$$

$$\overline{5 - 80 + 100 - 40\sqrt{5}} =$$

In the next couple of sections we will touch lightly on some issues involved with measurements such as units of measure, accuracy and precision. For a fuller treatment of these and other matters see the Appendices.

Unit Systems and MKS Units

Units of measure are crucial in science. Science is about making measurements, and a measurement without units of measure is a meaningless number. The two major systems for units of measure are the SI (from the French *Système international d'unités*), typically known in the United States as the metric system, and the USCS (U.S. Customary System) with which all Americans are familiar.

The USCS is very cumbersome, and not especially useful for scientific work. One problem is that there are many different units of measure for every kind of physical quantity. Just for measuring distance, for example, we have the inch, foot, yard, and mile. The USCS is also full of random numbers like 3, 12 and 5,280, and there is no inherent connection between units for different types of quantities.

By contrast, the SI system is simple and has many advantages. There is one basic unit of measure for each kind of quantity, such as the meter for measuring length. Instead of having a bunch of different unrelated units of measure for measuring quantities of different sizes, prefixes based on powers of ten are used on all of the units to accommodate different sizes of measurements. And units for different types of quantities relate to one another in some way. Unlike the gallon and the foot, which have nothing to do with each other, the liter[1] is 1,000 cubic centimeters. For all of these reasons the USCS is not used much in scientific work. The SI system is the international standard and students should be exposed to it early and often.

A subset of the SI system is the *MKS system*. The MKS system uses the *meter*, the *kilogram*, and the *second* (hence, "MKS") as primary units. There are also four other primary units, some of which we will encounter later on. There are also many derived units that are combinations of these three primary units. Examples of derived units that we will encounter in this book are the newton (N) for measuring force, the joule (J) for measuring energy, and the watt (W) for measuring power.

Dealing with different systems of units can become very confusing. But the wonderful thing about sticking to the MKS system is that any calculation performed with MKS units will give a result in MKS units. This is why the MKS system is so handy and why calculations in physics make use of it almost exclusively.

> In the MKS System of units (meter-kilogram-second), any computation undertaken with values expressed in MKS units will produce a result in MKS units.

---

1   Technically, the liter is not an official SI unit of measure. It is, however, commonly used as a metric unit in scientific work.

For more information about the SI system, refer to Appendix D.

Accuracy and Precision

Science is all about investigating nature and to do that we must make measurements. In the study of science the terms *accuracy* and *precision* are technical terms that refer to the limitations inherent in making measurements. These terms are often used interchangeably in common speech, but in the context of measurement they have specific, distinct meanings. Accuracy may be defined as follows:

> Accuracy refers to freedom from error in a measurement. The lower the error, the more accurate the measurement.

The error in a measurement is the difference between the value of a quantity obtained from a measurement and the actual, true value of the quantity. The lower the error in a measurement, the better the accuracy. There are many potential sources of error in measurements, including human mistakes, malfunctioning equipment, incorrectly calibrated instruments, or lurking variables. All measurements contain error, because (alas!) perfection is simply not a thing we have access to in this world.

Precision may be defined as follows:

> Precision refers to the resolution in a measurement, indicated by the number of significant digits in the value of the measurement.

The term *precision* refers to the resolution or degree of "fine-ness" in a measurement. The limit to the precision that can be obtained in a measurement is ultimately dependent on the instrument being used to make the measurement. If one wants greater precision, one must use a more precise instrument. The precision of a measurement is indicated by the number of *significant digits* included in the value when the measurement is written down.

An example will illustrate the difference between accuracy and precision. Let's say Shana and Marius each buy digital thermometers for their homes. The thermometer Shana buys cost $10, and measures to the nearest 1°F. Marius pays $40 and gets one that reads to the nearest 0.1°F. Shana reads the directions and properly installs the sensor for her new thermometer in the shade. Marius doesn't read the directions and mounts his sensor in the direct sunlight, which causes a significant error in the measurement for much of the day. The result will be that Shana has lower-precision, but higher-accuracy measurements!

For a more complete description of how significant digits work, see Appendix B.

Motion, Velocity and Acceleration

In this book we will examine two types of *motion*: motion at a constant *velocity*, when an object is not accelerating, and motion with a *uniform acceleration*. Defining these terms is a lot simpler if we stick to motion in one dimension, that is, motion in a straight line. So in this book this is what we will do. With this simplification we can define velocity as follows:

> To keep our discussion both simple and accurate, we will consider only motion in a straight line.

> The velocity of an object is the rate at which the distance to where it started is changing.

Thus, a girl walking at a velocity of three miles per hour is increasing the distance between herself and where she started at a rate of three miles every hour.

Note that an object's velocity is a measure of how fast the object is going, *not* whether its velocity is changing or not. When the velocity of an object is not constant the object is *accelerating*. This gives us the following definition for acceleration:

> The acceleration of an object is the rate at which the object's velocity is increasing or decreasing.

If an object's velocity is increasing or decreasing at a constant rate, as in the case of a falling object, we say the acceleration is *uniform*. In this book we will consider only situations involving constant velocity or uniform acceleration. (Calculus is required to solve problems in which the acceleration is not uniform. We will leave that for some other book.) One way to rephrase our definition for acceleration would be to say that if an object is not accelerating it must be either at rest or moving with a constant velocity.

> If an object is not accelerating it must be either at rest or moving with a constant velocity.

As an aside, the terms "at rest" and "moving with a constant velocity" refer to two different "states of motion." This state-of-motion language is important for a very good reason: Isaac Newton. Newton's Laws of Motion are universally studied by all students of physics. And Newton's First Law of Motion, which we will get into in the next chapter, makes use of this language.

There are two important equations used for solving problems involving motion with a constant velocity or motion with uniform acceleration. One equation is for motion at a constant velocity, and the other is for motion with uniform acceleration. For motion with a *constant velocity*, the equation is

$$d = vt$$

where d is the distance an object travels in meters (m), v is the object's velocity in meters per second (m/s) and t is time interval in seconds (s).

Note here that using the MKS units of meters and seconds for the distance and the time, the MKS units for velocity will be meters per second (m/s). We can see this by taking the equation above and dividing both sides by t, giving

$$\frac{d}{t} = \frac{vt}{t} = v$$

$$v = \frac{d}{t}$$

Since velocity is calculated as distance divided by time, the units for velocity will be the distance units divided by the time units, or meters per second (m/s).

For the case of uniform acceleration we calculate the acceleration over a specific interval of time. We call the velocity at the beginning of the time interval the initial velocity, symbolized v_i. The velocity at the end of the time interval is the final velocity, v_f. The time interval is simply denoted t, as in the equation above for constant velocity motion.

The equation we use to calculate uniform acceleration in terms of the initial final velocities is

$$a = \frac{v_f - v_i}{t}$$

where a is the acceleration in units of meters per second squared (m/s²).

Example Problem

Sound travels approximately 342 m/s in air. At this velocity, how far will the sound from the starter pistol at a race travel in 0.0500 s?

The given quantities are

$$v = 342 \ \frac{m}{s}$$

$$t = 0.0500 \ s$$

Inserting these into the distance equation and solving we have

$$d = vt = 342 \ \frac{m}{s} \cdot 0.0500 \ s = 17.1 \ m$$

The MKS unit for acceleration, meters per second squared (m/s^2), often drive people crazy until they get their brains wrapped around it, so we will pause here and discuss it. (Then you can sleep peacefully tonight.) We noted just above that the acceleration is the rate at which the velocity is changing. The acceleration simply means that the velocity is increasing or decreasing by so many meters per second, every second. Now, the terms "per" and "every" in the preceding sentence indicate fractions, and if a velocity is changing so many meters per second, every second, we would write these units in a fraction this way and simplify the expression using the "invert and multiply" rule for dividing fractions:

$$\frac{\frac{m}{s}}{s} = \frac{\frac{m}{s}}{\frac{s}{1}} = \frac{m}{s} \cdot \frac{1}{s} = \frac{m}{s^2}$$

So the m/s^2 units for acceleration are really no mystery. If we subtract two velocities we get a velocity. And if we divide that velocity by time, we get m/s^2.

We must be very careful to distinguish between velocity (m/s) and acceleration (m/s^2). Acceleration is a measure of how fast an object's velocity is changing, not

Example Problem

A truck is moving with a velocity of 18.8 m/s when the driver hits the brakes and brings the truck to a stop. The total time required to stop the truck is 8.75 s. Determine the acceleration of the truck, assuming the acceleration is uniform.

We note that since the truck stopped, the final velocity is zero. Writing down all the given quantities,

$$v_i = 18.8 \ \frac{m}{s}$$

$$v_f = 0$$

$$t = 8.75 \ s$$

Now we place these quantities into the equation for acceleration and solve the problem.

$$a = \frac{v_f - v_i}{t} = \frac{0 - 18.8 \ \frac{m}{s}}{8.75 \ s} = -2.15 \ \frac{m}{s^2}$$

The negative sign in this result simply means that the trucking is slowing down.

how fast it is going. To help emphasize the difference, note that an object can be at rest ($v = 0$) and accelerating at the same instant!

Now, although this may not be at all clear at first, it is very important to think this through and understand how this counter-intuitive situation can come about. Here are two illustrations. Every time an object starts from rest, such as the instant when the driver hits the gas while sitting at a traffic light, the object will be simultaneously at rest and accelerating. This is because if an object at rest is to ever begin moving its velocity must *change* from zero to something else. In other words, the object must accelerate. Of course, this situation only holds for an instant; the velocity instantly begins changing and does not stay zero.

Perhaps this point will be easier to see with this second illustration. As depicted in Figure 3-1, when a ball is thrown straight up and reaches its highest point it must stop for an instant before coming back down. At its highest point the ball is simultaneously at rest and accelerating. As before, this situation only holds for a single instant.

The point of these two illustrations is to emphasize the difference between the two variables we are discussing, velocity and acceleration. If an object is moving at all, then it has a velocity that is not zero. The object may or may not be accelerating. But acceleration is about whether the velocity itself is changing or not. If the velocity is constant, then the acceleration is zero. If the object is speeding up or slowing down, then the acceleration is not zero.

Historically, the study of motion was closely related to the study of the motions of the planets. So for the rest of this chapter we will survey the scientific thinking of the past 2,500 years on this subject. It is quite a story!

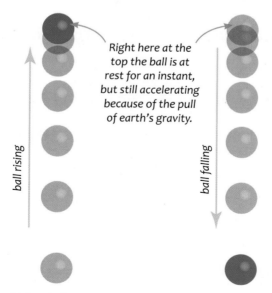

Right here at the top the ball is at rest for an instant, but still accelerating because of the pull of earth's gravity.

ball rising

ball falling

Figure 3-1. A rising and falling ball.

Crisis: What Happens When Theories are Mistaken for Truth

The view people had of the planets and stars in the medieval period began back with the Greek philosophers Plato and Aristotle in the fifth and fourth centuries BC. The famous Alexandrian astronomer Ptolemy (Figure 3-2) worked out a detailed mathematical system for this model in the second century AD. Over the next thousand years this model of the heavens was adopted by everyone in the West, including the Christian Church. Unfortunately, the Church adopted this model as the *truth*, and not as a model that could change when new information came to light. This error led to an increasing crisis as more and more discoveries seemed to conflict with Ptolemy's model.

This led to the Copernican Revolution, and over the course of 150 years the Ptolemaic model completely collapsed. The reason we study the Ptolemaic model now is that the history of how it developed and how it crashed is a world-class example of how science works through theories to model nature.

Figure 3-2. Ptolemy of Alexandria.

Seeing the Heavens from an Ancient Point of View

We will consider some of the mechanical details of Ptolemy's model soon, but before we do we need to consider a few things about the way the motion of the planets in the night sky appears to observers on earth. Now, to you and I, who all grew up in a time when it is quite clear that the planets and the earth orbit the sun, it seems obvious to us that day and night are caused by the earth's rotation on its axis. We have heard about this all of our lives.

But stop and consider how things would appear if all we had to go on was our simple observations. It does *appear* that everything is orbiting around the earth while the earth sits still, doesn't it? Don't the sun and moon rise each day and track across the sky and set? Don't the planets and stars all do the same thing? Also, it doesn't feel at all like earth is moving or rotating. We all know that anytime we spin in a circle, like people on a merry-go-round, we have to hold on to keep from falling off. We can also feel the wind in our hair. Again, if we had something with us on the merry-go-round that was tall and flexible, like a sapling, it would not stay vertical when it is moving in a circular fashion like this. Instead, it would bend over because of the acceleration pulling it in its circular motion.

These principles seemed *obvious* to *everyone* before 1500, and to everyone except a few cutting-edge astronomers right up to 1642 when Galileo died. Only a crazy person would imagine that the earth was spinning. They all knew that the earth was huge—Eratosthenes had made a very accurate estimate of the earth's circumference as far back as 240 BC. So if something that big were spinning in

> Only a crazy person would imagine that the earth was spinning.

a circle once a day the people on its surface would be moving very fast (1,000 miles per hour on the equator, actually!) and we would have to be hanging on for dear life! The trees would be laying down, and we would be constantly feeling winds that would make a hurricane feel like a calm summer day! People used these arguments all the way up until the time of Galileo to prove that there was no way the earth was orbiting the sun and spinning around on an axis once a day. And back then these were very persuasive arguments.

Retrograde Motion

To understand the reason for some of the features of Ptolemy's model we need to take a quick look at the phenomenon known as *retrograde motion*. If a person goes out and looks at, say, Mars each night and makes a note of its location against the stars, she will see that Mars appears in a slightly different place each night. The planet will gradually work its way along a pathway against the starry background night after night. If our observer tracks the planet for several months or a year it will move quite far. Moreover, there will be periods of time lasting several weeks when the nightly progress of the planet reverses course. Mars appears to be backing up! This apparent backing up is called retrograde motion.

Nowadays we easily explain the movement of the planets in the sky, as well as retrograde motion, by looking at the geometry of where earth is and where the planets are as we all orbit around the sun. No planet actually reverses course in its orbit, but depending on where earth is and where a planet is (on the same side of the sun, on opposite sides of the sun, and so on) a given planet will appear to be moving one direction or another relative to the stars.

But in the Ptolemaic model the earth is stationary. All of the planets, and the sun as well, orbit around the earth, not the sun. Additionally, the heavenly bodies move together, all rotating around the earth once each day. This makes the smaller motion of the planets, and their retrograde motions, harder to explain. Ptolemy explained it by assuming the planets all moved in *epicycles*. An epicycle is a circular path around a center point, and the center point itself travels on a circular path around the earth. Figure 3-3 depicts a planet moving in a path defined by an epicycle. The motion of a planet moving on an epicycle would be like that of a person in the "tea cup" ride at an amusement park.

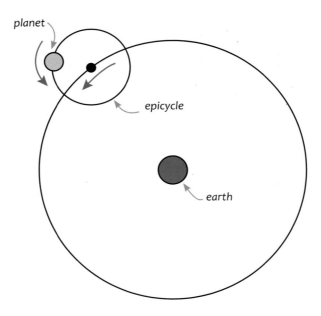

Figure 3-3. A planet moving in a path defined by an epicycle around the earth.

The Medieval Model of the Heavens

The prevailing model of the heavens continued to be the Ptolemaic model for a very long time, right up into the mid-seventeenth century. The basic features of the Ptolemaic model included these:

- There are seven heavenly bodies: the moon, Mercury, Venus, the sun, Mars, Jupiter and Saturn.

- All heavenly bodies are perfectly spherical.

- All heavenly bodies move in circular orbital regions, called spheres.

- All of the spheres are centered on the earth, making this system a *geocentric* system.

- Corruption and change only exist on earth. All other places in the universe, including all the heavenly bodies and stars, are perfect and unchanging.

- All of the spheres containing the heavenly bodies and all the stars rotate completely around the earth every 24 hours.

- Scores of epicycles are used to explain retrograde motion.

- The heavenly bodies inhabit spheres around the earth where their orbits are. In the model there are nine spheres plus the region beyond the spheres. The first seven spheres contain the heavenly bodies. The arrangement of the spheres is as follows:

Sphere 1	Moon
Sphere 2	Mercury
Sphere 3	Venus
Sphere 4	Sun
Sphere 5	Mars
Sphere 6	Jupiter
Sphere 7	Saturn
Sphere 8	*The Firmament.* This region consists of the stars arranged in their constellations according to the zodiac.
Sphere 9	*The Primum Mobile.* This Latin name means "first mover." This sphere rotates around the earth every 24 hours and drags all the other spheres with it, making them all move.
Beyond	*The Empyrean.* This is the region beyond the spheres. The Empyrean is the abode of God, or the gods.

Among the different astronomers of the ancient world there were those who held to variations on this basic model. For example, some astronomers reckoned that Mercury and Venus orbited the sun while the other heavenly bodies orbited the earth. But the basic Ptolemaic model was as described here. Figure 3-4 on the next page depicts this arrangement graphically.

From Ptolemy to Einstein via Copernicus

As we have seen, the model outlined above was first suggested by Plato and Aristotle in the fifth and fourth centuries BC, but was worked out into full mathematical detail by the Alexandrian astronomer Ptolemy in the second century AD. By the time of the medieval period 1,000 years later, the theology of the Christian Church had become closely intertwined with the geocentric Ptolemaic model.

> By the time of the medieval period the theology of the Christian Church had become closely intertwined with the Ptolemaic model.

The Ptolemaic model made sense to everyone at the time. To the authorities in the Church, the Ptolemaic model seemed to line up with the Bible in many ways. Because of the seemingly close linkages between the Bible and the Ptolemaic model, the Church in the medieval period made the category error of believing the model to be the truth. In Chapter 1 we saw that this confusion of scientific theory and truth is a mistake. The confusion in the medieval period was a very bad mistake, with horribly tragic consequences.

Scientific theories are not truth, they are models we use to understand the natural world. But Church doctrine in this period was closely linked with the

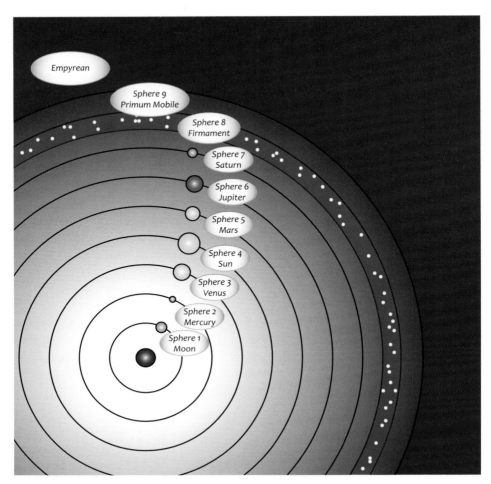

Figure 3-4. The Ptolemaic model of the heavens.

geocentric view of the heavens, so to the Church authorities, rejecting this view was tantamount to rejecting the teachings of the Church and the Bible itself. Such rejection was regarded as heresy, and was punishable by excommunication, banishment or death. The woeful episode that followed was not finally over until the year 2000, when Pope John Paul II issued a formal apology for the trial of Galileo.

The aftermath of the Copernican Revolution was not finally over until the year 2000, when Pope John Paul II issued a formal apology for the trial of Galileo.

Nicolaus Copernicus (1473-1543), a Polish astronomer, first proposed a detailed *heliocentric* model, with the earth rotating on its axis, all the planets moving in circular orbits around the sun, and the moon orbiting the earth (Figure 3-5). Copernicus' system was about as accurate, and about as complex, as the Ptolemaic system. Copernicus' model still used circular orbits, and because of this he still had to use epicycles to make the model work. Still, the model was an arrangement that was a lot closer to today's understanding than the Ptolemaic model was. Copernicus knew how committed the Church was to the Ptolemaic system

> Copernicus' new heliocentric model still used circular orbits, necessitating the use of epicycles to correct the resulting errors in astronomical predictions.

and being a sensitive and godly man, he didn't want to offend the Church with his ideas. So he published his work privately to his close friends in 1514. His work only became public at his death in 1543 when one of Copernicus' admirers got it published.

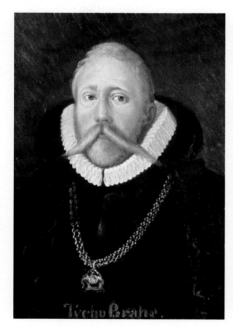

Figure 3-5. Polish astronomer Nicolaus Copernicus.

Tycho Brahe (1546-1601), whom I will call Tycho, was a Danish nobleman and astronomer (Figure 3-6). (I know it is appropriate to refer to scientists by their last names, but most references in the literature refer to Tycho; historians rarely call him Brahe. I love the name Tycho, so I will call him that, too.) Tycho built a magnificent observatory called the Uraniborg on an island Denmark ruled at the time (Figure 3-7).

Tycho was a passionate and hotheaded guy, as evidenced by the fact he had the bridge of his nose cut off in a duel. (If you look closely at Figure 3-6 you can see his prosthesis.) Even though Tycho had what must have been the most palatial observatory in the world, he had a falling out with the new King of Denmark and decided to leave. In 1597 Tycho moved to Prague in Bohemia (the modern day Czech Republic) and became Imperial Mathematician for Rudolph II, who was King of Bohemia and Holy Roman Emperor there. Tycho spent his life cataloging astronomical data for over 1,000 stars (doing this without a

Figure 3-6. Danish astronomer and mathematician Tycho Brahe.

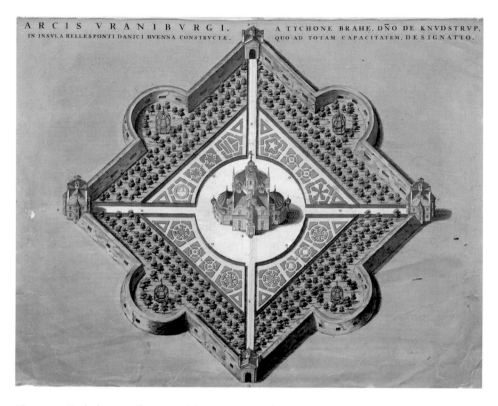

Figure 3-7. Tycho's magnificent Danish observatory, the Uraniborg.

telescope), and he published a catalog identifying the positions of 777 stars with unprecedented accuracy.

Tycho witnessed two astronomical events that are particularly important for the history of the Ptolemaic model. First, in 1563 he observed a conjunction between Jupiter and Saturn. A conjunction is when two planets are in a straight line with the earth, so that from earth they appear to be in the same place in the sky. Tycho predicted the date for this conjunction using Copernicus' new heliocentric model. The prediction was close (this is good) but was still off by a few days (not so good) indicating that there was still something lacking in Copernicus' new model. (There was. The orbits are not circular as Copernicus had assumed.) Second, in 1572 Tycho observed what he called a "nova" (which is Latin for *new*; today we would call it a supernova) and demonstrated that it was a new star. This discovery rocked the Renaissance world because it was very strong evidence that the stars were not perfect and unchanging

> Tycho witnessed a supernova—the birth of a new star—that the "perfect and unchanging" heavens of the Ptolemaic model could not explain.

Figure 3-8. German astronomer and mathematician Johannes Kepler.

as Aristotle had thought and as medieval cosmology and Church doctrine declared.

Johannes Kepler (1571-1630, Figure 3-8), a German astronomer, was invited in 1600 to join the research staff at Tycho's observatory in Prague, and became the Imperial Mathematician there the very next year after Tycho's death. He had access to Tycho's massive body of research data and Kepler used it to develop his famous three Laws of Planetary Motion, the first two of which were published in 1609. He discovered the third law a few years later and published it in 1619.

Kepler was a godly man, and took his faith very seriously, even though he was caught in the middle during a time of serious disagreement between the Roman Catholics and the Protestants. In addition to his astronomical discoveries, he made important discoveries in geometry and optics. He figured out some of the major principles of gravity later synthesized by Isaac Newton, and he was the first to hypothesize that the sun exerted a force on the earth.

Kepler's Laws of Planetary Motion are very beautiful in their simplicity and explanatory power, so it is worth reviewing them. Kepler's First Law of Planetary Motion is stated as follows:

First Law	Each of the planetary orbits is an ellipse, with the sun at one focus.

An ellipse is a geometric figure similar to a circle, except instead of having a single point locating the center, an ellipse has two points called *foci* (plural, and pronounced FOH-sigh; the singular is *focus*) that define the shape of the ellipse. Out in space the planets travel on paths defined by geometrical ellipses. The planetary orbits all have one focus located at the same place in space, and this is where the sun is. A planet in an elliptical orbit is depicted in Figure 3-9.

It seems incredible that Kepler figured this out. He was a monster mathematician (no calculator of course) and an extremely careful scientist, and the fact that scientists had understood the orbits to be circular for two thousand years did not prevent him from imagining a different possibility. This accomplishment is simply amazing.

Kepler's Second Law is in the next box.

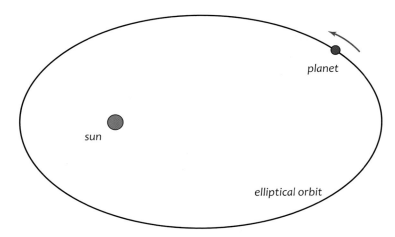

Figure 3-9. A planet in an elliptical orbit around the sun.

Second Law	A line drawn from the sun to any planet will trace out a region in space that has equal area for any equivalent length of time.

The Second Law is depicted in Figure 3-10. The idea is that for a given period of time such as a month or a week, the shaded region in the figure will have the same amount of area, no matter where the planet is in its orbit. Now, since the sun is off-center, this law implies that the planets travel faster when they are closer to the sun and slower when they are farther away. Again, it is stunning that a guy

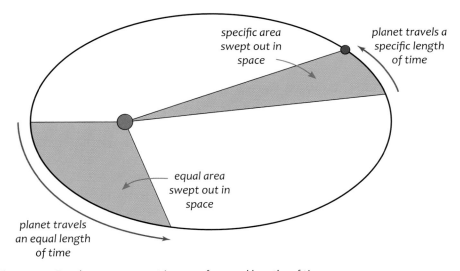

Figure 3-10. Equal areas are swept in space for equal lengths of time.

without a telescope, calculator or any modern computer could figure this out, all from the data that Tycho had assembled.

Kepler's Third Law of Planetary Motion is more mathematically complex than the first two. It is a magnificent example of the mathematical modeling that physicists do all the time, so let's look more closely at it for a bit. The law may be stated as follows:

Third Law   Any two planets will obey this law:

$$\left(\frac{T_1}{T_2}\right)^2 = \left(\frac{R_1}{R_2}\right)^3$$

where T_1 and T_2 are the planets' orbital periods, and R_1 and R_2 are their mean distances from the sun.

The Third Law is quite accurate. The equation can also be expressed in a way that shows that the orbital period, T, for any planet is a function of the planet's mean distance from the sun, R. In other words, there is a fixed relationship—that applies to all planets—between a planet's average distance from the sun and the length of time it takes the planet to complete its orbit. In equation form, this expression of the Third Law can be written as

$$T = kR^{3/2}$$

In this equation k is just a constant that depends on the units used for T and R.

When we see an equation as amazing and as simple as this, a couple of things stand out. First, Kepler's work as a scientist was first class. He figured this out from data collected in the era before telescopes, before calculators, before computers. This was only three years after Shakespeare died!

Second, this equation says something deep about the universe we live in. The universe has characteristics that can be modeled with simple mathematics that can be understood by high school kids. There is a deep mathematical structure to the universe that has always amazed scientists.

An important contemporary and theoretical sparing partner of Kepler was Galileo Galilei (1564-1642, Figure 3-11), who lived in Florence, Italy. Before Galileo, scientists had thought all the way back to Aristotle that forces were need to keep an object moving. Galileo broke with this 2,000-year-old idea and hypothesized that force was needed to *change* motion, but not to *sustain* motion as Aristotle had taught.

Galileo discovered that all falling objects accelerate at the same rate (the acceleration of gravity, 9.80 m/s²), which is mathematically very close to Isaac Newton's Second Law of Motion (our topic in the next chapter). He made significant improvements to the telescope and used it to see the craters on the moon and sunspots, which provided more powerful evidence that the heavens were not perfect and unchanging after all. In January, 1610 he used the telescope to discover four of the moons around Jupiter, which was clearly in conflict with the seven heavenly bodies idea. He was fully on board with all the new science of the Copernican model, but, oddly, he never did accept Kepler's discovery that the planets' orbits were elliptical rather than circular. Because of his outspoken Copernican views, Galileo was tried for heresy by the Church in 1633 and forced to recant his beliefs about the heliocentric model.

Figure 3-11. Florentine scientist Galileo Galilei.

> Among Galileo's long list of scientific achievements are the discovery of Jupiter's moons, and the fact that all falling objects accelerate at the same rate.

The saga of the Copernican Revolution ends more or less with Galileo. Within a few decades of Galileo's death the heliocentric model of the planetary orbits was well established. But while we are studying the planets and gravity the whole story just isn't complete unless we mention two more key figures in the history of science.

Sir Isaac Newton (1643-1727, Figure 3-12) is perhaps the most celebrated mathematician and scientist of all time. He was English, as his title implies, and he was truly phenomenal. He held a famous professorship in mathematics at Cambridge University. He developed calculus. He developed the famous Laws of Motion, which we will examine in detail in the next chapter. He developed an entire theory of optics and light. He formulated the first quantitative law of gravity called the Law of Universal Gravitation. His massive work on motion, gravity and the planets, *Principia Mathematica*, was published in 1686. This work is one of the most important publications in the history of science.

Newton's Law of Universal Gravitation is another law that is a bit mathematically complex, but worth taking a closer look at. The law may be written as

What else was Galileo able to discover with his telescope?

Galileo put his new telescopes in service during the period 1608-1609. As we saw, right away he discovered four of Jupiter's moons and was able to measure their orbital periods. Due to the conflict between the discovery that heavenly bodies were orbiting Jupiter and the Ptolemaic model, many at the time refused to accept that Galileo could have discovered the moons as he claimed.

Later in 1610, Galileo observed that Venus exhibited a complete set of phases—crescent, gibbous and full—just like the moon. The Ptolemaic model could be made to account for some, but not all, of the phases of Venus, so this observation provided more strong evidence for the Copernican model.

Galileo was the first to understand that the patterns of light seen on the moon's surface are caused by the way lunar mountains and craters block sunlight.

In 1612, Galileo observed the planet Neptune. He logged the celestial object in his observations, but did not realize the object was a planet before he lost track of it.

$$F = G \frac{m_1 m_2}{d^2}$$

In this equation F is the force of gravitational attraction between any two objects, G is a constant, m_1 and m_2 are the masses of the two objects (such as the sun and a planet) and d is the distance between the centers of the two objects.

Newton theorized that every object in the universe pulls on every other object in the universe, which is why his law is called the Law of *Universal* Gravitation. He was right. *Everything* in the universe pulls on *everything* else. As with Kepler's work, is it difficult to imagine how Newton could have figured this out. Newton's equation gives the force of gravitational attraction between any two objects in the universe, and it is very accurate. A detail that is important to note is that Newton's gravitational model depends on each object having mass, because the force of gravity has both masses in it multiplied together, and if either mass was zero the gravitational attraction would be zero.

> With his Law of Universal Gravitation Newton theorized that every object in the universe exerts a gravitational pull on every other object, and he was right.

While we are here looking at Isaac Newton we should pause and consider the relationship between his physical theories (including Law of Universal Gravitation and his Laws of Motion) and Kepler's mathematical theory of planetary motion. It turns out that Kepler's discovery about the elliptical orbits and

Figure 3-12. English scientist Sir Isaac Newton.

the relationship between the period and mean radius of the orbit can be directly derived from Newton's theories, and Newton does derive them in *Principia Mathematica*. But Newton's equations apply much more generally than Kepler's do. As we will learn in the next chapter, Newton's Laws apply to all objects in motion—planets, baseballs, rockets—while Kepler's Laws apply to the special case of the planets' orbits. If we consider this in light of the discussion in Chapter 1 about the way theories work, we see that Newton's Laws explain everything Kepler's Laws explain, and more. This places Newton's theory about motion and gravity above Kepler's, so Newton's theories took over as the most widely-accepted theoretical model explaining motion. However, even though Newton's Laws ruled the scientific world for nearly 230 years, they were not the end of the story.

This is where the German physicist Albert Einstein (1879-1955, Figure 3-13) comes in with his new general theory of relativity, published in 1915. Einstein's theory explains gravity in terms of the curvature of space (or more precisely, "space-time") around a massive object, such as the sun or a planet. It is fascinating that since Einstein's theory is about curving space, even phenomena without mass, such as rays of light, will be affected by it. Einstein noticed this and made the stunning prediction that starlight bends as it travels through space when it passes near a massive object such as the sun. He formed this hypothesis based on his general theory of relativity, which was based *completely on mathematics*. What should a person think about that? The entire theory can be summarized in a single equation, but the mathematics in that equation are so sophisticated that not even undergraduates studying physics get into it. What a genius!

Einstein predicted that light from stars bends in space as it travels past other stars, an incredible prediction that was experimentally confirmed in 1919.

Einstein became instantly world famous just a few years later when his prediction about bending light was amazingly confirmed. To test this hypothesis Einstein proposed photographing the stars we see near the sun during a solar eclipse. This has to be done during an eclipse, because trying to look at starlight while the sun is nearby would mean it was broad daylight and we wouldn't be able to see the stars. Einstein predicted that the apparent position of the stars would shift a tiny amount relative to where they are when the sun is not near the path of the star light. British scientist Sir Arthur Eddington commissioned two teams of photographers to photograph the stars during the solar eclipse of 1919. After analyzing their photographic plates they found the star light to have shifted exactly the amount Einstein said it would. Talk about sudden fame—Einstein became the instant global rock star of physics when this happened! (And his puppy dog eyes contributed even more to his popularity.)

Figure 3-13. German physicist Albert Einstein.

Just as Kepler's Laws were superseded by Newton's Laws and can be derived from Newton's Laws, Newton's Law of Universal Gravitation was superseded by Einstein's general theory of relativity and can be derived from general relativity. Einstein believed that his own theories would some day be superseded by an even more all-encompassing theory, but so far (after 98 years) that has not happened. The general theory of relativity remains today the reigning champion theory of gravity, our best understanding of how gravity works, and one of the most important theories in twentieth- and twenty-first-century physics.

What do Jupiter's moons look like?

Jupiter's four largest moons are Io, Ganymede, Europa and Callisto. Images of these moons were captured by NASA's deep space probe, Voyager 2, launched in 1977. The first image shows Io transiting Jupiter. To the right a volcano is seen erupting on Io's surface. In the second row are

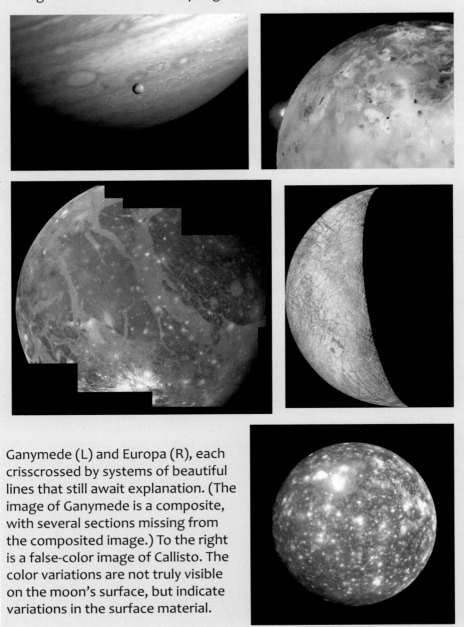

Ganymede (L) and Europa (R), each crisscrossed by systems of beautiful lines that still await explanation. (The image of Ganymede is a composite, with several sections missing from the composited image.) To the right is a false-color image of Callisto. The color variations are not truly visible on the moon's surface, but indicate variations in the surface material.

Ideas for Your Classroom

1. Using chalk and a long measuring tape, have your students construct a scale model of the contemporary solar system on the pavement of a long sidewalk. For a sun drawn about three inches in diameter the distance from the sun to Neptune will be about 80 yards. Unfortunately, at this scale Mercury will only be about a hundredth of an inch in diameter! This can be handled by drawing the relative sizes of the planets separately from their placement in the solar system.

2. With older students plot a scale model of the solar system on a map of your city or town. If possible, use a neighborhood they are familiar with so they have a feel for the distances involved. Increasing the scale of the distance from the sun to Neptune up to 5.5 miles would allow the sun to be about nine feet in diameter and the earth to be one inch in diameter.

3. In a class discussion ask students if they can tell that the earth is rotating instead of the sun and planets orbiting the earth. Ask them to try to think of ways that one could tell if the earth was rotating or not. Optionally, include a web research challenge to find ideas for experiments that would demonstrate the earth to be rotating. (One such is known as Foucault's Pendulum.)

4. Have students build a model of the Ptolemaic arrangement of the planets going around the earth. Compare this to a contemporary heliocentric model.

5. In a dark room, use a flashlight and rotating globe to show how the sun causes day and night.

6. Let students investigate the lives of the scientists mentioned in this chapter. There are many online sites with information about these famous men, as well as Uraniborg and Galileo's telescope.

7. Using models or mobile humans to represent the earth, sun and a planet, act out the planetary movements that lead to retrograde motion in both the Ptolemaic system and Copernican system. For a visual aid to illustrate, see the animations at http://www.lasalle.edu/~smithsc/Astronomy/retrograd.html.

8. Use a tablet with a free app such as GoSkyWatch to identify planets and constellations in the sky in real time.

9. Build a replica of Galileo's telescope using inexpensive plastic lenses (see also Chapter 15).

Goals for Chapter 4

1. Define and distinguish between matter, inertia, mass, force and weight.

2. State Newton's Laws of Motion.

3. Give several examples of applications of the Laws of Motion that illustrate their meaning.

4. Explain why the First Law is called the Law of Inertia.

5. Use Newton's Laws of Motion to explain how a rocket works.

About This Chapter

One of the most influential events of pre-modern physics was the publication of Isaac Newton's *Principia Mathematica* in 1686. The basic principles of force, motion, states of motion and acceleration that we still use today were systematically developed in the *Principia*. The Laws of Motion Newton put forward are deceptively simple, but they are subtle, and careful attention to the examples and applications is advised.

Chapter 4
Newton's Laws of Motion

Matter, Inertia, Mass and Force

To study Sir Isaac Newton's three Laws of Motion one needs to have a clear understanding of three closely related and easily confused terms, *matter*, *inertia*, and *mass*. Matter is simply the term we use for anything made of atoms or parts of atoms. Examples of matter are all around us, and include things like bananas, protons, carbon atoms, gas molecules, and planets. Examples of things that are *not* matter include light, radio waves, Beethoven's Third Symphony, justice, and truth. These are all real things, but they are not material objects.

> Matter is anything made of atoms, or parts of atoms.

To set the stage for the other two terms, consider that all matter possesses certain properties. For example, one of the properties of matter is that matter takes up space. We quantify the amount of space that a material object occupies with the variable *volume*, and our measurements of the volume of an object are stated in certain units of measure. In the MKS system the units for volume are cubic meters (m^3).

Another property all matter possesses is called inertia. The effect of this property is that a material object will always resist changes to its state of motion. Another way to say this is that to change the state of motion of an object a force is required. If an object is at rest and no net force is acting on it, it will remain at rest.

> Inertia is a property of all matter that makes matter resist change to its state of motion.

The same applies to an object moving with a constant velocity; if there is no net force acting on it, it will continue moving with a constant velocity.

In the previous chapter we saw that a changing velocity is called acceleration. It should now be clear that to say an object's state of motion is changing is equivalent to saying its velocity is changing, which is also equivalent to saying that the object is accelerating. In summary, a net force on an object is required to make it accelerate. No net force, no acceleration. Without a net force on an object, the object's inertia will make it keep doing whatever it is presently doing.

Finally, *mass* is the variable we use to quantify how much inertia an object has. In the MKS system the unit of measure for mass is the kilogram (kg). One way to emphasize the difference between inertia and mass is to say that inertia is a *quality* and mass is a *quantity*.

> Mass is the variable we use to quantify how much inertia an object has.

Now that we have a handle on matter, inertia and mass, there is one more pair of terms we need to discuss before getting to Newton's three famous Laws of Motion. These are the terms *force* and *net force*. A force is any push or a pull, regardless of how it happens. The concept of force is fairly easy to understand, and Newton's Laws of Motion tell us very specific things about the way forces work in nature.

> A force is any push or pull.

Now, to illustrate the concept of *net force*, consider the forces presently acting on me as I sit here at my computer writing this book. Because of the gravitational attraction of the earth, the earth is pulling me toward its center, which is *down* from my point of view. If this were the only force on me right now I would be accelerating downward, that is, falling. Luckily for me, there is another force pushing up on me from the chair I am sitting in. So although there are these two forces acting on me at present, they happen to be equal and directed in opposite directions, so they cancel each other out. This means there is no *net force* on me at the moment.[1] A net force is a force that is not balanced out or cancelled out by some other force.

Newton's Laws of Motion

Newton's Laws of Motion may be the three most famous scientific statements ever made. Here is the first one:

> First Law   An object at rest will remain at rest and an object in motion will continue moving in a straight line at a constant speed, unless it is compelled to change that state by forces acting on it.

The First Law applies when there is no net force acting on an object, and describes what objects will do in such circumstances. In the absence of a net force, an object at rest will remain at rest. Likewise, in the absence of a net force an object moving at a constant speed in a certain direction will continue moving in the same way on the same course forever. As mentioned previously, objects behave the way this law describes because of their inertia. For this reason the First Law is sometimes called the Law of Inertia.

In this book so far we have avoided using the term *speed*, and have used the term *velocity* instead in our discussion about motion. But in the statement of Newton's First Law the term speed is more appropriate since the speed and direction of motion are mentioned separately in the statement. The velocity of

---

1   Technically, if we consider the big picture of the rotating and orbiting earth, there *are* net forces acting on me. But we are here only considering the simplified context in which my chair, body and computer are all at rest. This is called the "frame of reference" for my example.

an object actually specifies not only *how fast* an object is moving, which is what we discussed in the previous chapter, but also the *direction* in which the object is moving. By contrast, the term speed denotes only the "how fast" part of an object's motion, not the direction part. So the term speed is more appropriate for the First Law statement. But for the purposes of this book, since we are considering only motion in a straight line, the terms speed and velocity are essentially synonyms.

Here is Newton's Second Law:

> **Second Law**   The acceleration of an object is proportional to the force acting on it, or
>
> $$a = \frac{F}{m}$$
>
> where *a* is the acceleration of the object (m/s²), F is the net force on the object in newtons (N), and *m* is the object's mass (kg).

I must now inform you that by writing the Second Law as $a = F/m$ I have boldly written it differently than the way it is written in nearly every physics book in the world, which is the equivalent expression $F = ma$. If you ask nearly anyone to state Newton's Second Law, they will say $F = ma$. Some people reading this might wonder if I have taken leave of my senses to restate one of the most famous equations in physics! No I haven't. I have a good reason for stating the law this way: This is the way Isaac Newton stated it! I don't know why everyone started saying $F = ma$. Mathematically, the equation $F = ma$ implies that force is dependent on acceleration. This is because when writing algebraic equations we customarily call the variable on the left the *dependent variable*, and we think of it as depending on the values we put in for the variables on the right, which are called *independent variables*.

> If it seems presumptuous to change one of the most famous equations in physics, remember that this is closer to the way Newton himself wrote it!

When we write $F = ma$, F is in the position of the dependent variable in the equation. But we do not usually think of objects this way. When we think of objects accelerating, we usually think of the acceleration as being dependent on the force acting on the object. If a certain net force is applied to an object, the object will accelerate in proportion to the force. This is the way we think, and this is the way Newton expressed it. So this is the way I have chosen to write it.

The Second Law applies when there is a net force present, and it says what the object will do as a result. As we saw previously, when a net force is present on an object, the object will change its state of motion. In other words, the object will accelerate, and according to Newton's Second Law, the acceleration is directly proportional to the force. This means if we double or triple the net force on an object, we double or triple its acceleration.

The MKS unit of measure for force is the newton (N), in honor of Sir Isaac Newton's contributions to science. This is the first derived unit we have encountered. As mentioned in Chapter 3, the MKS system of units uses the meter, kilogram and second as primary units. Many of the other units of measure are derived from combinations of these three main units. Since force is mass times acceleration (that is, $F = ma$), the unit for force is the product of the units for mass and acceleration, or

$$1\,\text{N} = 1\,\text{kg} \cdot \frac{\text{m}}{\text{s}^2}$$

One newton is defined as one kg·m/s^2, and we use newtons as a force unit for convenience. This is the case for all derived units. We could write all units of measure as combinations of the seven basic units. But using derived units for quantities we deal with all the time (like newtons for force) is much simpler.

Now for the Third Law, which is going to require some wordsmithing. The traditional way to state the Third Law is, "For every action there is an equal and opposite reaction." Newton himself wrote this law as, "To every action there is always opposed an equal reaction." The problem with this statement is that the words *action* and *reaction* in the traditional statement of Newton's Third Law do not mean anything like what we mean today when we use those words (leading to severe misunderstanding among contemporary students about the meaning of this law). Newton meant these terms to refer to *forces*. They are not, in the way we use the terms today, actions, or reactions, or events or processes. So a better way to state the law now would be: For every force, there is an equal and opposite push-back force. That is, if object A pushes to the right on object B, object B pushes to the left with the same strength on object A.

> In Newton's use of the terms, *action* and *reaction* both refer to *forces*.

Of course, it is well to know about the traditional language. So I have developed a hybrid version of the Third Law that connects the terms action and reaction to the term force. Here it is:

Third Law	For every action force, there is an equal and opposite reaction force.

The Third Law describes the way objects always act on *one another* when forces are present. If an object experiences a force—any force—a second object is experiencing one too, identical in strength but in the opposite direction. These two forces are the so-called "action-reaction pairs" the Third Law is famous for. It is not possible for one object to push on another object without the second object pushing back in the opposite direction on the first one with the same amount of force. The Third Law applies all the time, whether the forces result in the acceleration of one or both of the objects involved, or the objects just remain motionless, as in the example of sitting in my chair at my computer.

As another example, consider again Newton's Law of Universal Gravitation that we bumped into briefly near the end of Chapter 3. The Law of Universal Gravitation says that every object in the universe pulls on every other object. If objects are large enough and close enough together, as in the case of a planet and the sun, these forces are very large and keep the planet in its orbit. Without a large attractive force the planet's huge inertia would cause it to fly away in space, as Newton's First Law says.

As illustrated in Figure 4-1, a planet going around the sun is attracted to the sun with an amount of force given by the equation in Newton's Law of Universal Gravitation, which can be written as

$$F = G\frac{m_1 m_2}{r^2}$$

(In the last chapter I used the variable d in the denominator of this equation. Here I used r because it is common to use the variable r instead of d when orbital types of motion are involved.) But let's consider this situation from the sun's point of view. Newton's Third Law of Motion says for every force there is an equal and opposite reaction force, another force pushing

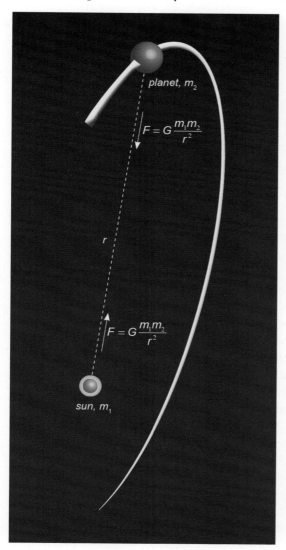

Figure 4-1. Newton's Third Law applied to a planet and the sun.

Example Problem

A force of 8.61 x 10⁻¹⁹ N is applied to a proton with a mass of 1.673 x 10⁻²⁷ kg. Determine the acceleration of the proton. (The force in this problem is one 10 billionth of a billionth of the weight of a mosquito.)

The given quantities in this example are extremely small, so they are written in scientific notation. (For more on scientific notation, see Appendix C.)

$$F = 8.61 \times 10^{-19} \text{ N}$$

$$m = 1.673 \times 10^{-27} \text{ kg}$$

Inserting these values into the Newton's Second Law equation and solving, we have

$$a = \frac{F}{m} = \frac{8.61 \times 10^{-19} \text{ N}}{1.673 \times 10^{-27} \text{ kg}} = 5.15 \times 10^{8} \ \frac{\text{m}}{\text{s}^2}$$

Even with the extremely small force, this is an enormous acceleration, and would accelerate the proton to the speed of light in about half a second. (However, this wouldn't happen because Einstein's special theory of relativity predicts that as the proton's velocity approached the speed of light the mass of the proton would increase too, so the force would accelerate the proton less and less as the proton accelerated. But that's another story altogether!)

back with the same amount of force but in the opposite direction. This means that not only is the planet attracted to the sun, but the sun is attracted to the planet with the exact same amount of force, pointing in exactly the opposite direction.

The result of these forces for the planet is that planet stays in orbit. But the result for the sun is that it wobbles in place as the planet goes around. Now, since the sun is so much more massive than any of the planets, it doesn't move very far. Additionally, the sun is being tugged on by all of the planets at once, and since they are spread out around the sun their forces on the sun tend to cancel each other out to some extent. Nevertheless, the sun does wobble because of all the planets pulling on it. In fact, all the planets wobble too because they are all pulling on each other. (Observing these wobbles in the past enabled astronomers eventually to discover the planets Uranus and Neptune, which could almost not be seen with the telescopes from Galileo's era.) On top of that, planets with moons, like the earth and Jupiter, wobble even more because of their moons pulling on them! All of these forces of the planets and moons and sun

The sun and each of the planets are constantly pulling on one another, causing each of them to wobble around.

pulling on each other produce an interacting system of forces that is so complex no one has ever been able to develop equations to model it that can be solved exactly. Instead, we model the planetary motions using approximations and the aid of sophisticated modern computers!

When discussing the Third Law it must be emphasized that the actions and reactions in the law are pushes or pulls, not events or processes. A generic statement of how action-reaction pairs of forces work is "A pushes B, and B pushes back equally and oppositely on A." As an illustration of how students often misunderstand this, consider the following scenario, illustrated in Figure 4-2: A glass of milk is sitting on a table. A boy walks by and accidently bumps the table, causing the glass of milk to spill. It would not be uncommon for students to say that the action is the boy bumping the table and the reaction is the milk spilling, but this is not a correct way to identify the forces involved. "Spilling milk" is not a force. The correct way of describing the action-reaction pairs is "the boy bumped the table, and the table bumped the boy."

So why did the milk spill if it was not involved in the action-reaction pair? When the boy bumped the table, the table accelerated briefly just as the Second

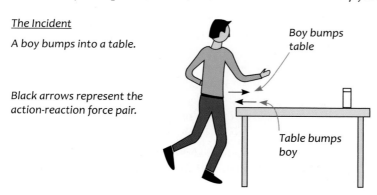

The Incident

A boy bumps into a table.

Black arrows represent the action-reaction force pair.

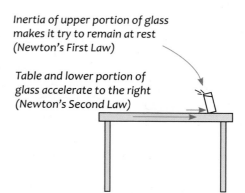

The Results

Results of the boy bumping the table: table accelerates to right.

Results of the table bumping the boy: boy feels the bump on his leg.

Figure 4-2. *Force analysis of the boy bumping the table and the table bumping the boy (top). Several different outcomes result from these bumps (bottom).*

Law states. The glass was sitting on the table, so friction between the table and the bottom of the glass caused the bottom portion of the glass to accelerate with the table. But the inertia of the upper part of the glass made the upper part of the glass resist change to its state of motion. If the bottom of the glass moves while the top part stays put, the glass tips over. In this illustration all three of Newton's Laws of Motion are involved.

Weight

The term *weight* simply means the force acting on an object due to gravitational attraction. Newton's Second Law can be used to calculate the weight of an object from its mass, or vice versa. This works because we know (from Galileo's work) that on earth at sea level all falling objects accelerate at the same rate, 9.80 m/s². This value, always referred to as *g*, is the acceleration of an object due to gravity. So the force of gravity pulling on an object on earth must equal the mass of the object times this acceleration. Writing this acceleration in the Second Law equation we have

> Weight is the force on an object due to gravitational attraction.

$$F_w = mg$$

Written this way, the symbol F_w is used to represent the force that is the weight of the object.

When the astronauts were walking on the moon back in the late 1960s, they weighed only 1/6 of their earth weight. This is because the moon's gravitational attraction is only 1/6 as great as the earth's. However, the astronauts' masses were unchanged, because mass is directly related to the atoms in an object. The difference in gravitational attraction is depicted in Figure 4-3 (in which I decided to imagine a female astronaut). The astronauts' weights depended on the acceleration

Example Problem

A certain athlete weighs 245 lb, which is equivalent to 1,090 N. Determine the athlete's mass.

We solve this problem by dividing both sides of the weight equation by g. This gives us

$$F_w = mg$$

$$m = \frac{F_w}{g} = \frac{1{,}090 \text{ N}}{9.80 \ \frac{\text{m}}{\text{s}^2}} = 111 \text{ kg}$$

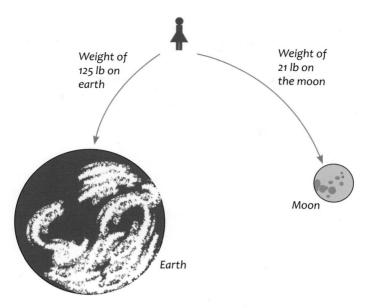

Figure 4-3. A person weighing 125 lb on earth would weigh only 21 lb on the moon.

of gravity where they were. The same equation for weight would apply on the moon or other planets as well, but the value of *g* would be different on the moon or other planets.

Applying Newton's Laws of Motion

To see how Newton's Laws of Motion would apply to a few more actual situations, here are a few case studies. In each case, a hypothetical scenario is followed by an explanation for what happened based on one or more of Newton's Laws.

1. An asteroid speeding through space comes close to a star. As it does, it begins to speed up and turn in its course. (Note that since a force is required to change the direction of a moving object, turning is an example of acceleration.)

    The asteroid is accelerating because of the attraction of the star's gravitational field. Since there is a force (gravity) on the asteroid, its velocity is changing. That is, it is speeding up and changing direction. The acceleration of the asteroid will be according to Newton's Second Law, $a = F/m$. The acceleration of the asteroid will be in proportion to the strength of the gravitational attraction of the star.

2. While driving, a man wearing glasses falls asleep at the wheel and runs into a tree. The man is wearing his seat belt, and is unharmed, but his glasses fly right off his face.

Is the value of g the same everywhere on the earth's surface?

The earth is not quite spherical, because its rotation causes it to bulge a little at the equator. Its diameter is about 26.6 miles greater at the equator than it is from pole to pole. As a result, the value of g is slightly lower at the equator, because a person standing on the equator is 13.3 miles farther from the center of the earth than a person standing on the north pole.

The value of g varies from about 9.78 m/s² at the equator up to 9.83 m/s² at the north pole. The value of 9.80 m/s² commonly used in physics problems applies to the central and northern United States. Down here in Texas g is only about 9.79 m/s² and up in Winnipeg, Canada it is 9.81 m/s². So if you weigh yourself in Winnipeg and then hop a flight to Austin, your weight will drop about 0.2%.

The glasses are moving with the same velocity as the man and car. While the man and the car experienced forces that make them stop (according to Newton's Second Law) there is no force on the glasses. In the absence of a force the inertia of the glasses makes them continue moving in a straight line at a constant speed, just as Newton's First Law says, until they hit the windshield. We also know from Newton's Third Law that when the car hit the tree (action force), the tree hit the car just as hard (reaction force). The effect of the car hitting the tree was that the tree was knocked over and damaged. The effect of the tree hitting the car was to stop the car and total it.

3. Susie wants to go hunting with her dad. Her father decides to let her shoot his .308 calibre rifle at a target out in the country. She places the rifle against her shoulder and fires at the target. The rifle fires the bullet, and Susie feels the painful kickback of the gun on her shoulder.

    The firing of the bullet and the kickback of the gun are explained by Newton's Third Law of Motion. The gun pushes the bullet (action force), and the bullet pushes the gun equally and oppositely (reaction force). The force of the gun on the bullet is very high, and causes the bullet to accelerate out of the gun barrel. The force of the bullet on the gun is equal, and in the opposite direction. This high kickback force causes the gun to hit Susie's shoulder hard.

How a Rocket Works

Rockets are a great way to see Newton's Third Law in operation. In outer space there is no friction or air, so normal methods of accelerating or stopping a vehicle on earth cannot be used. Cars accelerate by using the friction between the tires and the road to speed the car up or to slow it down. Airplanes and boats push against the air or water. These vehicles all use Newton's Third Law. The tires push against the road, the road pushes against the tires in the opposite direction. The boat propeller pushes against the water, and the water pushes against the propeller, equally and in the opposite direction.

But in space there is nothing there to push against. No road, no water, no air. Rockets speed up or slow down by using Newton's Third Law of Motion just like every other vehicle does, but a rocket has to do it without anything to push against.

A rocket engine works by throwing the mass of its own burnt fuel (the products of combustion) out of the rocket engine with a massive amount of force. In the parlance of rocketry, this force is called *thrust*. The combustion of the fuel is really only needed to get the fuel to fly out of the rocket with a great deal of force, producing a large thrust. In Third Law terms, we can say, "The rocket engine pushes the fuel." And the rocket pushes the fuel very *hard*! This is the action force in the Third Law. The reaction force is, "The fuel pushes the rocket engine." This push is *just as hard*. Since the rocket engine is, of course, connected to the rest of the space ship, the force of the fuel pushing on the rocket engine accelerates the space ship according to the Second Law. The action-reaction pair is illustrated in Figure 4-4.

To slow down, the space ship again has nothing to push against, and so must again use a rocket engine. However, in this case the ship will use *retro-rockets*,

What do astronauts or pilots mean when they refer to "g-forces"?

You may have heard a pilot speak of enduring a force of so many "g's" while banking or ascending. The g-force terminology is a short hand for expressing the magnitude of forces acting on people while they are being accelerated. The term is technically incorrect, since g is an acceleration, not a force.

A force of "one g" is equal to a person's weight. This would be the force we are normally accustomed to, acting on us by the ground or a chair to counteract the gravitational pull of the earth. A zero-g environment is synonymous with weightlessness or free fall. The g-forces we normally feel when accelerating in cars or aircraft are mild, but extreme conditions can produce accelerations of several g's.

When accelerating upward in an elevator one feels a vertical g-force of slightly greater than 1 g. Accelerating in one's car by increasing speed or by turning corners produces very slight horizontal g-forces.

Pilots can experience large g-forces during extreme maneuvers of aircraft. Normally, a person can handle a vertical g-force of about 5 g's before blacking out due to the blood rushing down out of the brain and into the body. With special flight suits and muscle strains people can handle up to 9 g of vertical acceleration. Humans can handle much higher horizontal accelerations, depending on whether the acceleration is "eyeballs in" or "eyeballs out."

which are small rocket engines that point toward the front of the space ship. When the "engine pushes the fuel" from the front of the space ship, the "fuel pushes the engine" from the front, against the motion of the ship, thus slowing the ship down.

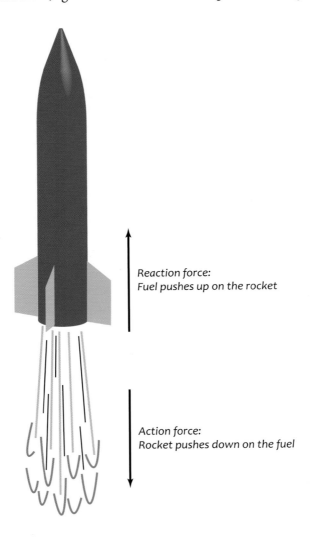

Reaction force:
Fuel pushes up on the rocket

Action force:
Rocket pushes down on the fuel

Figure 4-4. Action-reaction pairs associated with a rocket.

Ideas for Your Classroom

1. Let students work in groups to think of examples illustrating each of the laws of motion. Challenge them to correctly identify the action-reaction pairs when one object pushes or pulls on another object.

2. Watch videos of astronauts while weightless in the space craft. Ask the students what would happen if a weightless astronaut decided to throw a heavy object, say, a bowling ball. What would the bowling ball do? What would the astronaut do? What would the spacecraft do when the bowling ball hit the wall? What would the space craft do when the astronaut hit the wall in the opposite direction?

3. To illustrate Newton's First Law and inertia, show the students a video of the old trick of pulling a table cloth out from under a table setting. Or, try this yourself in the classroom. Ask the students which laws explain what they see. (If you do this demonstration yourself, use a lightweight plastic cloth, such as the type that comes on rolls used by caterers. Use only a small piece, about two feet square. Instead of dishes, use some wood blocks. When you pull the cloth, pull it as suddenly and as horizontally as possible. It will work with a little practice.)

4. Ask students to use the Laws of Motion to explain why a car will roll to a stop if it runs out of gas. Then discuss whether a space ship in outer space would do the same thing or something different.

5. Make rockets out of plastic bottles, water and compressed air. NASA has instructions at http://exploration.grc.nasa.gov/education/rocket/rktbot.html.

Goals for Chapter 5

1. State the Law of Conservation of Energy.

2. Describe how energy can be changed from one form to another, including:

    a. different forms of mechanical energy (kinetic, gravitational potential, elastic potential)
    b. chemical potential energy
    c. electrical energy
    d. thermal energy
    e. electromagnetic radiation
    f. nuclear energy
    g. acoustic energy

3. Briefly define each of the types of energy listed above.

4. Describe two processes by which energy can be transferred from one object to another (work and heat), and the conditions that must be present for the energy transfer to occur.

5. Describe in detail how energy from the sun is converted through various forms to end up as energy in our bodies, or as energy used to run appliances in the home or machines in industry.

6. Explain how conservation of energy principles apply to simple mechanical systems such as a swinging pendulum.

About This Chapter

One of the central concepts of physics, and science in general, is energy. Even so, no one can really define this most fundamental of quantities. So the goal of this chapter is more about how to think about the way energy works than to understand its fundamental essence. The physical universe consists of matter and energy. Physics is all about how these two interact.

Chapter 5
Energy

What is Energy?

Defining energy is tricky. Dictionaries usually say, "the capacity to do mechanical work," which is not particularly helpful. So we are not going to try to define it accurately, we are just going to accept that energy exists in the universe and it exists in many different forms. It is fairly obvious that a bullet traveling at 2,000 ft/s has more energy than a bullet at rest. This is why the high speed bullet can kill but the bullet at rest cannot. This chapter is mainly about tracking energy as it changes from one form to another, and calculating the quantities of three particular forms of energy.

The Law of Conservation of Energy

The *Law of Conservation of Energy* is:

> Energy can be neither created nor destroyed, only changed in form.

Energy can be in many different forms in different types of substances, such as in the molecules of gasoline, in the waves of a beam of light, in heat radiating through space, in moving objects, in compressed springs, or in objects lifted vertically on earth. As different physical processes occur such as digesting food, throwing a ball, operating a machine, heating due to friction, or accelerating a race car, energy in one form is being converted into some other form. Energy might be in one form in one place, such as in the chemical potential energy in the muscles of a person's arm, and be converted through a process like throwing a ball to become energy in another form in another place, like kinetic energy in the ball.

Mass-Energy Equivalence

In 1905, Albert Einstein published his now-famous equation $E = mc^2$. The E and m in this equation stand for energy and mass; c stands for the speed of light. With this equation, Einstein theorized that mass and energy are really just different forms of the same thing. That is, all mass has associated with it an equivalent amount of energy (given by $E = mc^2$), and vice versa. This theory of mass-energy equivalence is now considered to be a fundamental property of the universe.

I mention mass-energy equivalence here because since mass is a form of energy, matter must be taken into consideration for a completely accurate statement of the Law of Conservation of Energy. In nuclear reactions, such as take place in the sun (fusion) or in nuclear power plants (fission) quantities of matter are converted completely into energy. Einstein's equation $E = mc^2$ also gives the amount of energy that appears when a quantity of matter in converted to energy in one of these nuclear processes. Thus, to be completely accurate, the Law of Conservation of Energy includes all mass as well, as one of the forms energy can take.

> The Law of Conservation of Energy is strictly correct only if we include the equivalent energy associated with mass.

However, most of the problems we encounter in physics and chemistry don't involve nuclear reactions (thankfully). This means that for most purposes we can consider the common forms of energy listed below without worrying about the complicated issue of mass-energy equivalence.

Forms of Energy

Here are some common forms energy can take:

GRAVITATIONAL POTENTIAL ENERGY

This is the energy an object possesses because it has been lifted up in a gravitational field. If such an object is released and allowed to fall, the gravitational potential energy will convert into kinetic energy. The term *potential* in the name of this form of energy indicates that the energy is stored and has the capability of converting into another form of energy when released. There are other forms of energy listed below that use this term for the same reason.

KINETIC ENERGY

This is the energy an object possesses because it is in motion. The faster an object is moving, the more kinetic energy the object has.

ELECTROMAGNETIC RADIATION

This is the energy in electromagnetic waves traveling through space, or through media such as air or glass. This type of energy includes all forms of light, as well as radio waves, microwaves, and a number of other kinds of radiation. We will study electromagnetic waves in detail in a later chapter.

CHEMICAL POTENTIAL ENERGY

This energy is in the chemical bonds of molecules. Burning or combustion is a type of chemical reaction. In the case of substances that burn, the chemical potential energy in the molecules is released in large quantities as heat and light when the substance is burned, making these substances useful as fuel.

ELECTRICAL ENERGY

This is energy flowing in wires, such as from a power station to your house to power your appliances.

THERMAL ENERGY

This is a vague term we will define better in Chapter 8 on heat. It basically means the energy in hot things that got there by heating them.

ELASTIC POTENTIAL ENERGY

This is the energy contained in any object that has been stretched (like a rubber band or a hunter's bow) or compressed (like a compressed spring).

NUCLEAR ENERGY

This is energy released from the nuclear processes of fission (when the nuclei of atoms are split apart) or fusion (when atomic nuclei are fused together). As mentioned previously, these processes convert matter into energy.

ACOUSTIC (SOUND) ENERGY

This is the energy carried in sound waves, such as from a person's voice, the speakers in a sound system or the noise of an explosion. Since sound consists of waves of moving air molecules, this is really a special form of kinetic energy.

Energy Transfer

Two more important energy-related terms are those associated with the process of energy being transferred from one place, substance or object to another. These two terms are:

WORK

Work is a mechanical process by which energy is transferred from one object to another. Objects do not possess work energy, like they do other forms of energy. Instead one object "does work" on another by applying a force to it and moving it a certain distance. When one object does work on another, energy is transferred from the first object to the second. We will study work in more detail later in the chapter.

HEAT

Heat is energy in transit, flowing by various means from a hot substance to a cooler substance when a difference in temperature is present. We will study heat in more detail in Chapter 8. As with work, objects do not possess heat.

> Objects do not possess work or heat. These terms refer to energy in transit from one object or substance to another.

Energy Transformations

Let's look at a common example of energy changing from one form into others. We all know what happens when a person lights a firecracker. (It explodes!) What forms of energy are present during the explosion, and where did all this energy come from? As shown in Figure 5-1, the energy released in the explosion was the chemical potential energy in the molecular bonds of the chemicals inside the firecracker. When these chemicals burn they release a lot of energy. An exploding firecracker gives off a flash of light and heat (both are forms of electromagnetic radiation), a loud bang, and the fragments of the firecracker are blown all over the place. Thus, the chemical potential energy in the powder inside the firecracker was converted into several different kinds of energy during the explosion.

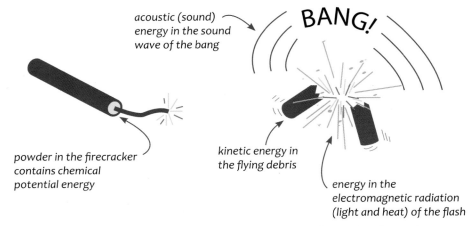

Figure 5-1. Chemical potential energy in a firecracker is converted into other forms of energy when the firecracker explodes.

Now let's consider how the Law of Conservation of Energy would apply to this explosion. All of the energy present in the chemicals before the explosion is still present in various forms after the firecracker explodes. This is what "conservation" of energy means. None of the energy went away and no new energy was created. We could represent the conservation of energy in a sort of equation like this:

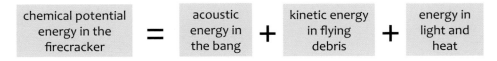

This equation shows an accounting of the energy, and indicates that the energy present before the explosion and the total of the energy present in different forms during and after the explosion must equal.

The "Energy Trail"

Much of the energy we depend on here on earth comes to us from the sun. As we track the forms this energy takes in its journey from the sun to, say, the energy in our bodies, we might call this the "energy trail." We will follow the trail of energy beginning with the sun, through different processes of conversion, and arriving at different places where energy is commonly found.

The sun's energy is produced by nuclear fusion reactions as the nuclei of hydrogen atoms "fuse" or stick together to form helium. This is so hard to do that we have not yet succeeded in doing it here on earth in a controlled way. However, we have succeeded in doing it in an uncontrolled way. Fusion is the same nuclear reaction as the reaction in a nuclear bomb. A nuclear explosion is an uncontrolled nuclear fusion reaction.

When referring to this energy being produced on the sun we will simply call it nuclear energy. The energy leaves the sun as electromagnetic radiation, a different form of energy, and travels through space to us. As mentioned previously, electromagnetic radiation consists of waves of light, heat, infrared light and so on traveling through space. When this energy lands on earth most of it warms the ground, oceans or atmosphere. This is very important for stabilizing the earth's climate and making earth habitable, but unless we collect the energy in a solar collector of some kind we are not able to use this energy directly.

However, some of the electromagnetic radiation streaming from the sun is captured by plants and converted through photosynthesis into chemical potential energy in the molecules in the plants, which eventually become the foods we eat or the fuels we burn. In ancient eras in the earth's history, many vast forests were buried and the plant matter was converted underground into what we now call "fossil fuels" (crude oil, coal, and natural gas). Some fuels come from living plants too, such as firewood from trees, and automotive alcohol from corn. The energy in the molecules of these fuels is chemical potential energy which is converted into heat energy when the fuels are burned.

Tables 5-1 through 5-4 below illustrate a few examples of following the trail of energy from the sun to different places it can end up here on earth.

Where is the energy?	The Sun	Electro-magnetic waves in space	Plants on earth	Breakfast cereal	Muscles in the human body	Stretched bow	Flying arrow
What form is the energy in?	Nuclear energy	Electro-magnetic radiation	Chemical potential energy	Chemical potential energy	Chemical potential energy	Elastic potential energy	Kinetic energy

Table 5-1. Energy transformations from the sun to a flying arrow, assuming the archer was on a vegetarian diet.

Where is the energy?	The Sun	Electro-magnetic waves in space	Plants on earth	Chicken feed	Muscles in the bodies of chickens	Muscles in the hu-man body	Moving kid on skate-board
What form is the energy in?	Nuclear energy	Electro-magnetic radiation	Chemical potential energy	Chemical potential energy	Chemical potential energy	Chemical potential energy	Kinetic energy

Table 5-2. Energy transformations from the sun to a kid on a skateboard, assuming the kid was eating chicken.

Where is the energy?	The Sun	Electro-magnetic waves in space	Plants on earth	Fossil fuel (crude oil, coal, natural gas)	Spin-ning gas turbine generator at power station	Wires from the power station to houses	Heat radiating from the coils in a toaster
What form is the energy in?	Nuclear energy	Electro-magnetic radiation	Chemical potential energy	Chemical potential energy	Kinetic energy	Electrical energy	Electro-magnetic radiation

Table 5-3. Energy transformations from the sun to the heat from a toaster in someone's house.

Where is the energy?	The Sun	Electro-magnetic waves in space	Plants on earth	Fossil fuel (coal)	Heat from burning coal	Steam in the boiler	Moving train
What form is the energy in?	Nuclear energy	Electro-magnetic radiation	Chemical potential energy	Chemical potential energy	Heat	Thermal energy	Kinetic energy

Table 5-4. Energy transformations from the sun to a moving steam locomotive.

Energy "Losses" and Efficiency

For all these different forms of energy we have considered, there are many different kinds of processes that might be involved in converting energy from one form to another. Combustion is a process that converts chemical potential energy into heat. Photosynthesis converts electromagnetic energy from the sun into chemical potential energy in the cells of plants. Photovoltaic cells convert the sun's energy into direct current (DC) electricity—electrical energy.

The industrial revolution began when humans learned how to design machines and systems to convert energy from various forms found in nature into forms that can be harnessed to do useful work for us. Since then, scientists and engineers have continued to improve energy conversion technologies and to develop new ones.

Let's consider one of these processes, such as an engine in a car converting the chemical potential energy in the gasoline into kinetic energy in the moving car. According to the theory of thermodynamics, it impossible for a conversion process to capture all of the energy involved and convert it to a form that can do useful work. Whether we want it to or not, some of the energy will always be converted to heat which radiates out into the environment. The laws of thermodynamics state that this must always be the case.

> The efficiency of any energy conversion process will always be less than 100%.

This situation is represented in Figure 5-2. It is common to speak of the energy converted into heat as "lost." Keeping the Law of Conservation of Energy in mind, it should be clear that what we mean by this is not that the energy has ceased to exist, but only that the energy has escaped into the environment where it is no longer available to us in a usable form.

The efficiency of an energy conversion process is the ratio of the usable energy coming out of the process to the energy that went into the process,

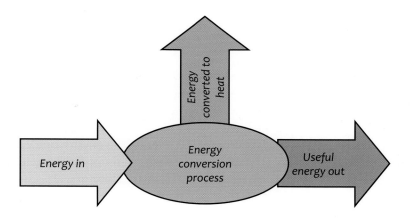

Figure 5-2. In any energy conversion process some energy is converted to heat that is not available to do useful work.

Why are perpetual motion machines impossible?

As mentioned above, the laws of thermodynamics state that in any energy conversion process some energy must always leave the system as unusable heat energy. As a result, the energy coming out of the machine is always less than the energy going in.

The same holds true even if the machine simply tries to retain the energy inside itself to sustain its own motion. As the machine operates, some energy will always be lost to the environment and the machine will eventually wind down and stop.

$$Efficiency = \frac{E_{out}}{E_{in}}$$

Since some energy must always be lost as heat, the efficiencies of our machines must always be less than 100%. As physical examples, the efficiency of typical automobile engines is only around 15%, which means that 85% of the energy in the fuel is not used to propel the car. Solar cells convert electromagnetic energy from the sun into electricity. At present the highest efficiencies realized with these technologies is around 25%. The overall efficiency of electric cars, for example, is around 20-25%. This figure may seem low, but there are a lot of losses in generating the electrical power at a power station and transporting the power to homes and other buildings where it is used.

Calculations With Energy

Two important forms energy can take in mechanical systems are gravitational potential energy, E_G, and kinetic energy, E_K. The gravitational potential energy an object possesses depends on how high up it is, and the kinetic energy of an object depends on how fast it is moving. Gravitational potential energy is calculated as

$$E_G = mgh$$

where E_G is gravitational potential energy in joules[1] (J), m is the mass (kg), g is 9.80 m/s^2, and h is the height (m). The gravitational potential energy of an object is directly proportional to its height. For example, if the height of an object increases by 50%, the gravitational potential energy of the object will also increase by 50%.

When calculating gravitational potential energy, the energy one calculates will always depend on the location used as the zero reference for the height. This zero reference might be sea level, or the ground, or the floor of a classroom, or a table top. It doesn't matter, because the E_G an object has is always relative to where $h = 0$ is. In physics problems the most logical location for $h = 0$ is generally clear from the context.

The equation for gravitational potential energy gives us another example of a derived MKS unit, joules. Multiplying the units together for the terms on the right side of the E_G equation, we can see that a joule is made up of fundamental units as follows:

$$1\,\text{J} = 1\,\text{kg} \cdot \frac{\text{m}}{\text{s}^2} \cdot \text{m} = 1\frac{\text{kg} \cdot \text{m}^2}{\text{s}^2}$$

---

1   Named after James Prescott Joule, a nineteenth-century English physicist whose work led to the discovery of the Law of Conservation of Energy.

Example Problem

A golf ball has a mass of 0.0459 kg. While climbing a tree near a driving range, little Janie finds a golf ball stuck in a branch 2.90 m above the ground. What is the gravitational potential energy of the golf ball at that height?

The given information is:

$m = 0.0459$ kg

$h = 2.90$ m

Inserting these values into the equation for gravitational potential energy we have

$$E_G = mgh = 0.0459 \text{ kg} \cdot 9.80 \ \frac{\text{m}}{\text{s}^2} \cdot 2.90 \text{ m} = 1.30 \text{ J}$$

This is not much energy—about enough to run a standard 60-watt light bulb for 0.02 seconds.

Another important form of mechanical energy is kinetic energy, the energy possessed by a moving object. Kinetic energy is calculated as

$$E_K = \tfrac{1}{2} mv^2$$

where E_K is the kinetic energy in joules (J), m is the mass (kg), and v is the velocity (m/s). The units for kinetic energy are joules, just as with all other forms of energy. Kinetic energy is proportional to the mass of an object, and to the square of the object's velocity.

Example Problem

An electron with a mass of 9.11 x 10^{-31} kg is traveling at 1.076% of the speed of light. Determine the amount of kinetic energy the electron has.

The speed of light in a vacuum is approximately 3.00 x 10^8 m/s. Thus, the velocity of the electron will be

$$v = 0.01076 \cdot 3.00 \times 10^8 \ \frac{\text{m}}{\text{s}} = 3.23 \times 10^6 \ \frac{\text{m}}{\text{s}}$$

Placing this value with the mass in the kinetic energy equation we have

$$E_K = \tfrac{1}{2} mv^2 = 0.5 \cdot 9.11 \times 10^{-31} \text{ kg} \cdot \left(3.23 \times 10^6 \ \frac{\text{m}}{\text{s}} \right)^2 = 4.75 \times 10^{-18} \text{ J}$$

Work

The way an object acquires kinetic energy or gravitational potential energy is that another object or person or machine does *work* on it. In physics, "work" is a technical term with a specific mathematical meaning. Work is the way mechanical energy is transferred from one machine or object to another. Work is a form of energy, but objects don't possess work. Work is the quantity of energy transferred from one mechanical system to another during the process of one system doing work on another. Work is defined as the energy it takes to push an object with a certain (constant) force over a certain distance, and it is calculated as

> When one mechanical system does *work* on another, energy is transferred between them, and the quantity of energy transferred is called *work*.

$$W = Fd$$

where W is the work done on the object in joules (J), F is the force on an object (N), and d is the distance the object moves (m).

The concept of work is the basic principle governing how energy is transferred from one device to another in a mechanical system. For example, as depicted in Figure 5-3, if an electric motor is used to lift a piece of equipment, the motor must reel in a certain length, L, of steel cable, and it must pull on the cable with a certain force, F, while doing so. The pulling force times the length of cable is the amount of work done by the motor. And where did this work energy supplied by the motor go? Assuming 100% efficiency in the lifting motor and cables (and electric motors have very high efficiencies, so this is not a bad approximation), the energy all went into the gravitational potential energy of the piece of equipment that was lifted. In actuality, since the efficiency of all systems must be less than 100% some of the energy left the system as heat. In the end, the gravitational potential energy of the lifted piece of equipment will not quite represent all of the energy the electric motor had to supply. (As a side note, a system designed to lift

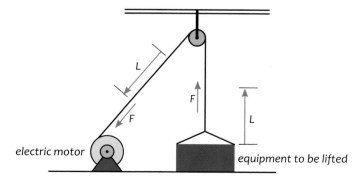

Figure 5-3. An electric motor raising an object to a height L by means of force F pulling on the cable.

an object using pulleys as in Figure 5-3 is called a *simple machine*. We will look at simple machines in the next chapter.)

We see here that work and conservation of energy are very closely related. As another example, if a man pushes a kid on a bicycle over a short distance to get the kid going, the man delivered energy to the kid on the bicycle equal to the pushing force times the distance pushed. Ignoring friction for now, that work energy from the man is now the kinetic energy of the kid on the bicycle.

There are two more important details to note about work. First, the equation for work, $W = Fd$, requires that the force applied to an object and the distance the object travels have to point in the same direction. If a person lifts a bucket of water, then work was done on the bucket of water. The force is applied vertically and the bucket moves vertically, so the work done to lift a bucket of water is the force required to lift it (its weight) times the distance it was lifted. But a person carrying a bucket of water down the road is *not doing any work on the bucket*. This is because the force exerted on the bucket to hold it up is vertical, but the distance the bucket is moving is horizontal. These two forces do not point in the same direction. In fact they are at right angles to one another, and no work is done on the bucket of water. This example is depicted in Figure 5-4.

Figure 5-4. In raising the bucket (left) work is done on the bucket. In moving the bucket horizontally no work is done on the bucket.

I hinted at the second detail in the previous paragraph. Most people will say that the force required to lift a bucket will be just a little larger than the weight, but this is not correct. If the upward force is at all greater than the weight, then we have a net upward force on the bucket. Recall from Chapter 4 that Newton's Second Law of Motion says that a net force will not just raise the bucket, it will *accelerate* the bucket. But for a bucket to move up with a *constant* speed requires no net force at all, according to the First Law of Motion. So after a little bump of force to get the bucket moving (which does briefly require a larger force and some energy) the bucket can be lifted to any height with a force equal to the bucket's weight.

The force required to lift an object is equal to its weight.

In physics problems of this kind we would normally just neglect the little bump of force necessary to get the bucket started and just assume that the force required to lift the bucket is equal to the weight of the bucket.

Example Problem

An elevator in a skyscraper weighs 8,868 N (about a ton). Inside the elevator are three people whose weights are 664 N, 548 N, and 736 N. Determine how much work the elevator motor has to do to lift this elevator and the people inside it from the ground floor up to the 47th floor, 171.9 m above the ground floor.

The total weight of the elevator and passengers is 10,816 N. This will be the force required to lift the elevator, since the force required to lift an object is equal to its weight. Placing this force and the height of 171.9 m into the work equation gives

$$W = Fd = 10,816 \text{ N} \cdot 171.9 \text{ m} = 1,859,270 \text{ J}$$

For those who may really be enjoying these examples, we must note that there is a small problem with this result. As it turns out, we are not technically allowed to state our result with this much precision. Recall from Chapter 3 that the precision in a value is indicated by the number of significant digits in the value. The weight has five digits of precision, and the height has four digits of precision. The height is less precise, and its precision governs the precision we are allowed to have in any calculated result. Thus, we must round off our result to 1,859,000 J, a value with four significant digits.

Again, the rules for using significant digits in measurements and calculations may be found in Appendix B.

Applying Conservation of Energy

When an object is thrown or fired straight up from the ground it leaves the ground with a certain velocity, and thus a certain amount of kinetic energy, E_K. As it goes up what happens to this E_K? It is converted to gravitational potential energy, E_G, of course, as the object goes higher and higher, and slower and slower. At the top of its flight all of the energy the object had at the ground in E_K will have been converted into E_G. We can use the Law of Conservation of Energy, along with the equations for E_G and E_K, to determine how high the object will go.

The same thing works in reverse. An object at a certain height has E_G. If the object is released to fall, as it falls the E_G is gradually and continuously converted into E_K. Just before it hits the ground all of the E_G it had at the top has been converted into E_K. We can use the Law of Conservation of Energy, along with the equations for E_G and E_K to find out how fast the object is going just before it strikes the ground.

In problems of this type it is customary to ignore friction. In reality, friction is always present in any so-called *mechanical system*, such as moving objects or

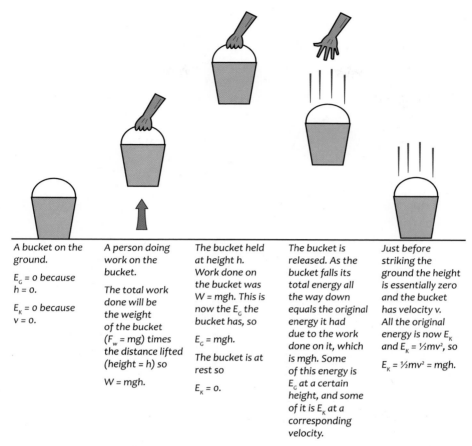

A bucket on the ground.	A person doing work on the bucket.	The bucket held at height h.	The bucket is released. As the	Just before striking the

A bucket on the ground.

$E_G = 0$ because $h = 0$.

$E_K = 0$ because $v = 0$.

A person doing work on the bucket.

The total work done will be the weight of the bucket ($F_w = mg$) times the distance lifted (height = h) so

$W = mgh$.

The bucket held at height h. Work done on the bucket was $W = mgh$. This is now the E_G the bucket has, so

$E_G = mgh$.

The bucket is at rest so

$E_K = 0$.

The bucket is released. As the bucket falls its total energy all the way down equals the original energy it had due to the work done on it, which is mgh. Some of this energy is E_G at a certain height, and some of it is E_K at a corresponding velocity.

Just before striking the ground the height is essentially zero and the bucket has velocity v. All the original energy is now E_K and $E_K = \frac{1}{2}mv^2$, so

$E_K = \frac{1}{2}mv^2 = mgh$.

Figure 5-5. Conservation of energy applied to a lifted and falling bucket.

machines. I will say a few words at the end of this chapter about the effect friction has on mechanical systems, but in introductory-level computations we typically ignore it. Many physical systems can be approximated pretty well even if friction is ignored.

Let us now look at a simple example of the conservation of energy in action. Figure 5-5 illustrates the application of the Law of Conservation of Energy to a person lifting a bucket and letting it drop. When a person lifts a bucket vertically the person does work on the bucket. To compute this work, the force to lift the bucket is the weight of the bucket, and the distance involved is the height it is lifted, so the work done on the bucket by the person is

$W = F_w h$

Since the weight, F_w, is equal to mg, this equation can be written

$W = F_w h = mgh$

Example Problem

A certain bucket of yellow paint with a mass of 3.85 kg is carried up a ladder until it is 1.52 m (about 5 ft) above the ground. Sadly, the bucket then falls off the ladder. How fast will the bucket of water be moving just before it hits the ground (and makes a colossal mess)?

The given information is:

$m = 3.85$ kg

$h = 1.52$ m

From this we calculate the gravitational potential energy the bucket will have at the top of the ladder.

$$E_G = mgh = 3.85 \text{ kg} \cdot 9.80 \ \frac{\text{m}}{\text{s}^2} \cdot 1.52 \text{ m} = 57.3 \text{ J}$$

As the bucket falls this E_G will gradually convert to E_K, which we can symbolize as $E_G \rightarrow E_K$. This tells us that the E_K the bucket will have just before it strikes the ground will be 57.3 J.

Now, to calculate the velocity that corresponds to the kinetic energy, we will have to perform a bit of algebra that is a tad more advanced than what we have seen so far. We will start with the equation for E_K, which is

$$E_K = \tfrac{1}{2}mv^2$$

We need to solve this equation for v, so we start by multiplying both sides by 2 and dividing both sides by m.

$$E_K = \tfrac{1}{2}mv^2$$
$$2E_K = mv^2$$
$$\frac{2E_K}{m} = v^2$$

Now we will flip this around and take the square root of both sides to have an equation for v, based on the E_K. Then we just insert the values and compute.

$$v^2 = \frac{2E_K}{m}$$

$$v = \sqrt{\frac{2E_K}{m}} = \sqrt{\frac{2 \cdot 57.3 \text{ J}}{3.85 \text{ kg}}} = 5.46 \ \frac{\text{m}}{\text{s}}$$

Energy was transferred from the person (the chemical potential energy in the person's muscles) to the bucket, and the bucket now has gravitational potential energy equal to

$$E_G = mgh$$

Right here we can see the conservation of energy at work. The work done by the person to lift the bucket is mgh. Where did that energy go? It went into the E_G the bucket has at the top, which is mgh, the same amount of energy. If the person releases the bucket, then as the bucket falls the gravitational potential energy begins to convert to kinetic energy. At any point as the bucket is falling, energy is conserved, which means that the total energy the bucket has is still the same as the energy it started with, but some of the energy is in kinetic energy and some of it is in gravitational potential energy. At the instant before the bucket hits the ground there will be no more gravitational potential energy because the height then is zero, so all of the energy originally given to the bucket by the work done on it is in the kinetic energy of the bucket.

The Effect of Friction on a Mechanical System

In our discussion of energy and work we did not consider friction in the examples. However, in all real mechanical systems friction plays a significant role. Friction is caused when parts of the system rub against each other, or when parts of the system move through a fluid such as air or water. Just as when a person rubs her hands together on a cold day, friction always results in heating. When the parts of a mechanical system such as a machine get warm, heat flows from the warm parts into the cooler surrounding environment. (We will look more at how this happens in a later chapter.) This heat energy flowing out of the system is energy that was formerly in the system in some other form.

> The effect of friction on any mechanical system is to convert energy into heat, which flows out of the system into the environment.

When heat energy flows out of a system due to friction the Law of Conservation of Energy still applies. No energy is created or destroyed. However, the energy remaining in the system is reduced by the amount of energy that has flowed out of the system due to heating from friction. A scientist or engineer may refer to energy "lost" due to friction. This does not mean the energy was destroyed or ceased to exist, only that it flowed out of the system and into the environment as heat and is no longer available as energy in the system. The net effect, of course, is that left to themselves (that is, without a continuing source of energy coming in) things will slow down while energy gradually leaves the system as heat due to friction.

Energy in the Pendulum

A swinging pendulum provides us with one final example of the conservation of energy at work. To begin, note that because of friction between the swinging pendulum and the air, and friction at the pivot at the top of the pendulum, any actual pendulum will lose energy to the environment as heat. This is why any actual free-swinging pendulum will always come to a stop.

But let's imagine a perfect pendulum, one that loses no energy due to friction. Physicists call this an *ideal pendulum*. In an ideal pendulum no energy would leave the "system" (the swinging pendulum) as heat and the pendulum would just keep on swinging without slowing down. The total amount of energy in the system is always the same.

> In an "ideal system," the total amount of energy in the system is always the same.

From the discussion in this chapter about the forms of energy and energy conservation, it should be pretty clear how energy transformation will work in this ideal pendulum. As shown in Figure 5-6, we will let the height of the pendulum when it is at rest (that is, not swinging) be our reference for height measurements. This means when the pendulum is straight down its height is zero and its gravitational potential energy is also zero. When the pendulum swings up to its highest point

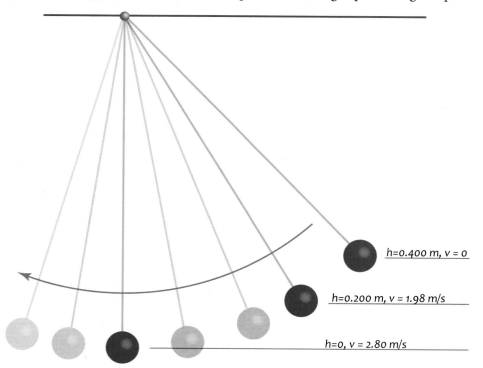

h=0.400 m, v = 0

h=0.200 m, v = 1.98 m/s

h=0, v = 2.80 m/s

Figure 5-6. Conservation of energy in a swinging pendulum.

it momentarily comes to rest. At this moment its velocity is zero and so its kinetic energy is zero. Put these facts together and let the pendulum start swinging.

Because of the conservation of energy, the pendulum always has the same amount of energy no matter where it is. When someone lifts the pendulum to get it started the person does work on the pendulum equal to the force it takes to lift it times the height (just as we saw with the bucket example). Since the pendulum is ideal, no energy is leaving the system as it swings. This means that no matter where the pendulum is, the total amount of energy in the system is always the same, and is equal to the amount of energy put into the system in the first place by the work done on it to lift it to the starting position. As the pendulum swings down E_G converts into E_K, and as the pendulum swings up E_K converts back into E_G. At all times the total energy the pendulum possesses always equals the sum of the E_G and the E_K, and this sum must always add up to the same value no matter where the swinging pendulum is.

Just to run through a quick calculation, let's say the mass at the end of the pendulum is 2.00 kg and we lift it up 0.400 m above its lowest point to release it. The total E_G at this starting point will be *mgh*, which gives $E_G = 7.84$ J. The kinetic energy here is zero, so now we know that the pendulum has a total of 7.84 J of energy no matter where it is.

How fast will it be going when it is halfway down, 0.200 m high? Well, the E_G at that position will be *mgh* = 3.92 J, so the E_K will be 7.84 J – 3.92 J = 3.92 J. Calculating the velocity from this kinetic energy value (see the example problem in the box on page 76) gives a velocity of 1.98 m/s. At the bottom all of the energy (7.84 J) is kinetic energy, so the velocity will be 2.80 m/s. In summary, if one knows how high the pendulum is at any point, the velocity at that point may easily be determined.

Nuclear Energy Calculations (Just for Fun!)

Back at the beginning of the chapter I mentioned Einstein's equation for mass-energy equivalence, $E = mc^2$. Some readers may have been wondering what a real calculation with this equation would look like. Well, why not have a look at one? The results are amazing.

A common nuclear process we often hear about is *nuclear decay*. Nuclear decay is a natural process in which the nucleus of an atom basically falls apart, one little bit at a time. The elements that exhibit nuclear decay are said to be *radioactive*. During each step in the decay process of an atom, some kind of particle comes flying out of the nucleus, carrying away mass and kinetic energy. (This constant stream of particles flying out of a radioactive material is what nuclear radiation is.) As an atom decays, the atom repeatedly mutates from its original identity, changing from one element to another as it goes through the decay process. The decay continues until the atom has turned into lead (usually), at which point the decay process stops.

There are three different kinds of nuclear decay, named with the first three letters of the Greek alphabet, α (alpha), β (beta), and γ (gamma). In alpha decay the nucleus of an atom fires out an alpha particle, which contains two protons and two neutrons. (We are going to run into alpha particles again in Chapter 8.) This particular cluster of particles is identical to the nucleus of a helium atom, and we can symbolize an alpha particle as ^4_2He . This type of notation is used in nuclear physics to represent any particle or atom that contains protons, neutrons or both. The upper number indicates the total number of protons and neutrons in the particle. (Together these are called *nucleons*, because they are the particles located in the nucleus of an atom.) The lower number indicates the number of protons in the particle.

There are two other kinds of nuclear decay. In beta decay, the nucleus fires out a beta particle, which is an electron. This is a nice trick, since there *are no electrons* in the nucleus of an atom! Nevertheless, it happens. The way this works is that the mass of a neutron is a teeny bit higher than the mass of a proton. When beta decay occurs, a neutron in the atom's nucleus mutates into a proton (!), and the difference in mass comes flying out of the atom as an electron with kinetic energy. Finally, in gamma decay the nucleus fires out a photon, which is a massless particle of light energy. (All these types of decay happen around us all the time and we are never even aware of it. The world is a strange place.)

With these basics, let's now look at an example of nuclear decay and see how matter gets turned into energy. Radium is a radioactive element that can undergo alpha decay. When an atom of radium goes through alpha decay it turns into a radon atom. An atom of radium has 88 protons and 138 neutrons, so we symbolize it as $^{226}_{88}\text{Ra}$. Radon has 86 protons and 136 neutrons and is symbolized as $^{222}_{86}\text{Rn}$. We can write the decay process in the form of an equation as follows:

$$^{226}_{88}\text{Ra} \rightarrow \, ^{222}_{86}\text{Rn} + \, ^4_2\text{He}$$

This equation says that one atom of radium decays to produce one atom of radon and one alpha particle.

Let's look at the masses and energies involved in this nuclear process. Looking up the masses for these three particles in a standard reference source, we find the masses to be:

Radium $m = 3.753242 \times 10^{-25}$ kg

Radon $m = 3.686691 \times 10^{-25}$ kg

alpha $m = 0.06646481 \times 10^{-25}$ kg

The sum of the masses of the radon nucleus and the alpha particle is 3.753156×10^{-25} kg. This is less than the original radium nucleus mass by 8.6×10^{-30} kg. (We don't get to keep all our significant digits when we subtract like this.) The Law of Conservation of Energy tells us the missing mass has been converted into the kinetic energy the alpha particle has when it comes flying out of the atom. Let's now figure out how fast this alpha particle will be going. Using Einstein's equation $E=mc^2$ and $c = 3.00 \times 10^8$ m/s, we find the missing mass is equal to 7.7×10^{-13} J of energy. Finally, loading this energy and the alpha particle mass into the velocity equation we get a velocity of 15,000,000 m/s, or 9,300 *miles per second*, which is 5.0% of the speed of light! Yikes! Those ordinary, everyday alpha particles are moving with incredible speed!

Ideas for Your Classroom

1. Make pictures depicting common objects and the kinds of energy they might possess. Examples:

    a. football stuck on a roof (gravitational potential)

    b. boiling water (thermal)

    c. moving train (kinetic)

    d. green laser light (electromagnetic)

    e. music (acoustic)

    f. loaded dart gun (elastic potential)

    g. foghorn (acoustic)

    h. speeding bullet (kinetic)

    i. data cables (electrical)

    j. unlit candle (chemical potential)

    k. firewood (chemical potential)

    l. pop fly baseball (kinetic and gravitational potential)

    m. stretched rubber band (elastic potential)

2. Make collages or charts showing the energy transformations and types of energy as energy travels from the sun to machines, people, or objects on earth, or from one object or machine to another.

3. Design a game in which groups compete by identifying the form of energy present in a given example.

Goals for Chapter 6

1. Name the six types of simple machines.

2. Explain the concept of mechanical advantage.

3. Explain how mechanical advantage is achieved with each of the basic simple machines.

4. Explain why it might be desirable to construct a machine with a mechanical advantage less than 1.

About This Chapter

Simple machines is a topic often included in elementary and middle school curricula, so we include it here. But since this topic is about *applied* physics, it more properly belongs to the subject of mechanical engineering. For this reason, simple machines is not a topic generally found in college physics courses.

Chapter 6
Simple Machines

Archimedes, a third-century BC mathematician, inventor and engineer in Syracuse, is famously supposed to have said, "Give me a place to stand and I will move the world with a lever." This statement is, of course, hyperbole, but everyone who has ever had to change a tire should be thankful for the lever and the screw, two of the six *simple machines*. The six simple machines have all been used from ancient times, and all remain in wide use to this very day.

Figure 6-1. Archimedes lifting the world with a lever.

Simple machines make it possible to do hundreds of simple tasks inexpensively and by hand, tasks that otherwise would require a more complicated machine or assistance from Superman. Every time a person pops the top off a glass bottle, winches a boat onto a trailer, rolls a wheel chair up a ramp, or pulls out a nail with a hammer, a simple machine is being put to use.

Understanding how simple machines work requires only an understanding of the work equation from the previous chapter. In that chapter we saw that the energy required to lift or push an object is called *work*. Work, W, is a quantity of energy, defined by the equation

$W = Fd$

where W is the work done on an object in joules (J), F is the force on the object (N), and d is the distance the object moves (m). For any given task, such as any of those listed above, a specific amount of energy is required to perform the task, regardless of whether the task is performed by a human, a machine or a gorilla. That energy will be delivered to the task at hand by applying a certain amount of force to an object and moving the object a certain distance.

The fact that *both* distance *and* force are involved is the key to how simple machines can make tasks easy to perform by hand. To perform a task, such as pulling a nail out of a board, a force must be applied to the nail, and the nail moved a certain distance. The force times the distance must equal the work (energy) required to remove the nail. But it doesn't matter at all how large the force or the distance applied by the human operator are, as long as their product equals the energy required, and as long as the end of the device actually touching the nail exerts a force high enough to pull the nail.

Of course, pulling a nail out of a board does require a specific amount of force, a lot more force than a person can produce with bare hands. But the idea of a simple machine is that it has an input side and an output side. The input side is where the human applies a force. The output side is where the machine applies a force to the task at hand. The output force will match the force required to pull the nail, but the input force will be reduced by a factor inherent in the design of the machine. Or stated the other way around, the force applied by the person operating the machine will be *multiplied*, and this multiplied force will appear at the output of the machine. So simple machines may be defined as follows:

> A simple machine is a device that mechanically trades distance for force to produce a given amount of work. The simple machine reduces by a certain factor the force required to perform a task, and multiplies the distance required by the same factor.

The design of the machine determines the multiplying factor achieved. This multiplying factor is called the *mechanical advantage, MA*, of the machine, defined as:

> The mechanical advantage, *MA*, of a simple machine is the ratio of the output force to input force, that is, the output force that will be produced for a given input force applied. The *MA* may also be computed as the ratio of input distance to output distance.

Thus, if 400 lb of lifting force is produced by a person applying 40 lb of force to the handle of a machine, the mechanical advantage of the machine is $MA = 400/40 = 10$.

With respect to the energy required to perform a task (that is, the work, $W = Fd$), simple machine provides a trade-off of distance for force. This means if the force required to perform a task is reduced by a certain factor, the mechanical advantage of the machine, the distance required to perform the task will be *increased* by the same factor. So consider a person who wants to hoist a 400-lb carton upward 10 feet to an upper storage platform in a warehouse. We will assume this task will be performed using a simple machine with a mechanical advantage of $MA = 8$. We will further assume that this simple machine makes use of a rope, and the worker pulls down on the rope to lift the carton. With this machine the person will only have to pull on the rope with 50 lb of force to lift the carton (since $400/8 = 50$). The trade-off is that the worker will have to pull not 10 ft of rope, but 80 feet of rope (since $8 \times 10 = 80$). In summary, the force required to accomplish a task is reduced by the mechanical advantage of the machine; the distance required to perform the task is multiplied by the same factor.

There are six basic types of simple machines. We will examine each type separately and show how mechanical advantage is achieved in each case. When discussing simple machines the conventional parlance is to use the term *effort* for the force applied to the machine (whether this force is applied by a human or by another machine), and *resistance* to the load the machine is moving.

1. The Lever

One of the most common simple machines is the lever, a device that is ubiquitous in every day life. Examples of levers are see-saws, crow bars, wheel barrows, and claw hammers. There are three separate classes of levers, distinguished by the locations of the effort and the resistance relative to the location of the *fulcrum*, that is, the pivot point.

CLASS 1 LEVERS

The see-saw is a common illustration of a Class 1 lever. As shown in Figure 6-2, the effort is applied to one side of the fulcrum, and this lifts the load or resistance on the other side of the fulcrum. The lever is the "board" of the see-saw, shown as a long, thin rectangle in the figure. In the illustration, the effort is applied twice as far from the fulcrum as the resistance. This means that to lift the resistance a certain distance, the effort will have to move down for double that distance. Since the effort distance is twice the resistance distance, the effort force is only half of the resistance force, so the *MA* of the machine is *MA* = 2. If the effort were five times as far from the fulcrum as the resistance was, the *MA* would be 5. The same principles apply even if the lever is not a simple straight line. Figure 6-3 shows a pry-bar pulling a nail, with the locations of the effort, resistance and fulcrum marked on the photograph. The effort is applied 10.5 inches from the fulcrum, and the resistance is 1.5 inches from the fulcrum, so the *MA* for this lever is *MA* = 10.5/1.5 = 7. A person pushing the lever with a force of 30 lb would produce a force of 210 lb on the nail, enough to pull it out.

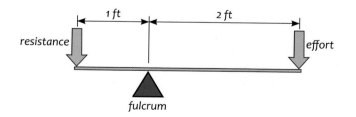

Figure 6-2. A Class 1 lever with MA = 2.

Figure 6-3. Using a pry-bar as a Class 1 lever.

CLASS 2 LEVERS

As shown in Figure 6-4, the Class 2 lever has the fulcrum on one end, with the resistance in between the fulcrum and the effort. In the diagram the effort is four times as far from the fulcrum as the resistance is, so the mechanical advantage is $MA = 4$. Classic examples of the Class 2 lever are the bottle opener and the wheelbarrow, shown in Figures 6-5 and 6-6.

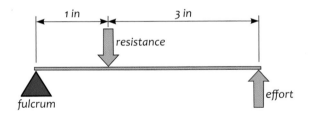

Figure 6-4. A Class 2 lever with MA = 4.

CLASS 3 LEVERS

In the Class 3 lever, depicted in Figure 6-7, the effort is in between the fulcrum and the resistance. This is the only lever class in which the effort is closer to the fulcrum than the resistance is. As seen in the figure, for this lever to work the fulcrum must actually be a hinge so the end of the lever is pinned down. In Class 3 levers the mechanical advantage is less than one, meaning that *more* force is required at the effort than if the lever were not used at all. Obviously, the purpose for Class 3 levers is not to make jobs easier. Instead, the purpose is to make them convenient. There are many cases in which the load or resistance needs to be at the opposite end of the lever from the fulcrum. A fascinating example is the lower human jawbone, or mandible. In an adult male the jaw muscles attach to the

Figure 6-5. A bottle opener as a Class 2 lever with MA of approximately 6.

Figure 6-6. A wheelbarrow as a Class 2 lever with MA of approximately 7.

mandible about 1.5 cm from the jawbone hinge, while the front teeth are about 9 cm from the hinge. This results in a mechanical "advantage" of $MA = 1.5/9 = 1/6 = 0.17$. The advantage here is obviously to keep the muscles that work our jawbones back out of the way, but the result is that to bite through a carrot with the front teeth requires six times as much force as cutting through the carrot on a cutting board! No wonder our jaw muscles are so strong! Other classic examples of Class 3 levers are tweezers and the construction machine known as a "front-end loader." These are shown in Figures 6-8 and 6-9.

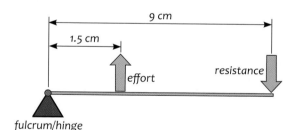

Figure 6-7. A Class 3 lever with $MA = 1/6$.

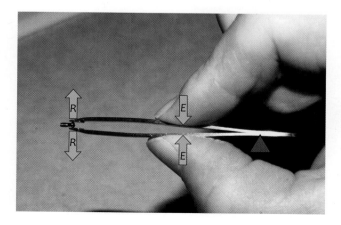

Figure 6-8. Tweezers are an example of a Class 3 lever.

Figure 6-9. The front-end loader applies the effort with the hydraulic cylinders attached to the underside of the main arms.

2. The Inclined Plane

The inclined plane is no mystery; it is simply a ramp. We see ramps everywhere, like in the back of a moving van or at building entrances with disabled access. If an object needs to be lifted a few feet, the force required to roll the object up a ramp will be lower than the force required to hoist it straight up. The mechanical advantage of the inclined plane depends on how long the ramp is (the input distance) in proportion to how high it is (the output distance), as shown in Figure 6-10.

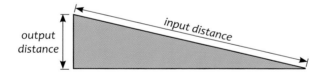

Figure 6-10. Input and output distance relations for a ramp.

Figure 6-11. This ramp for disabled access is an inclined plane with MA = 10.

For example, the disabled access ramp shown in Figure 6-11 is 25 feet in length and 2.5 feet high. The effort is applied as a force pushing a wheelchair up the ramp, with the goal (output) of raising the wheelchair (and the person in it) up 2.5 feet. So the ratio of input distance to output distance is 25/2.5 = 10. This value is the mechanical advantage of the ramp. As a result, if the combined weight of the person and wheelchair is 200 lb, the force required to push the chair up the ramp will be only 200 lb/10 = 20 lb.

3. The Wedge

The wedge is similar to the ramp, and common examples are splitting wedges used to split firewood, axes, knives, and chisels. With a ramp, the ramp is stationary and the task is accomplished by moving an object up the ramp. With a wedge, it is the wedge that moves by being forced into a stationary object to split it open, or under the object to lift it.

The mechanical advantage of the wedge is simply the length of the wedge

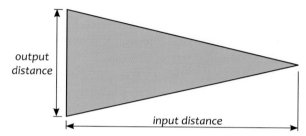

output distance

input distance

Figure 6-12. Input and output distance relations for a wedge when the wedge is fully driven in.

Figure 6-13. A splitting wedge is driven into the wood.

divided by the width, as suggested by Figure 6-12. The thinner the wedge is, the greater the mechanical advantage. The image in Figure 6-13 shows a wedge being driven into a piece of wood. The effort is the force of the hammer, and the resistance is the force of the log pushing horizontally on the wedge that tries to hold the log together. The width of the wedge, which is the output distance when the wedge is fully driven in, is the limit of how wide the wedge can push the two pieces of the log away from each other.

As mentioned, the thinner the wedge is the higher its mechanical advantage is. An axe head is only about half as thick as a splitting wedge, so its mechanical advantage is about twice as high. However, with a task such as splitting a log a thin wedge is much more likely to become tightly lodged in the log due to friction. (And spending a half hour trying to figure out how to get an axe head unstuck from a log can really put a damper on one's enthusiasm for splitting wood.) This is why splitting wedges are more often used for splitting larger pieces of wood as opposed to axes.

Efficiency in Simple Machines

So far in our discussion of simple machines we have not addressed the issue of friction. Friction is not much of an issue with levers, and with good wheels it is not much of an issue with the inclined plane, either. But with the wedge (previous section) and the screw (next section), friction is a significant factor.

The energy to drive in the wedge is coming from the kinetic energy of the hammer head. When a lot of friction is present, as with a wedge, a lot of the incoming kinetic energy is converted to heat due to the friction of the wedge, as, for example, it penetrates the tight grain of the wood. The friction does not nullify the practical advantage afforded by using the wedge, but it does mean that a lot of the energy spent by the person hammering the wedge will be dissipated as heat due to the friction, rather than being available to accomplish the task at hand. Mathematically, we would express this loss of energy by saying the machine's efficiency is less than 100%, because less than 100% of the input work is being utilized as output work.

The typical way of handling this in solving problems is to calculate the ideal *MA* of the machine, and multiply this figure by the efficiency of the machine to get the *actual* or *effective MA*. For such a calculation the efficiency would probably be determined experimentally by measuring the actual values of input work and output work. In the case of the wedge and the screw such measurements can get pretty complicated.

A different way of incorporating the effect of friction into the *MA* of a machine is to distinguish between the ideal *MA*, as calculated from the ratio of input distance to output *distance*, and the actual or effective *MA*, calculated from the ratio of output force to input *force*. The effect of friction is to reduce the output force applied to the resistance. Experimentally, this method is generally easier to implement. One simply measures the amount of force required (input force) to lift a known weight (output force), and the ratio of output force to input force is the actual *MA* of the machine.

> In a simple machine where friction is a significant factor, the actual MA may be experimentally determined as the ratio of the measured input force required to lift a known weight.

4. The Screw

These days the most common example of the screw is the car jack supplied with most contemporary automobiles, shown in Figure 6-14. The car jack makes use of levers to raise the car, and the screw provides a very high mechanical advantage for this purpose.

To turn any screw, whether it be a wood screw, a bolt, or the screw in the jack in the photo, requires rotating the screw with some kind of lever. This lever applies a force to the screw at some distance from the center of the screw. This means that the mechanical advantage of the screw depends not only on the screw itself, but also on the length of the lever used to turn the screw.

For the car jack shown in Figure 6-14, the hand turning the handle is held 10 inches from the center of the screw. To turn the handle through one complete rotation, the hand will travel around the circumference of a circle,

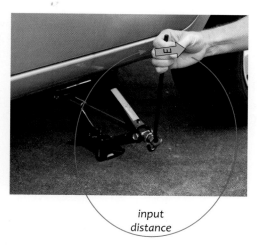

Figure 6-14. A typical car jack is a screw with high MA.

which is a distance of $2\pi r$. This distance is the input distance, and for the jack shown will be 2 x 3.14 x 10 inches = 62.8 inches.

The jack has 13 threads per inch on the screw shaft. This means for one turn of the handle the shaft will travel forward 1/13 inch, or 0.0769 inches. This is the output distance. Thus, the mechanical advantage afford by this screw is MA = 62.8/0.0769 = 817! This high mechanical advantage is why a person with even modest physical strength can raise the corner of a car off the ground. However, as with the wedge, there will be a lot of friction in the screw where the threads are in contact with the material they are threading into, so the actual MA will be less than the ideal MA we just calculated.

5. The Pulley

The fifth type of simple machine is the pulley. As shown back in Figure 5.3 in Chapter 5, a single pulley provides a mechanical advantage of 1. In that figure, the force with which the motor is pulling the cable is the same as the force lifting the load. In such an arrangement the advantage of using the pulling is simply to change the direction in which the force is applied for convenience. Without the pulley the motor would have to be mounted on the ceiling directly above the equipment being lifted. This restriction may not be very practical.

The real advantage of the pulley comes when multiple pulleys are used in an arrangement called a block and tackle, illustrated in Figure 6-15. In the photo, the yellow objects, the blocks, each house three pulleys, called sheaves. The tackle is the rope wound through the sheaves. The load to be lifted is attached to the ring hanging from the lower block. The load is lifted by pulling on the rope seen angling off to the left from the upper block.

To work out the *MA* for this simple machine we first need to mention how forces work in ropes. When a pulling force is applied to the end of a rope the force within the rope making it taught is called *tension*. The tension in a rope is a force, and its magnitude is the same as that of the force applied to the end of rope. Further, in the absence of friction the tension in a rope is the same everywhere in the rope, from one end to another.

Now here is a handy way to figure out the *MA* for a block and tackle. Consider the lower block to be part of the object it is connected to for lifting. The *MA* is determined by how many sections of rope are pulling up on that lower block, because each section has the same tension in it. In Figure 6-15 there are six vertical sections of rope

Figure 6-15. Block and tackle.

leading from the lower block to the upper block. Since each of these six sections of rope is pulling up on the lower block with the same tension, and since this tension is the same as the force applied to the end of the rope, the applied force or effort is being multiplied by six to lift the load, giving a mechanical advantage of *MA* = 6.

Although it is difficult to visualize, the same distance relationship applies to the pulley or block and tackle as to the other machines. With a mechanical advantage of six, the person pulling on the rope will have to pull six feet of rope in order to lift the load one foot.

The more sheaves there are in the blocks of a block and tackle system, the more friction there will be in the operation. Friction is caused not only by the bearings in the sheaves, but also by the stiffness and roughness of the cord. With ordinary hemp rope such as shown in Figure 6-15, the friction builds up pretty fast when the number of sheaves is increased. If appropriate for the purpose, friction will be reduced considerably by using a smooth, flexible rope such as nylon cord.

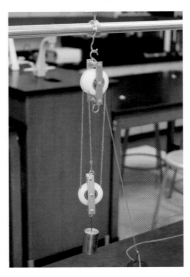

Figure 6-16. A small demonstration block and tackle in the lab, MA = 3.

Figure 6-16 shows a small block and tackle set-up using laboratory apparatus. Since three sections of cord lead up from the lower block, the mechanical advantage is $MA = 3$.

6. The Wheel and Axle

The last simple machine is the wheel and axle, depicted in Figure 6-17. One rarely sees the wheel and axle applied with two actual wheels and two cords, the way the figure shows. More commonly the large wheel where the effort is applied is actually some kind of handle, as shown in the old water well sketch of Figure 6-18. The steering wheels in cars and boats are somewhat similar to the water well machine. In fact, in some simple, inexpensive powered boats the steering system is identical to the system in Figure 6-18. In these boats the large wheel is the steering wheel. Under the dashboard there are two cables wrapped around the shaft connected to the steering wheel, and these two cables are directed with pulleys to the rear of the boat where they turn the engine, steering the boat.

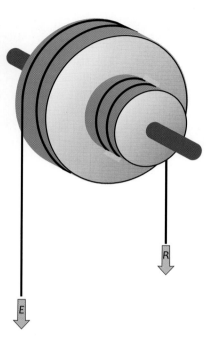

Figure 6-17. The wheel and axle.

The mechanical advantage of the wheel and axle is most easily determined by considering that the entire assembly rotates together, so that one full rotation occurs simultaneously for the effort wheel and the resistance wheel. The distance the cord wrapped around the wheel will travel during one rotation is, in each case, $2\pi r$. If we call the effort wheel radius r_E and the resistance wheel radius r_R, then the ratio of input distance to output distance is

$$MA = \frac{2\pi r_E}{2\pi r_R} = \frac{r_E}{r_R}$$

A very familiar application of the wheel and axle is the pedaling arrangement of a bicycle, shown in Figure 6-19. The effort is applied on the pedals, which are attached at a

Figure 6-18. A wheel and axle applied at a water well.

certain radius from the axis of rotation of the chain ring (the technical term for the front sprocket). The resistance is the force of the chain pulling on the chain ring.

From the equation above, the mechanical advantage gained from the front section of a bicycle is the pedal radius divided by the chain ring radius. For a bicycle like the one shown, the mechanical advantage depends on which

Figure 6-19. The pedals and chain rings of a bicycle.

chain ring is selected by the gear changer. The mechanical advantage will be highest when the chain is engaged on the smallest chain ring, so the bike will be easiest to pedal with the chain in this position. For the bicycle in the photo, the pedal radius is 6.75 inches, and the radius of the small chain ring is 2.5 inches, giving a mechanical advantage of MA = 6.75/2.5 = 2.7.

But on a bicycle this is not the end of the story; there is another wheel and axle system at the real wheel! Here the effort is applied at the chain, and the resistance is the pavement, applied at the radius of the much larger back tire. Since the radius of the back tire is several times the radius of any of the rear sprockets, the mechanical advantage at the rear axle is much less than one. The MA of the rear system will be as high as possible when the chain is engaged on the largest of the rear sprockets, but even there the rear axle MA for the bicycle shown is 1/6 with the chain on the largest sprocket. The overall MA of the bicycle is the product of the MA from the front and the MA from the back. For this bicycle, the maximum mechanical advantage is 2.7 x (1/6) = 0.45.

As with the Class 3 lever, the fact that the mechanical advantage of a bicycle is less than 1 indicates that convenience rather than force multiplication is the point of the machine. It is not at all difficult for humans to propel themselves down the road on foot, so we don't require mechanical advantage to help us. The convenient thing about a bicycle is the way one can maximize speed, and coast at speed without having to pedal at all (especially when going down hill). All simple machines make the same force-distance trade-off. With a bicycle, we are happy to make this trade. It is harder to propel oneself than walking, but still easy enough for most people. And the distance trade means the machine covers a lot more distance for the same expenditure of energy.

Yet another example of the wheel and axle is a device known to every rancher as a come-along, shown in Figure 6-20. Ranchers use the come-along to stretch a long section of steel fence wire tight and hold it tight while the wire is stapled to the

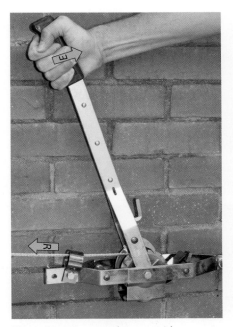

Figure 6-20. A come-along provides a
relatively high mechanical advantage.

Figure 6-21. A laboratory wheel and axle
set-up, MA = 2.

fence posts. As the handle is pulled the steel cable (seen going off to the left in the photo) is wound onto a small drum. A locking system locks the drum to prevent it from unwinding, so the drum turns only when the handle is being pulled to reel in the cable. As the handle is pulled repeatedly back and forth the cable gets tighter and tighter. For the come-along shown in the figure, the effort is applied at about 16.5 inches from the axis of rotation, and the cable is reeled in on a drum 1.5 inches in radius, for a mechanical advantage of $MA = 16.5/1.5 = 11$. This is a fairly high mechanical advantage, and the friction in this machine is minimal. As a result, the come-along allows the user, whether rancher or otherwise, to exert several hundred pounds of force without much difficulty on whatever the cable is attached to.

Finally, Figure 6-21 shows a wheel and axle system assembled from laboratory apparatus. The radius of the larger wheel is twice that of the smaller wheel, giving the machine a mechanical advantage of $MA = 2$. As a result, the smaller weight can balance or lift the larger weight, even though the smaller one weighs half as much.

Combinations of Simple Machines

We will end this chapter with a brief look at a few devices that use combinations of simple machines.

Every auto repair shop makes use of the floor jack, shown in Figure 6-22. The floor jack uses a complex arrangement of several different levers. These levers in turn actuate a small hydraulic cylinder, another device that provides mechanical advantage but which is not one of the ancient simple machines. The resulting mechanical advantage is very high without sacrificing much in the way of distance. A mechanic slides the floor jack under one end of the car so the blue lifting pad (at the far right of the device in the photo) is under something solid. Then with just a few pumps of the handle one end of the car will be off the floor. Figure 6-23 shows a small-scale, working model of a floor jack. The base of this cute little gadget is only about 8 inches long, making this device a terrific demonstration item.

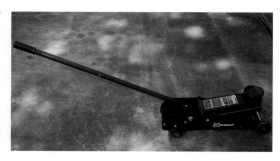

Figure 6-22. A floor jack combines multiple levers and a small hydraulic cylinder to achieve very high MA.

Figure 6-24 shows the bolt cutter, a tool used for cutting steel cable, metals rods, and so on. A pair of bolt cutters (the plural is often used to refer to a single tool) uses a combination of two Class 1 levers and some nice long handles

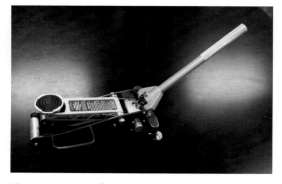

Figure 6-23. A small-scale, working model floor jack is great for demonstrations.

to generate a mechanical advantage of over 80. This would mean that with 50 lb of force applied at the handle, over 4,000 lb of cutting force appears at the blades. Of course, the blades are wedges, another simple machine incorporated into this tool.

Many households are familiar with the levered cork screw, shown in Figure 6-25. The screw is first screwed into the cork, and the levers are used to extract the cork from the bottle. Though old-school European waiters may scoff, this tool is actually a pretty handy way of getting a cork out without straining your shoulder.

There are many other devices around that make use of combinations of

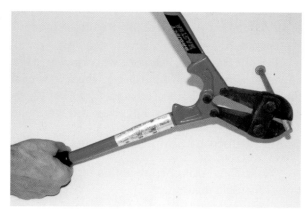

Figure 6-24. A bolt cutter combines levers to achieve a mechanical advantage of over 80.

simple machines. A pair of scissors is a combination of the Class 1 lever and the wedge; positioning the material to be cut closer the to the pivot increases the *MA*. A door knob is a wheel and axle combined with a Class 2 lever. Venetian blinds incorporate pulleys, levers, and sometimes screws. Just about every tool in the tool box or kitchen uses or connects to simple machines in some way. Simple machines are all around us. They make use of basic principles known in ancient times, and continue to be applied today in many fascinating ways.

Figure 6-25. A common levered cork screw combines the screw and the Class 1 lever.

Ideas for Your Classroom

1. Allow students to experience as many actual simple machines in person as possible. Many of the examples in this chapter are tools that may be purchased at reasonable expense and used in the classroom (with plenty of adult supervision) for students to see and use.

2. Have students perform historical research to see how simple machines were used in ancient times. (Archimedes is a good place to start.)

3. Have students research developing countries to see how simple machines are used today in pre-industrial cultures for work such as drawing water from rivers, hauling heavy loads, and other tasks.

4. Challenge students to identify common devices in the environment around them that make use of simple machines. (The kitchen is a great place to look.)

5. Using an inexpensive spring scale, measure input and output forces to calculate the effective mechanical advantage of a simple machine such as an inclined plane (with and without wheels under the load) or block and tackle. Compare these effective *MA* values to the ideal values determined from the input and output distances.

Goals for Chapter 7

1. Define interaction.

2. State the law of conservation of momentum.

3. Distinguish between elastic and inelastic collisions.

4. Use the principle of conservation of momentum to describe the possible outcomes of an elastic collision between equal or unequal masses, with one mass initially at rest.

5. Describe how the law of conservation of momentum relates to Newton's Third Law of Motion.

About This Chapter

Momentum may not be a topic that comes up much in the context of elementary school science. But the law of conservation of momentum is one of the most fundamental laws in physics and is not hard to understand, so we include this chapter here for completeness.

Chapter 7
Momentum

One of the basic principles of physics, and a fairly simple one to understand, is the principle of *momentum*. The study of momentum is important in physics because momentum relates very closely to Newton's Third Law of Motion. With the study of momentum we also encounter another of the important "conservation laws" in physics. There are several of these so-called conservation laws, and in studying them one actually learns a lot about our understanding of the way nature works. Conservation principles show up in many different contexts in nature.

The law of conservation of momentum is one of the primary tools physicists have used to investigate the world of subatomic particles. And since subatomic physics has been one of the primary research objectives in physics throughout the twentieth and twenty-first centuries, the law of conservation has played a major role in the developments in physics over the past 100 years.

> Conservation principles show up in many different contexts in nature.

The momentum of an object is the product of its mass and its velocity. In physics, we use the variable p to represent momentum. Thus, the equation for momentum is

$$p = mv$$

where p is an object's momentum (kg·m/s), m is the mass of the object (kg), and v is the velocity of the object (m/s).

Conservation of Momentum

The *law of conservation of momentum* is another of the famous conservation laws in physics. The first conservation law we encountered was the conservation of energy in Chapter 5.

The law of conservation of momentum is about what happens during a collision between two objects. The law applies to a collision between cars, a collision between billiard balls, or a collision between two atoms. It doesn't matter what the objects are, or how it is that they collide, the law of conservation of momentum will apply.

In fact, the objects don't even have to touch for the law of conservation of momentum to apply. Two protons fired directly at one another in a physics experiment will actually never "touch." They will just get so close together that their repulsive electric charge makes them bounce apart. Because of this, we prefer to use the term "interaction" instead of collision. An "interaction" could be two cars colliding,

Example Problem

A proton at the Large Hadron Collider in Switzerland is traveling with a velocity of 12,200,00 m/s (4% of the speed of light). The mass of a proton is 1.673×10^{-27} kg. Determine the momentum of this proton.

From the given information,

$$v = 12,200,000 \ \frac{m}{s}$$

$$m = 1.763 \times 10^{-27} \ kg$$

Inserting the values and compute the result we have

$$p = 1.673 \times 10^{-27} \ kg \cdot 12,200,000 \ \frac{m}{s} = 2.04 \times 10^{-20} \ \frac{kg \cdot m}{s}$$

two charged particles repelling one another, two magnets pushing apart, or the sun and a planet pulling on each other with gravitational attraction. In summary, one can think of the terms interaction and collision as synonyms in this context.

The Law of Conservation of Momentum may be stated as follows:

> In any interaction between objects, the total momentum of the objects involved is conserved.

As we discussed back in Chapter 5, when we say that a quantity is "conserved" during a certain event, what we simply mean that the total amount of this quantity before the event is equal to the total amount of the same quantity after the event. In the case of momentum, we are talking about the total of all the momentum values of all the objects involved in the interaction.

Types of Collisions

There are two basic types of collisions or interactions. In an *elastic collision*, the objects bounce perfectly apart without any damage. When this happens, not only is the momentum conserved but the total kinetic energy of the moving objects is conserved as well. In other words, no energy is lost from heat or friction as the objects collide. In an *inelastic collision*, the kinetic energy of the moving objects is not conserved. This is because in inelastic collisions some of the initial kinetic energy the objects had was converted to other forms of energy during the collision. Some of the original kinetic energy may have be converted

Momentum is conserved in all interactions. In *elastic* interactions, kinetic energy is also conserved.

to heat due to friction as the objects collided. Or, some of the original energy may have been used to bend or break parts of the objects, such as with most car collisions. Or again, some of the kinetic energy before the collision may have been converted into sound or light from the impact of the crash. When some of the initial kinetic energy is converted into heat or other forms of energy, the kinetic energy of the objects after the collision will not be the same as it was before the interaction.

In *inelastic* collisions, some kinetic energy is converted into heat or other forms of energy.

action. (Though, of course, the total of all types of energy will be conserved.) Momentum will still be conserved, because momentum is always conserved. But the kinetic energy is only conserved in elastic collisions.

Working Assumptions

To keep this presentation as straightforward as possible, we will establish a few working assumptions to simplify the discussion while keeping it accurate. The first is that we will examine only elastic collisions. In the real world, there are many interactions that are so close to being elastic that we can study them as if they were perfectly elastic. Examples of these would be collisions between billiard balls, between smooth steel spheres, and between subatomic particles such as protons. In actuality, there are no perfectly elastic collisions; there are always energy losses of some kind. But the elastic collision assumption is a very good assumption in some important cases.

Another assumption we will make to keep things manageable is that the objects in the collisions we study will always move in a straight line with respect to each other. When things bounce apart at different angles the conservation of momentum still applies, but the math involved is a lot more complex. A third assumption we will apply is that prior to the collision one of the objects will be at rest but free to move when hit. This assumption will also simplify the math in the example problems quite a bit. In summary, there are three working assumptions that will apply to the considerations in this chapter:

Our Working Assumptions

1. The interaction is elastic.
2. All the motion before and after the collision is in a single straight line.
3. One of the objects is at rest before the collision, but is free to move.

An important issue for us to consider at the beginning is whether or not the two objects involved in the collision have the same mass. Of course, in the case of billiard balls the two objects do have the same mass. When the two objects have the same mass and one of them is at rest the outcome is totally predictable. The initially moving object will always stop dead, and the other object will begin moving at the same speed as the original object and in the same direction. This is illustrated in Figure 7-1 with two billiard balls.

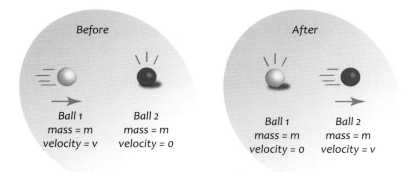

Figure 7-1. The interaction of two billiard balls (equal masses) colliding.

The figure shows a blue ball at rest and a white ball heading toward it. Since the blue ball is at rest, its velocity is zero, and it has no momentum. The white ball is moving with a certain velocity, so the white ball does have momentum. The total momentum before the collision is simply the momentum of the white ball, because it is the only one moving.

After the collision, the blue ball will, of course, be moving off to the right. But since the masses are equal, the white ball will come to a complete stop. This means that for momentum to be conserved, the blue ball will have to move off after the collision with the same velocity as the white ball had originally. Anyone who has played pool (or billiards) enough will have seen this kind of momentum transfer in action. Of course, putting spin ("English") on the cue ball changes the interaction considerably—an issue we will not be dealing with here.

This case seems simple enough. But in general, we need to consider what happens when two objects with different masses interact. No doubt every reader of this chapter has had many experiences watching things bump into each other. In addition to billiard balls, you may have seen bumper cars colliding, or toy cars, or marbles. You have seen things collide all of your life. From all these experiences, you know that when a moving object collides with a stationary object there are three possibilities for what the objects could do after the collision.

The first possibility is the one we just considered. When the objects have equal masses the moving object will stop dead and the stationary object will begin moving. The second possibility is that the first moving object could continue moving in the same direction but at a slower speed than before, so that both objects move off after the collision in the same direction. This is exactly what will happen if the first moving object has a greater mass than the stationary object, illustrated in the upper part of Figure 7-2. Because the moving object is more massive, it will keep moving in the same direction, rather than bouncing back.

The third possibility is that the first moving object bounces backward, going back toward where it originally came from, while the stationary object moves off in the original direction. This is what will happen if the moving object is less massive than the stationary one. This situation is illustrated in the lower half of in Figure 7-2. For this illustration I chose two hockey pucks to use for the collision.

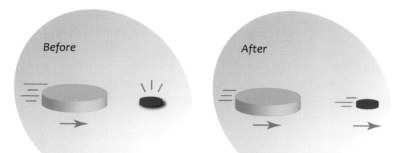

When a large mass collides with a small mass at rest, both masses will move off in the original direction of motion.

When a small mass collides with a large mass at rest, the small mass bounces back, while the large mass moves off in the original direction of motion.

Figure 7-2. The interaction of unequal masses colliding: a large mass striking a small mass (top), and a small mass striking a large mass (bottom).

The Directionality of Momentum

The third of the three scenarios we have just considered raises an important question. In the third scenario, after the collision occurs the two objects are moving in opposite directions. Will motion in two different directions make a difference in our mathematical approach to solving problems using the law of conservation of momentum? Yes, indeed! Momentum is one of the types of quantities in physics that have a *direction* associated with them. That is, they *point* somewhere. Recall from Chapter 4 that the term velocity connotes both the speed and direction of the motion of an object. Quantities like this are called *vectors*. A vector quantity has both magnitude and direction associated with it. Other vector quantities we have already encountered are acceleration and force. Now momentum may also be added to the list of vector quantities we have studied.

Hopefully, it will seem intuitive that the direction of these quantities is important. A positive or negative velocity is the difference between driving north and driving south. A positive or negative acceleration is the difference between speeding up and slowing down. A positive or negative force is the difference between pushing an object to the right or pushing it to the left.

With our motion constrained to a straight line, we model vector quantities mathematically by using positive and negative signs. All we have to do is identify the two possible directions, such as left and right, and call one of them positive and one of them negative. It doesn't matter which is which, but conventionally we identify motion to the right as positive and motion to the left as negative. If we do this, all the math will work.

While we are on the subject, you may be interested to know there are other variables in physics that have no direction associated with them, such as mass, energy and temperature. Quantities like these are called *scalars*. The temperature at a certain place in the room you are in right now has no direction associated with it, that is, it doesn't point anywhere. Mass is another variable that has no direction. To be sure, the force of gravity acting on a mass *does* have a direction (down), which is why force is a vector. But mass has no direction and is a scalar quantity.

> A *vector* is a physical quantity that possesses both magnitude and direction. A *scalar* is a physical quantity that possesses only magnitude.

Solving Problems with Conservation of Momentum

One of the most powerful features about the law of conservation of momentum is the fact that the law can be used to solve very complex problems in physics. As mentioned at the beginning of the chapter, the application of the law of conservation of momentum has been a big factor in discoveries in physics for over a century.

The task of applying conservation of momentum to physical problems begins by stating the law of conservation of momentum in the form of an equation. In this chapter, one of our operating assumptions is that before the collision only one of the objects will be in motion. We will call this object 1. The other object is at rest, and we will call it object 2. After the collision we will always have either only one object moving (which would be object 2, in the case when the masses are equal), or both objects moving.

The law of conservation of momentum says that the total momentum of all the objects before the collision must equal the total momentum of all the objects after the collision. Assuming the most general case, that both objects are moving after the collision, this statement would be written mathematically this way:

$$p_{1i} = p_{1f} + p_{2f}$$

In this equation the subscripts *i* and *f* mean *initial* and *final*, just as in the acceleration equation from Chapter 3. The subscripts 1 and 2 refer to *object* 1 and *object* 2, respectively. Before the collision, the *initial* (or before) part of the problem, the only object moving is object 1, so its momentum, on the left side of the equation, is p_{1i}. The momenta (plural for momentum) of the two objects after the collision, the *final* (or after) part of the problem, are added together on the right side of the equation. The equation simply sets the momentum before the collision equal to the total momentum after the collision, as the law of conservation of momentum says.

Now, each of the three momentum terms in the equation above is simply the product of a mass and a velocity. Assuming that the masses of object 1 and object 2 do not change during the interaction, we can write the equation as

$$m_1 v_{1i} = m_1 v_{1f} + m_2 v_{2f}$$

In this equation there are five variables—two masses and three velocities. Solving problems involving the conservation of momentum boils down to solving this equation for the quantity that is unknown, inserting values for the other quantities, and computing the result.

If you have been following the example problems, please do take a crack at the one that begins below. Although the math is straightforward, there are several steps and a bit of algebra involved, and as a result this example is the most complicated one in this volume. (Of course, the most complicated example had to occur somewhere.) But the example itself is taken from an actual historical event, one we will explore further in the next chapter.

Example Problem

In 1909 Ernest Rutherford discovered the atomic nucleus with his famous "gold foil experiment." In this experiment, small "alpha particles" were fired at much larger gold atoms and some of them bounced straight back, a perfect example of the third type of collision we studied. As we saw in an example in Chapter 5, an alpha particle contains two protons and two neutrons. Let's calculate the rebound velocity for an alpha particle after a head-on collision with an atom of gold, assuming the gold atom is free to move. An alpha particle has a mass of 6.646 x 10^{-27} kg, and the much larger gold atom has a mass of 3.271 x 10^{-25} kg. The gold atom is at rest when Rutherford fires the alpha particle at it with a velocity of (incredible as it may sound) 15,000,000 m/s. After the collision, the gold atom recoils with a velocity of 597,000 m/s. What was the rebound velocity of the alpha particle after the collision?

Summarizing the given information and the unknown quantity we have:

$$v_{1i} = 15,000,000 \ \frac{m}{s}$$

$$m_1 = 6.646 \times 10^{-27} \ kg$$

$$m_2 = 3.271 \times 10^{-25} \ kg$$

$$v_{2f} = 597,000 \ \frac{m}{s}$$

$$v_{1f} = ?$$

The next step is to write down the conservation of momentum equation and solve it for the unknown, v_{1f}. This is done as follows (keeping the equals signs lined up to make the steps easier to follow):

$$m_1 v_{1i} = m_1 v_{1f} + m_2 v_{2f}$$

$$m_1 v_{1i} - m_2 v_{2f} = m_1 v_{1f}$$

$$\frac{m_1 v_{1i} - m_2 v_{2f}}{m_1} = v_{1f}$$

$$v_{1f} = \frac{m_1 v_{1i} - m_2 v_{2f}}{m_1}$$

We can now compute the unknown velocity by inserting the values.

$$v_{1f} = \frac{m_1 v_{1i} - m_2 v_{2f}}{m_1}$$

$$= \frac{6.646 \times 10^{-27} \ kg \cdot 15,000,000 \ \frac{m}{s} - 3.271 \times 10^{-25} \ kg \times 597,000 \ \frac{m}{s}}{6.646 \times 10^{-27} \ kg}$$

$$v_{1f} = -14,000,000 \ \frac{m}{s}$$

Well! That alpha particle came at the gold atom moving 15 million meters per second, and when it rebounded it was going 14 million meters per second. That is amazing!

Final notes:

As expected, the velocity came out to be negative, indicating that the alpha particle bounced back the way it came. This is because the alpha-particle is much less massive than the gold atom.

Also, the velocity for the alpha particle has been rounded to two significant digits. The reasons for this were described briefly in the elevator example from Chapter 5, and we will repeat them here. In this example we are not technically allowed to state our result with more than two digits of precision. Recall from Chapter 3 that the precision in a value is indicated by the number of significant digits in the value. The initial velocity given in the problem has only two digits of precision, and this precision governs the precision we are allowed to have in the calculated result. Thus, even though the calculator gives us –14,382,891.9651 m/s, we must round off our result to –14,000,000 m/s, a value with two significant digits.

Again, the rules for using significant digits in measurements and calculations may be found in Appendix B for those who are interested.

Momentum and Newton's Third Law of Motion

Recall that Newton's Third Law of Motion states, *For every action force there is an equal and opposite reaction force.* Any time *anything* pushes or pulls on *anything else*, the forces on each object are the same. The forces on the two objects are also in opposite directions, because as we saw earlier, force is a vector quantity. That is, forces have direction.

The thing is, even though the forces acting on two objects are the same, the effects on those two objects will not be the same. Sure, while the forces are acting during a collision, both objects will accelerate, according to Newton's Second Law of Motion, $a = F/m$. But this law is very difficult to apply in a situation like a collision. We almost never know how long the forces between objects last. This is where the law of conservation of momentum comes in.

Newton's Third Law tells us that when one object pushes on another, the second one pushes back on the first, equally and oppositely. The law of conservation of momentum tells us what the effects of this exchange will be: the total momentum of the interacting objects will be conserved. If one object is moving and the collision makes it stop, or if both objects are moving and continue to move, whether they bounce apart or both move off in the same direction, it doesn't matter. The total momentum of the objects must remain unchanged during the interaction.

This principle can blow your mind if you think about it for a while. It basically means that the total momentum of the universe is zero and always stays at zero! The reason for this goes back to the Big Bang, the original explosion that most astrophysicists say initiated the universe. At the Big Bang everything blew out from the initial point in all directions. For every kilogram of matter going in one direction, there was another kilogram of matter heading off in the opposite direction. Assuming that the momentum of the universe before the Big Bang was zero (if we can even conceive of such a thing), adding together all of the momentum of the matter emerging from the explosion gives zero.

> The total momentum of the universe is zero and stays zero!

Ever since this original event, every time one particle or object in the universe gains some momentum in one direction by being pushed, one or more other objects must gain an equal amount of momentum in the opposite direction by being pushed equally and oppositely. Think about that.

In summary, Newton's Third Law tells us that when A pushes on B, B pushes back on A equally and oppositely. The law of conservation of momentum informs us about the effects these pushes or pulls have on the objects involved. Momentum must be conserved!

Momentum and Newton's First and Second Laws of Motion

It is also worth pointing out the straightforward connection between the concept of momentum and Newton's first two Laws of Motion. *The net force on an object may be thought of as the rate at which the momentum is changing with time.*

According to the First Law, when there is no net force present on an object, the velocity is a constant. So when $F = 0$, change in momentum $= 0$.

According to the Second Law, force equals mass times acceleration, or $F = ma$. In Chapter 3, we defined acceleration as the rate at which an object's velocity is changing (see page 28). This means that ma is the rate at which the momentum is changing, and this is equal to the net force on the object, F.

How does a bicycle keep its balance?

The conservation of momentum also applies to rotating objects, where it is referred to as *angular momentum*. With angular momentum, the direction of the momentum lies along the *axis of rotation*. (This may sound weird, but this is the way the math works.) A rotating system will always preserve a constant angular momentum, which often means the system will maintain a balance as long as it continues to rotate. If you try to change the direction of the axis while an object is spinning, something else will have to change with it in order to make the total angular momentum of the system remain the same.

The conservation of angular momentum is the explanation behind the behavior of spinning tops and gyroscopes. Conservation of angular momentum is also the reason a bicycle can balance on two wheels, and why leaning a bicycle while it is moving causes it to turn, even without turning the handle bars.

Ideas for Your Classroom

Momentum is not normally a topic in the curriculum in the elementary grades, so the subject is not likely to come up except as a question from a curious student. As a result, the ideas list is shorter than usual this chapter.

1. Demonstrate conservation with the interesting demonstration device known as a Newton's Cradle. In this device, swinging steel balls interact in nearly perfectly elastic collisions. No matter how many balls swing down to hit those at rest at the bottom, conservation of momentum requires that the same number of balls must swing up on the other side.

2. An older and really curious elementary student might be fascinated by thinking about the claim that the total momentum of the universe is and must always be zero. Such a student might wish to try illustrating this by a sequence of collision events that fan out in a chain reaction and never stop.

Goals for Chapter 8

1. Define and describe atom and molecule.

2. Describe John Dalton's atomic model.

3. Describe each of the following three major experiments: J. J. Thomson's cathode ray tube experiment, Robert Millikan's oil drop experiment, and Ernest Rutherford's gold foil experiment.

4. Describe the new atomic models that resulted from Thomson's and Rutherford's experiments.

5. Describe the Bohr and quantum models of the atom.

6. Explain the phrase, "energy is quantized."

7. Use the Bohr model of the atom to explain the phenomenon of atomic spectra, that is, how atoms of each different element give off specific colors of light when they are excited.

About This Chapter

This chapter is perhaps a bit more conceptually difficult than other chapters, but everyone should be able to follow it with some effort. The material covered here is of central importance for many topics in physics, so you are encouraged to read thoughtfully.

Chapter 8
Atoms and Atomic Spectra

Atomic Basics

We will begin this chapter with a review of the basic facts about the atomic structure of matter. All matter is made of *atoms*, which are the smallest basic units matter is composed of. An atom of a given element is the smallest unit of matter that possesses all of the properties of that element.

Atoms are mostly empty space. Each atom has an incredibly tiny nucleus in the center which contains all of the atom's *protons* and *neutrons*. Since the protons and neutrons are in the nucleus, they are collectively called *nucleons*. The masses of protons and neutrons are very nearly the same, although the neutron mass is very slightly greater. Each proton and neutron has nearly 2,000 times the mass of an electron, so the nucleus of an atom contains practically all of an atom's mass. Outside the nucleus is a weird sort of cloud surrounding the nucleus containing the atom's *electrons*. Sometimes people have modeled electrons as orbiting the nucleus like planets orbiting the sun, but we have known for a century that this is not at all an accurate description of what is going on with electrons. It is actually very hard to say what is *really* going on, but we are not going to get into that.

The emptiness of atoms can be hard to grasp. It's so easy for us to glibly pass over the "mostly empty space" remark without pausing to consider what it means, so here is an analogy. Assume that we imagine an atom to be the size of the huge Roman Coliseum, shown in Figure 8-1. Those tiny figures near the center are people. Imagine that one of those people has a flower on his lapel, held there by a straight pin. Suppose he removes the pin in order to straighten his flower. For a moment he holds the pin up and looks at the pinhead. Then he looks up all around at the distant outer edges of the massive Coliseum. If our atom were the size of the Coliseum, the nucleus of that atom would be the size of that pinhead! If you have ever been inside a football stadium you can try to imagine this for yourself. So what fills all this vast space inside the atom?

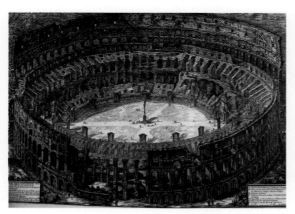

Figure 8-1. Engraving of the Roman Coliseum by Giovanni Piranesi.

Nothing, not even air! (Air is also made of atoms.) The inside of an atom is empty space.

Moving along, neutrons have no *electric charge*, one of the properties of subatomic matter. Benjamin Franklin was the first to apply the terms positive and negative to the two types of electric charge that occur in nature. It is hard to say exactly what electric charge *is*. However, we can say oppositely charged objects attract each other, and objects with the same type of charge repel each other. We can also say that the forces between charges are the extremely important forces that enable compounds to form, giving rise to all of chemistry. Protons and electrons each contain exactly the same amount of charge, 1.6×10^{-19} coulombs (C). (The coulomb is the MKS unit for charge, a derived unit. It is named after French scientist August Coulomb.) The charge on protons is positive and the charge on electrons is negative. If an atom has no net electric charge it must contain equal numbers of protons and electrons.

> The size difference between an atom and its nucleus is analogous to the difference between a stadium and a pinhead.

Atoms are significantly smaller than the wavelengths of light, which means light does not reflect off atoms and there is no way to see them. The same is true of molecules. *Molecules* are tiny clusters of atoms chemically bonded together. When atoms of different elements are bonded together in a molecule they form a *compound*, which we will discuss more in the next chapter. But sometimes atoms of the same element bond together in molecules. Examples of this are oxygen and hydrogen molecules, which are each composed of a pair of atoms. These two gases are examples of *diatomic gases*, so called because their atoms bond together in pairs to form molecules of gas.

The History of Atomic Models

The story of atomic theory starts back with the ancient Greeks. As we look at how the contemporary model of the atom developed we will hit on some of the great milestones in the history of physics and chemistry along the way. As with our review of the Copernican Revolution in Chapter 3, the history of our models or theories about atoms vividly illustrates the way theories evolve in the Cycle of Scientific Enterprise.

In the fifth century BC the Greek philosopher Democritus (Figure 8-2) proposed that everything was made of tiny, indivisible particles. Our word atom comes from the Greek word *atomos*, meaning "indivisible." Democritus' idea was that the properties of substances were due to characteristics of the atoms they are made from. So atoms of metals were supposedly hard and strong, atoms of water were assumed to be wet and slippery, and so on. At this same time there were various views

> Our term atom derives from the Greek word *atomos*, meaning indivisible.

about what the basic elements were. One of the most common views was that there were four elements—earth, air, water, and fire—and that everything was composed of these.

Not much real chemistry went on for a very long time. During the medieval period, of course, there were the alchemists who sought to transform lead and other materials into gold. But this cannot be done by the methods available to them and their efforts were not successful.

But in the seventeenth century things started changing as scientists became interested in experimental research. The goal of the scientists described here was to figure out what the fundamental constituents of matter were. This meant figuring out how atoms were put together, what the basic elements were, and understanding what was going on

Figure 8-2. Greek philosopher Democritus.

when various chemical reactions took place. The nature of earth, air, fire and water were under intense scrutiny over the next 200 years.

In 1803 English scientist John Dalton (Figure 8-3) produced the first actual scientific model of the atom. Dalton's atomic model was based on the five principles stated in the box on the next page.

The impressive thing about Dalton's atomic theory is that even today the last three of these points are regarded as correct, and the first two are least partially correct. On the first point, it is still scientifically factual that all substances are made of atoms, but we now know that atoms are not indivisible. This should be fairly obvious, since atoms themselves are composed of protons, neutrons and electrons. The second point is correct in every respect but one. Except for the number of neutrons in the nucleus, every atom of the same element is identical. However, we now know that atoms of the same element can vary in the number of neutrons they have in the nucleus. (These varieties of nuclei are called *isotopes*.)

Figure 8-3. English scientist John Dalton.

The Five Principles of John Dalton's Atomic Model

1. All substances are composed of tiny, indivisible particles called atoms.

2. All atoms of the same element are identical.

3. Atoms of different elements have different weights.

4. Atoms combine in whole number ratios to form compounds.

5. Atoms are neither created nor destroyed in chemical reactions.

Dalton's model was the first scientific model of the atom. Most of what Dalton proposed is still regarded as correct today.

Moving on toward the later part of the nineteenth century, many individual elements had been discovered by this time. Another huge milestone was the publication of the first Periodic Table of the Elements by Russian chemist Dmitri Mendeleev in 1869 (Figure 8-4). Mendeleev had discovered that there were patterns in the properties of the elements that he could use to order the elements into rows and columns. When he arranged the elements this way he noted that there appeared to be gaps between some of the elements. This led him to predict the properties of several elements which had not yet been discovered. One of these was the element germanium, which Mendeleev called *ekasilicon*. Germanium is right below silicon in the Periodic Table of the Elements. Mendeleev predicted the color, density and atomic weight of this unknown element. His predictions turned out to be quite accurate once the element was discovered 15 years later. Table 8-1 shows a comparison between Mendeleev's ekasilicon prediction and the actual properties of germanium. You will find a modern Periodic Table in Chapter 9.

Our attention now shifts from the chemists to the physicists as we take a look at the most famous developments that led to our contemporary understanding of how atoms are structured.

English scientist J. J. Thomson worked at the Cavendish Laboratory in Cambridge, England (Figure 8-5). In 1897 he conducted a series of landmark experiments that revealed

Figure 8-4. Russian scientist Dmitri Mendeleev.

"Ekasilicon" Prediction		Germanium Discovered	
Date Predicted	1871	Date Discovered	1886
Atomic Mass	72	Atomic Mass	72.6
Density	5.5 g/cm³	Density	5.32 g/cm³
Color	dark gray	Color	light gray

Table 8-1. Predicted and actual characteristics of germanium.

the existence of electrons. Because of his work he won the Nobel Prize in Physics in 1906 and was knighted in 1908. Thomson's ingenious set-up is sketched in Figure 8-6.

Thomson placed electrodes from a high-voltage source inside of a very elegantly made, sealed-glass vacuum tube. This apparatus can generate a so-called *cathode ray* traveling from the negative electrode, called the *cathode*, to the positive one, called the *anode*. A cathode ray is simply a beam of electrons, but this was not known at the time. (In the era prior to flat-screen displays, television sets and computer monitors used cathode rays to hit the screen from behind and create the picture on the screen. This is why computer monitors back in the 1980s and 1990s were called cathode ray tubes, or CRTs.) The anode inside Thomson's vacuum tube had a hole in it for some of the electrons to escape through, which created a beam of "cathode rays" heading toward the other end of the tube.

Figure 8-5. English physicist Sir J. J. Thomson.

Thomson placed the electrodes of another voltage source inside the tube, above and below the cathode ray and discovered that the beam of electrons deflected when this voltage was turned on. The dashed line in Figure 8-6 shows the direction of the beam without the deflection voltage turned on. The deflection of the beam toward the positive electrode led Thomson to theorize that the beam was composed of negatively charged particles (since opposite charges attract), which he called "corpuscles." (The name *electron* was first used a few years later by a different scientist.) By trying out many different arrangements of cathode ray tubes, including the use of a magnetic field to deflect the beam, Thomson confirmed that the ray was negatively charged. Then using the scale on the end of the tube to measure the deflection angle, he was able to determine the charge-to-mass ratio of the individual electrons he had discovered, which is 1.8×10^{11}. (The units

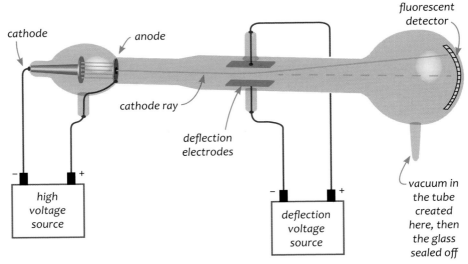

Figure 8-6. Thomson's cathode ray tube experiment.

of this value, as we would now say, are coulombs/kilogram, or C/kg.) When one considers all the work involved in the hand-blowing of every glass tube, the skill of getting the metal parts inside the glass vacuum tube, and the whole idea of this experiment, one has to admit that this is a *very* impressive experiment. Thomson was a truly great scientist!

Thomson went on to theorize that electrons came from inside atoms. This was a major break with the first principle of Dalton's model, which had been guiding research for nearly 100 years by this time. Thomson developed a new atomic model that envisioned atoms as tiny clouds of massless, positive charge sprinkled with thousands of the negatively charged electrons, depicted in Figure 8-7. This model is usually called the *plum pudding* model. But since Americans are less familiar with plum pudding than, say, watermelon, we might just as well think of it as the "watermelon model." The red meat of the watermelon is like the overall cloud of positive charge, and the seeds are like the negatively charged electrons scattered around inside it.

> In his plum pudding model Thomson proposed that atoms were massless clouds of positive charge, with thousands of tiny negatively charged particles distributed around on the inside.

In 1911 American scientist Robert Millikan (Figure 8-8) devised a brilliant experiment that allowed him to determine the charge on individual electrons, 1.6×10^{-19} coulombs (C). Using the value of the charge/mass ratio determined by Thomson, Millikan was also able to calculate the mass of the electron, 9.1×10^{-31} kg. Millikan's apparatus is sketched in Figure 8-9.

Millikan's famous experiment is called the *oil drop experiment*. Inside of a metal drum about the size of a large bucket Millikan placed a pair of horizontal

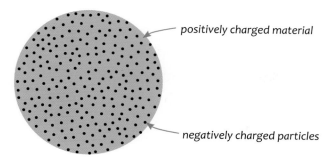

Figure 8-7. Thomson's "plum pudding" model of the atom.

metal plates connected to an adjustable high-voltage source. The upper plate had a hole in the center and was connected to the positive voltage, the lower plate to the negative. He used an atomizer spray pump (such as ladies used in the old days on bottles of perfume) to spray in a fine mist of watchmaker's oil above the positive plate. Some of these droplets would fall through the hole in the upper plate and move into the region between the plates. Connected through the side of the drum between the two plates was a telescope eyepiece and lamp so that Millikan could see the oil droplets between the plates.

Figure 8-8. American scientist Robert Millikan.

The process of squirting in the oil droplets with the atomizer sprayer caused some of the droplets to acquire a charge of static electricity. This means the droplets had excess electrons on them and were thus negatively charged. They picked up these extra electrons by friction as the droplets squirted through the rubber sprayer tube. As Millikan looked at an oil droplet through the eyepiece and adjusted the voltage between the plates, he could make the charged oil droplet hover when the voltage was just right. Millikan took into account the weight of the droplets and the viscosity of the air as the droplets fell and was able to determine that every droplet had a charge on it that was a multiple of 1.6×10^{-19} C. From this he deduced that this must be the charge on a single electron, which it is. Millikan won the Nobel Prize in Physics in 1923 for this work.

The last famous experiment in this short history of atomic models was initiated in 1909 by one of Thomson's students at Cambridge, New Zealander Lord Ernest Rutherford (Figure 8-10). Rutherford was already famous when this

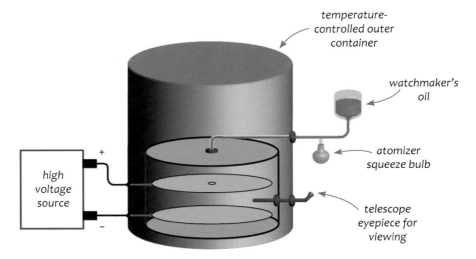

temperature-
controlled outer
container

watchmaker's
oil

+

high
voltage
source

−

atomizer
squeeze bulb

telescope
eyepiece for
viewing

Figure 8-9. Millikan's oil drop experiment.

experiment occurred, having just won the Nobel Prize in Chemistry the previous year. Rutherford's *gold foil experiment* resulted in the discovery of the atomic nucleus.

To understand Rutherford's experiment one needs to know that an "alpha particle," or α-particle (using the Greek letter alpha, α), is a particle composed of two protons and two neutrons. This particular combination of protons and neutrons is identical to the nucleus of a helium atom (two protons, two neutrons), although α-particles don't have anything to do with helium *per se*. Alpha particles are naturally emitted by various radioactive materials as their nuclei deteriorate in a process called nuclear decay (see examples on pp. 79 and 105).

Rutherford's experimental set-up is sketched in Figure 8-11. Rutherford created a beam of α-particles by placing some radioactive material (radium bromide) inside a lead box with a hole in one end. The α-particles from the decaying radium atoms streamed out of the hole. Rutherford aimed the α-particles at a thin sheet of gold foil that was only a few hundred atoms thick. Surrounding

Figure 8-10. New Zealander and physicist Lord Ernest Rutherford.

the gold foil was a ring-shaped screen coated with a material that would glow when hit by an α-particle. Rutherford could then determine where the α-particles went after encountering the gold foil by observing where the flashes of light occurred.

You may recall from the examples in Chapters 5 and 7 that when the α-particles exit the lead box they are traveling at 15 million meters per second. (Yes, that is mind boggling.) Rutherford found that most of them went straight through the foil and struck the screen on the other side. However, occasionally an α-particle (one particle out of every several thousand) would deflect with a large angle. Sometimes these deflected particles would bounce almost straight back. To Rutherford, this was astonishing and not at all what he had expected.

Twelve years before the gold foil experiment Thomson had theorized that the positive charge in the atom was dispersed around throughout the atom. Because of this Rutherford expected the massive and positively charged α-particles traveling at 15 million m/s to blow right through the gold foil. Most of them did, but when some of them ricocheted backward the astonished Rutherford commented that it

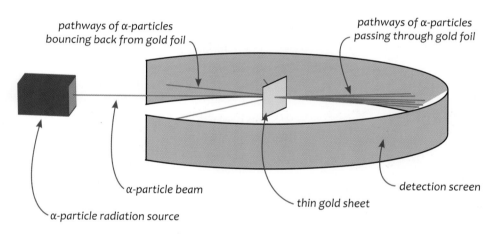

Figure 8-11. Rutherford's gold foil experiment.

was like firing a huge artillery shell into a piece of tissue paper and having it bounce back and hit you! Now, from our study of momentum last chapter, the only way for an object to bounce back from an elastic collision (and these essentially are elastic collisions) is for the object at rest to be more massive than the incoming object. This fact led Rutherford to begin thinking that the positive change in atoms was not spread out the way Thomson had theorized, but was concentrated into a very small region. Rutherford's work led to his new proposal in 1911 for a model of the atom. The key points of Rutherford's model are summarized in the next box.

And again, just what do we mean when we say that atoms are mostly empty space? Just think of that pinhead inside the Roman Coliseum! In 1917, Rutherford became the first to "split the atom." In this experiment he used α-particles again,

Ernest Rutherford's Atomic Model

1. The positive charge in atoms is concentrated in a tiny region in the center of the atom, which Rutherford called the nucleus.

2. Atoms are mostly empty space.

3. The electrons, which contain the atom's negative charge, are outside the nucleus.

this time striking nitrogen atoms. His work led to the discovery of the positively-charged particles in the atomic nucleus, which he named protons.

Figure 8-12. English physicist Sir James Chadwick.

It took another twenty years before James Chadwick, another Englishman, discovered the neutron (Figure 8-12). Before World War I Chadwick studied under Rutherford (at Cambridge, of course). Then the war began. Not only did the war interrupt the progress of the research in general, but Chadwick was a prisoner of war in Germany. Working back in England after the war he discovered the neutron in 1932 and received the Nobel Prize in Physics for his discovery in 1935. Ten years later he was knighted as well.

Chadwick's discovery of the neutron enabled physicists to fill in quite a few blanks in their understanding of the basic structure of atoms. But years before Chadwick made his discovery Rutherford's atomic model was already being taken to another level through the work of Niels Bohr.

The Bohr Model of the Atom

Danish physicist Niels Bohr is one of the major figures in the development of the modern physics of the twentieth century (Figure 8-13). For his work in the development of quantum physics he received the Nobel Prize in Physics in 1922. In 1913 Bohr theorized that atoms were like little planetary solar systems, with the electrons orbiting the nucleus the way planets orbit the sun. The negatively charged electrons were held in their orbits by electrical attraction to the positively charged nucleus. And a most significant aspect of the model is this: each electron in an orbit possessed a specific amount of energy. If an electron were to absorb additional energy somehow it would move to an orbit that was for electrons with

Figure 8-13. Danish physicist Niels Bohr

higher energy. And if an electron were to emit energy somehow, it would move to an orbit that was for electrons with lower energy.

Bohr's "planetary model" is usually depicted as illustrated in Figure 8-14. The model allows a maximum of two electrons in the first energy level, eight electrons in each of the second and third energy levels, and higher numbers in higher levels. In this depiction of Bohr's model, orbits that are farther out from the nucleus are for electrons possessing higher energy.

Even though we now know that electrons do not orbit the nucleus like planets, Bohr was completely right about the electrons possessing specific energies. This concept is now well established in contemporary atomic theory. Bohr's model was an important step forward in our understanding of atomic structure, even though the planetary model has since been discarded. Of course, when one looks at Figure 8-14 it is very difficult to think about the

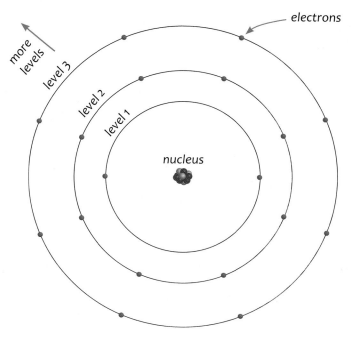

Figure 8-14. Bohr's planetary atomic model.

electron energy levels without thinking of them as *spatial*, like orbits. But a discussion of the spatial arrangement of electrons in atoms is beyond our objectives for this book. So my suggestion is to ignore how the electrons are arranged spatially, and simply think in terms of how much energy they have. Thinking of electrons as possessing specific energies brings us to our contemporary understanding.

> Though it is tempting to think of atoms like solar systems, with electrons orbiting the nucleus, they are not at all like that.

The Quantum Model of the Atom

The contemporary model or theory about atoms is called the *quantum model*. The quantum model was pieced together by a host of scientists over a period of decades in the early to mid-twentieth century. The quantum model includes Bohr's contribution that all electrons possess certain energies. But the big step forward in the quantum model was that energy itself was *quantized*. To say that energy is quantized is to say that there is a smallest unit of energy available in nature and all energies in the universe are multiples of this one. Energy is not a continuous quantity; it is granular; it comes in lumps. One lump of energy, such as the energy carried by a photon of light, is called a *quantum*.

Lots of common things are "granular" like this; that is, they come in lumps—eggs, m&m's, sand, and so on, as suggested by Figure 8-15. One cannot purchase 2.83 eggs because the smallest unit of eggs one can purchase is one egg. Whenever a quantity is granular and made up of chunks of a particular size, we say the quantity is quantized.

Our contemporary understanding that energy is quantized is analogous to our understanding that water is quantized. Water appears smooth, but is actually composed of huge numbers of individual water molecules. The smallest amount of water that can exist is one molecule of water, and all quantities of water are multiples of this smallest quantity, the single molecule. In the same way we now understand energy to be quantized, too. There exists a smallest quantum of energy and all energies that exist are multiples of the single quantum of energy, the inconceivably small amount of 6.6×10^{-34} J. So the quantum model of the

> Energy is quantized, just like eggs, m&m's and water molecules.

atom posits that every electron has a certain amount of energy. Electrons cannot possess just *any* amount of energy. The energy they possess must be a specific multiple of the smallest unit of energy that can exist. And as we will see shortly, when electrons absorb or emit energy, they do so in discrete packets of energy that possess specific amounts of energy.

Eggs are quantized.

m&m's are quantized.

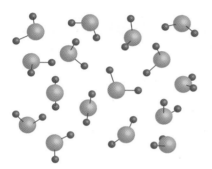

Water molecules are quantized.

Energy is quantized, too. (But it doesn't look like this—energy is not an object!)

Figure 8-15. Things that are quantized: they come in quanta.

Is Everything in Nature Quantized?

Maybe. Certainly matter is quantized, since all matter is made of individual atoms or parts of atoms. Energy too is quantized, as we have just seen.

Electromagnetic radiation—light—is also quantized. Isaac Newton first hypothesized this, using the term "corpuscles" to denote a single lump of light. But the new discoveries in the two centuries after Newton all strongly suggested that light consisted of continuous waves, not particles. In most of these experiments, phenomena were displayed that could only be explained in terms of continuous waves. By the mid-nineteenth century the wave theory of light was very solidly established. (We will get to the wave properties of light in Chapter 11.)

But by end of the nineteenth century there were a few puzzling phenomena that could not be explained by assuming that light was continuous waves. One of these was the so-called *photoelectric effect*. Think again of the cathode ray tube apparatus used by J. J. Thomson to discover the electron (Figure 8-6). It turns out that the "cathode ray," a beam of electrons, can be created merely by shining light on the metal cathode. By itself, this was not a mystery to the scientists at the time.

The problem was that the wave theory of light could not explain what happened. The wave theory predicts that a more intense light source should create faster moving electrons in the cathode ray. This is because more intense light has more energy, and electrons with more energy, kinetic energy, should be moving faster. But that's not what happens. Instead, more intense light just creates *more* electrons, all with the same energy. To get faster electrons one must change the *color* of the light source. Red light generates relatively slow moving electrons; blue or violet light generates faster electrons.

Albert Einstein won the 1921 Nobel Prize in Physics for his 1905 explanation of the photoelectric effect, an explanation that depended on the work of another physicist, Max Planck (Figure 8-16). In 1900 Planck had been attempting bizarre

What is a Photon? Can ray guns, light sabers or photon torpedoes really be made?

At present we understand light as having a dual nature. It has properties that all continuous waves have, so light has a wave nature. It also has granular properties, so it has a particle nature. To speak of light we must ascribe both natures to it; a theoretical description making use of one or the other description alone is not adequate.

A single particle of light is called a photon. To combine the wave and particle properties into a single term, physicists often define photons as "wave packets." The shorter a photon's wavelength is, the more energy the photon carries.

Photon torpedoes and light sabers are strictly science fiction. A photon torpedo would be a high-energy ball of light, which does not exist. However, we can make a high-energy beam of light with particularly destructive properties. These are lasers. The term "ray-gun" from the sci-fi films and cartoons of long ago can be thought of as similar to a laser.

A light saber would require two impossibilities. First, that a beam of light could stop suddenly in mid-air, four feet from the hilt of the weapon. This light does not do. Photons traveling through the air keep going until their energy is absorbed by a solid object. Air molecules do absorb light energy, but not much, and a beam of light has to travel a long distance in air before all its energy is absorbed. For the same reasons, a "Death Star" weapon that takes four beams of light traveling in different directions and combines them into a single beam at some spot in empty space is also fiction.

Second, a light saber would require a beam of photons to be impervious to an object made of atoms. In other words, to be used in a sword fight the light would have to act like a solid object itself when another solid object tried to pass through the beam. Alas, light doesn't do this either.

mathematical tricks while searching for an explanation of another phenomenon that defied the wave theory of light, so-called blackbody radiation. We will not go into the "blackbody problem" here. Suffice it to say that Planck solved the problem by recklessly introducing the idea of quantization into his calculations. Planck proposed that energy was quantized, and he came up with an equation that weirdly related energy to wavelength, which didn't make sense to anyone at the time. Nevertheless, these were game-changing proposals, and Planck won the 1918 Nobel Prize in Physics for this work.

Figure 8-16. German physicist Max Planck.

Einstein declared that there was more than a mere mathematical trick in play. He applied the idea of quantization to light, and bingo, the photoelectric effect was explained. We now call these light quanta *photons*, a term that was coined in 1926 by American chemist Gilbert Lewis.

> Albert Einstein first demonstrated the quantization of light.

Einstein theorized that if light came in lumps, then the electrons were being ejected from the metal cathode by absorbing the energy from the quanta of light. Different colors of light have different energies. If an electron absorbed the energy from a higher energy photon, say a blue or violet one, it would have more kinetic energy and would travel faster. Energy absorbed from a lower-energy red photon would produce a slower moving electron.

Atomic Spectra and the Bohr Model

We will conclude this chapter by going back to the Bohr model for a bit. The Bohr model became popular very rapidly because of the straightforward way it is able to explain the phenomenon of *atomic spectra*. The atoms of every element emit different colors of light when they are excited, as shown in Figure 8-17. In physics, when we say "excited" we simply mean that the atoms have absorbed energy somehow, such as by heating or being bombarded with electricity or light.

Atomic excitation is how the colors of fireworks are generated. If one wants a shower of green sparks one simply puts some copper in the explosion, because when copper atoms get excited they emit a strong green light. Are pale orange colors needed? Sodium atoms happen to give off just this color. Have you ever

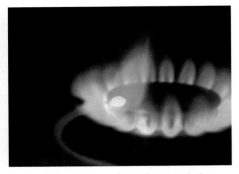

Figure 8-17. Flame tests of copper (left) and lithium (right) show some of the characteristic colors given off by excited atoms.

wondered why street lights these days have a pale orange glow? It is because there is sodium vapor inside the lamp fixture and the electricity excites those sodium atoms and causes them to emit their characteristic pale orange color. Similarly, neon signs are red-orange because neon atoms give off several specific strong orange and red colors when they are excited (shown at the top of Figure 8-19).

Different atoms don't give off just one color when they are excited. Every atom gives off an entire *spectrum* of specific colors, as illustrated in Figures 8-18 and 8-19. Some of the colors might be emitted very strongly, such as the green light emitted by copper, while other colors are emitted much more weakly. Moreover, the spectrum emitted by the atoms of each element is unique. This means the spectrum of the atoms of a particular element acts as a sort of fingerprint. Every atom of helium, when it is excited, emits the spectrum of colors unique to helium atoms. In fact, this is how we discovered that the sun was composed of a lot of helium, because the light the sun gives off contains the colors of the helium spectrum very prominently. (The Greek word for sun is *helios*, from which we get the element name helium.) *Spectroscopy* is the name for the study of these atomic spectra and the science of identifying the presence of particular elements by looking at light spectra. Astrophysicists use spectroscopy all the time to identify the substances present in distant objects in the galaxy, and chemists use it in the laboratory to identify the elements in unknown samples.

The Bohr model of the atom was very successful in explaining the atomic spectrum of hydrogen. (The much more complete quantum model was needed to explain the spectra of other elements.) To see how Bohr's model explained the hydrogen spectrum we need to know how photon energies correlate to light wavelengths. This was the work that won Einstein the Nobel Prize, discussed in the previous section. In summary, in the color spectrum of visible light, photons of red light have the longest wavelength and lowest energy; photons of violet light have the shortest wavelength and highest energy. Green light is in the middle, with respect to both energy and wavelength.

The spectrum of light from the sun includes all of the colors of the helium spectrum, indicating that the sun contains helium.

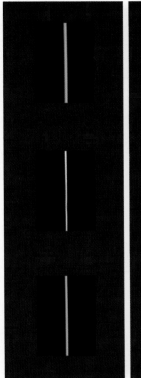

*Figure 8-18. The
light emitted by
gas spectrum tubes
containing neon (top),
mercury vapor (center)
and nitrogen (bottom).*

*Figure 8-19. Atomic spectra of neon (top), mercury vapor (center)
and nitrogen (bottom). These spectra are formed by passing the light
from the spectrum tubes through a diffraction grating, which acts
like a prism to separate the individual colors of light (discussed in
Chapter 11).*

Now let's apply these wavelength-energy relationships to see how the Bohr model of the atom explains atomic spectra. Recall that in Bohr's atomic model electrons are confined to specific energy levels. Let's abandon the idea of orbits and redraw the energy levels simply as lines across the page. Each line represents a different energy level, with the lowest energy at the bottom, as shown in Figure 8-20. In the figure a single electron is shown occupying the lowest energy level. Each one of these energy levels can hold two or more of the atom's electrons.

Now assume that we are going to excite the atom by bombarding it with light, that is, photons. Further assume that the light we use will be violet, which makes use of the highest energy/shortest wavelength photons in the visible spectrum. When we do this a series of events will take place in the atom, all within a tiny fraction of a second. Refer to Figure 8-21 as we go through this sequence.

1. When a photon hits an atom, the atom *absorbs* the photon's energy and the photon ceases to exist.

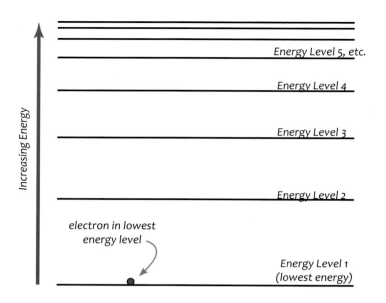

Figure 8-20. Electron energy levels in the atom.

2. The absorbed energy will go to one of the atom's electrons. Since the electrons are in energy levels according to how much energy they possess, an electron that absorbs the energy of an incoming photon will jump up to a specific higher energy level. This atom, as we say, has been *excited*. The absorption of the photon's energy will only happen if the energy in the incoming photon corresponds to the specific amount of energy the electron needs to jump to a higher energy level.

3. The more energy an electron absorbs, the higher up it will jump in the energy levels of the atom. Violet photons have high energies, and will cause the electron to make a large energy jump. Red photons have lower energies, and so cause a smaller energy jump when absorbed. Green photons have intermediate energies, and will cause an electron to make an intermediate jump in the energy levels.

4. When an electron absorbs energy from a photon, it will only stay briefly in the higher energy level. It will work its way back down to a lower energy level by *emitting* one or more new photons, energy packets of light that fly out of the atom. These emitted photons are the source of the specific colors of light the atom will emit. Even a tiny sample of a particular element contains a colossal number of atoms, and with all of them doing the absorption and emission at once, the light streaming out of the sample seems continuous.

5. In every atom there are many different energy levels available to the electrons in the atom. But a specific energy level can only hold a specific and restricted

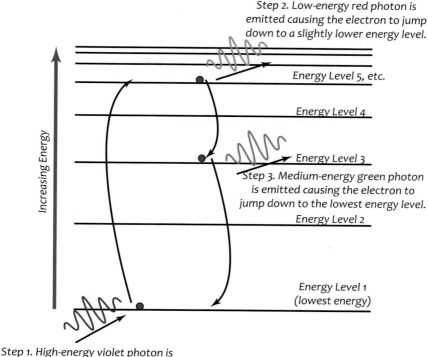

Step 2. Low-energy red photon is emitted causing the electron to jump down to a slightly lower energy level.

Energy Level 5, etc.

Energy Level 4

Energy Level 3

Step 3. Medium-energy green photon is emitted causing the electron to jump down to the lowest energy level.

Energy Level 2

Energy Level 1 (lowest energy)

Increasing Energy

Step 1. High-energy violet photon is absorbed causing the electron to jump up to a much higher energy level.

Figure 8-21. Example photon absorption and emission by an electron in an atom.

number of electrons. So when an electron in an excited atom jumps down an energy level and emits a photon of light, the energy it will emit, and thus the wavelength and color of the emitted light, will depend on where there are vacancies in the atom's energy levels for the electron to jump to. In other words, the energy levels available for all of this electron jumping depend on the atom. Atoms of every element have different numbers of electrons, and thus different energy levels will be in use or available. Thus, every element has its unique spectrum of light wavelengths it will emit. Every element has a unique atomic spectrum.

It is a lot of fun to use a *spectroscope* to look at the atomic spectra for different elements. A spectroscope contains a prism or diffraction grating that spreads out the colors in the light by refraction or diffraction (which we will discuss in a later chapter). One looks through the eyepiece to see the spectrum of light entering the spectroscope. If the light entering the spectroscope consists of specific wavelengths of light (instead of containing all of the colors, like the light from a flashlight), then when the light is spread out in the spectroscope the specific colors of light will appear as sharp, separate lines of color, as in the actual photographic images of Figure 8-19. These lines are called *spectral lines*, the lines in the spectrum of a particular element or compound.

In the lab we usually look at atomic spectra by heating a metallic sample in a flame, which is called a *flame test* (Figure 8-17), or by connecting a glass *spectrum tube* containing the vapor or gas of a particular element to a high-voltage power supply and zapping it with electricity to make it glow (Figures 8-18 and 8-19). The heat or the electricity provide the energy necessary to excite the electrons in the atoms of the sample. The sample will then begin emitting photons at the specific wavelengths in the spectrum for the particular element or elements in the sample. When one looks at the light emitted by the sample with a spectroscope one sees the individual lines of color in the spectrum. Particular electron energy transitions that happen frequently will produce lots of photons of the corresponding color, resulting in a very bright line in the spectrum. Less common energy transitions result in dimmer lines because fewer photons of that energy and wavelength are being produced.

How does a fluorescent light work?

The operation of a fluorescent light depends on the principles of photon absorption and re-emission discussed in the last section of this chapter. However, the operation of the fluorescent light will be easier to discuss after we have discussed the spectrum of different light wavelengths and colors in more detail. Thus, we will take up this question at the end of Chapter 11.

Ideas for Your Classroom

The ideas in this chapter are certainly far more advanced than what students will study in elementary school. But perhaps the task in the elementary grades might be to just start the conversation so that students begin associating together atoms of particular elements with specific color sets of light.

1. Look at images of flame tests. Better yet, get a qualified teacher or parent to demonstrate actual flame tests. Talk about the fact that the atoms in each of the elements will emit a set of colors that is specific to that element.

2. Compare the light given off by fluorescent lights, mercury vapor streets lights, and high-pressure sodium street lights. Research and find the spectra for each of these and compare.

3. Procure a class set of inexpensive spectroscopes (less than $10 each at a science supplier). These inexpensive spectroscopes are easily overwhelmed by intense light or stray ambient light, so these investigations must be performed in a totally dark room. Even the stray light through closed Venetian blinds is too much, so you will either need to find a room with no windows, or cover windows completely with foil. Also, to keep the light intensity from the source low enough so that the spectroscope works properly, use small battery-powered lights when possible. Place the light source in a cardboard box that has a slots cut in the top or sides. Make the slots about 3/4 inch long and 1/16 inch wide. Now students can look at the spectrum of the light coming through a slot.

Try each of the following light sources, observing safety precautions where appropriate.

-   A small, battery-powered fluorescent lamp. The fluorescent spectrum will show pronounced lines from the mercury, as shown in the middle spectrum of Figure 8-19. Other broad ranges of color will also be visible.

-   A neon light, such as are used in older-style circuit testers (see photo). For this light source, the amount of light emitted is very small, so you won't need to use the cardboard box. Instead, place the incoming light slot of the spectroscope right on the neon lamp. You should see a distinct neon line spectrum, similar to the top spectrum in Figure 8-19. For power, insert the leads of the circuit tester into an extension cord (do this when the cord is not plugged in). Then tape the leads thoroughly with black electrician's tape so that no metal parts are exposed.

-   A yellow fluorescent lamp (such as used for repelling insects). If you can't find a battery-operated yellow fluorescent, you can use a compact yellow fluorescent in a corded light socket inside the box. Take appropriate safety precautions with 120-VAC electrical wiring, and do not leave the lamp on long enough for the box to get warm enough to pose a fire hazard. You should see pronounced green, yellow and red lines in the spectrum.

-   An LED, such as for a clip-on book reader's lamp. The LED will provide a smooth, beautiful, full spectrum of light.

Goals for Chapter 9

1. Describe how mass and volume contribute to the density of a substance.

2. Draw the "family tree" of substances, including in it the following terms: substance, pure substance, alloy, mixture, compound, heterogeneous mixture, homogeneous mixture, suspension, element and solution.

3. Name two examples for each substance listed in the family tree.

4. Define each of the terms in the substances family tree.

5. Distinguish between compounds and mixtures.

6. Use the concept of internal energy to define the three common phases of matter, solids, liquids and gases, and distinguish between them at the molecular level.

7. Explain how evaporation occurs.

About This Chapter

The material in this chapter tends to fall in the ambiguous territory between physics and chemistry. This is because the Periodic Table of the Elements and discussions about the different types of elements and compounds are definitely within the discipline of chemistry, but the closely related topics of physical properties and phases of matter are always included in the discipline of physics. Accordingly, the material here also appears in *Science for Every Teacher Volume 2: Chemistry*.

Chapter 9
Substances

A Few Physical Properties

An important aspect of all scientific discussion about matter is the frequent reference to the physical properties of one substance or another. One physical property we have already seen (Chapter 3) is *inertia*, the property that matter resists change to its state of motion. Objects do not speed up or slow down by themselves. Left to itself, any object will either sit at rest and stay at rest, or move in a straight line at a constant speed forever. To change this state of affairs a net force is required. If a net force does happen to appear on any object, that object will accelerate. And the more massive the object is, the more slowly it will accelerate. All matter possesses this property, and we quantify the amount of inertia possessed by an object with the variable *mass*. The MKS unit for mass is the kilogram (kg).

A second physical property we have already mentioned is that all matter takes up space. This is a rather intuitive property, a lot easier to understand than inertia. We quantify the amount of space an object takes up with the variable *volume*. We make frequent use of the notion of volume in our daily lives. New cars have so many cubic feet of cargo space, soft drinks come in 1-liter and 2-liter bottles, milk is sold by the gallon, and so on. The MKS unit for volume is the cubic meter (m^3), a unit of measure Americans tend to be less familiar with than with USCS units such as gallons and cubic feet. The liter is a commonly-used metric unit, although it is not recognized as an official unit of the SI system of units.

The third and final physical property we will discuss here is *density*. The density of an object is a measure of how much matter there is in a particular amount of space. Density is simply a combination of the variables mass and volume. The more mass there is in a particular volume, the denser an object will be. The MKS units for density are kilograms per cubic meter, kg/m^3. However, the kilogram and the cubic meter are both much larger than the small samples scientists often work with, so another common set of units used for density is grams per cubic centimeter, g/cm^3. These small units are much more common in lab work. However, when the density of a substance is to be used in a calculation with other variables, MKS units should be used. The reason for this, as mentioned in Chapter 3, is that when working with MKS units any calculation will always give a result in MKS units. This is a very practical principle that removes a lot of confusion from the work of performing unit conversions and calculations in the physical sciences.

> Density is simply a combination of the variables mass and volume.

Water is a substance so familiar to us in daily life that we often compare the density of objects to the density of water, which is about 1.0 gram per cubic centimeter. Objects less dense than water will float; objects more dense than water will sink. There is even a term for the ratio of the density of a liquid to the density of water, the *specific gravity*. If a liquid has a specific gravity less than one, it is less dense than water. Oil is like this, with a specific gravity of 0.6 or so, which is why oil floats on the surface of water during an oil spill. Oil is less dense than water. Alcoholic beverages are also less dense than water, with specific gravities in the 0.7–0.8 range. This is why mixed drinks are made by putting the alcohol in the glass first. When the water is added the liquor will begin to rise and mix with the water on its way up.

Comparisons of Volume Units

Everyone is familiar with the common unit for volume in the U.S. Customary System, the gallon. A standard plastic jug of milk we obtain from a grocery store contains one gallon of milk. In the MKS system the standard volume unit is the cubic meter (m^3). Three other very common metric units are the cubic centimeter (cm^3), the liter (L) and the milliliter (mL). Images depicting these different quantities are shown in Figures 9-1a-f.

As seen in Figure 9-1a, a cubic meter (m^3) is quite a large volume, enough to hold several people. In Figure 9-1b, one-liter (1 L) and one-gallon (1 gal) containers are shown side-by-side to help visualize the fact that there are a bit less than 4 liters in one gallon. Figure 9-1c shows two different objects, each occupying a volume of one liter (1 L). The orange one has dimension of 10 cm x 10 cm x 10 cm to show that 1 L is equal to 1,000 cm^3. There are 1,000 liters in one cubic meter, as suggested by Figure 9-1d. Figure 9-1e shows a small cube with a volume of one cubic centimeter (cm^3) and a 10 x 10 array of 100 of these cubes, which has a volume of 100 cm^3. As we can see by comparing Figure 9-1a and 9-1e, a volume of 100 cm^3 is clearly *not* equal to 1 m^3, a common mistake made by older students learning to work with unit conversions. In fact, it takes 1,000,000 cm^3 to equal 1 m^3.

It takes 1,000,000 cm^3 to equal 1 m^3.

A milliliter (mL) is one one-thousandth of a liter (0.001 L). It is also the case that one mL is equal to one cm^3. It takes about 10 drops of liquid to make one milliliter (1 mL), as suggested by Figure 9-1f. This means that a single drop has a volume of about 0.1 mL.

By convention, the liter is generally used only in reference to liquid volumes. The cubic meter and cubic centimeter are commonly used for everything.

Calculating Density

As previously mentioned, density is a measure of how much matter is packed into a given volume for different substances. The concept of density is very familiar. We all know that if we hold equally sized balloons in each hand, one filled with

Figure 9-1a. The white frame encloses a volume of one cubic meter.

Figure 9-1b. One-gallon and one-liter containers.

Figure 9-1c. Each of these objects has a volume of one liter.

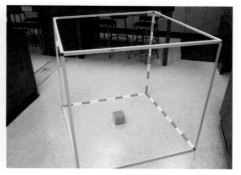

Figure 9-1d. To fill the 1-m³ cube would require 1,000 1-L cubes.

Figure 9-1e. One cubic centimeter (left) and 100 cubic centimeters (right).

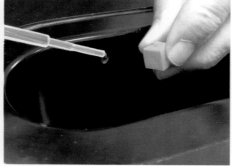

Figure 9-1f. It takes ten drops of 0.1 mL each to equal 1 mL, or 1 cm³.

water and one filled with air, the water balloon will weigh more because water is denser than air. We know that to have equal weights of sand and Styrofoam packing peanuts the volume of the packing material will be much larger because the packing material is much less dense.

The equation for density is

$$\rho = \frac{m}{V}$$

where the Greek letter ρ (spelled rho and pronounced like row, which rhymes with snow) is the density in kg/m³, m is the mass in kg, and V is the volume in m³. These are the variables and units in our familiar MKS unit system. As mentioned previously, it is common for densities to be expressed in g/cm³ in laboratory work.

Types of Substances

A *substance* is anything that contains matter. There are many different types of substances, but they all fall into two categories, *pure substances* and *mixtures*. We will examine pure substances first, but it will be helpful to know that a *mixture* is made any time different substances are combined together without a chemical reaction occurring. If a chemical reaction does occur when different substances

---

Example Problem

Dmitri Mendeleev predicted the existence of the element germanium 15 years before it was actually discovered. The density of germanium is 5.323 g/cm³. A small sample of germanium has a mass of 17.615 g. Determine the volume of this sample.

The given information and unknown we seek are:

$$\rho = 5.323 \ \frac{g}{cm^3}$$
$$m = 17.615 \ g$$
$$V = ?$$

We write the density equation and solve it for the volume. Then we insert the values and compute the result.

$$\rho = \frac{m}{V}$$
$$\rho V = m$$
$$V = \frac{m}{\rho} = \frac{17.615 \ g}{5.323 \ \frac{g}{cm^3}} = 3.309 \ cm^3$$

---

are combined, a pure substance called a *compound* is formed. Thus, these are the two major types of substances that are composed of combinations of other substances, compounds and mixtures. The major distinction between mixtures and compounds is that if no chemical reaction occurs when substances are combined, the resulting substance is a mixture. If a chemical reaction does occur when substances are combined, a compound (or perhaps more than one compound) is formed. We will come back to compounds in a moment.

> When substances combine without a chemical reaction occurring, a mixture is formed. When substances combine in a chemical reaction, a compound is formed.

There are two kinds of pure substances, one of which is compounds. The other kind of pure substance is a group of substances called *elements*. We will discuss elements first.

The Periodic Table of the Elements (PTE) lists all of the known elements. This famous table, shown in Figure 9-2, plays a major role in the study of chemistry. The characteristic that defines each element in the PTE is the number of protons the element has in each of its atoms. For example, carbon is element number six in the PTE. This means that an atom of carbon has six protons. All carbon atoms have six protons. If an atom does not have six protons, it is not a carbon atom, and if an atom does have six protons, it is a carbon atom. An element is therefore a type of atom, classified according to the number of protons the atom has. A lump of elemental carbon is therefore any lump of atoms that contain only six protons apiece. Oxygen is another example of an element. Pure oxygen is a gas (ordinarily) that contains only atoms with eight protons each, because oxygen is element number eight. Other examples of well-known elements are iron, gold, silver, neon, copper, nitrogen, lead, and many others.

For every element there is a chemical symbol which is used in the PTE and in the chemical formulas for compounds. For some elements a single uppercase letter is used, such as N for nitrogen and C for carbon. For other elements an upper case letter is followed by one lower case letter, such as Na for sodium and Mg for magnesium. (The three-letter symbols at the right side of the seventh row beginning with U are just placeholders until official names and two-letter symbols are selected by the appropriate governing officials.)

Some of the chemical symbols are based on the Latin names of elements, such as Ag for silver, from its Latin name *argentum*. Other examples are Au for gold, from the Latin *aurum*, and Pb for lead, from the Latin *plumbum* (everyone's favorite Latin name).

As the name implies, a *compound* is formed when atoms of two or more different elements are chemically bonded together, which is always the result of a *chemical reaction*. A chemical reaction is any process in which connecting bonds between atoms are formed or broken. It takes a chemical reaction to bond atoms together, and it takes a different chemical reaction to break them apart.

1	2	3	4	5	6	7	8	9	10	11	12	13	14	15	16	17	18
1 H Hydrogen 1.0079																	2 He Helium 4.003
3 Li Lithium 6.94	4 Be Beryllium 9.012											5 B Boron 10.811	6 C Carbon 12.011	7 N Nitrogen 14.007	8 O Oxygen 15.999	9 F Fluorine 18.998	10 Ne Neon 20.17
11 Na Sodium 22.990	12 Mg Magnesium 24.305											13 Al Aluminum 26.982	14 Si Silicon 28.086	15 P Phosphorus 30.974	16 S Sulfur 32.066	17 Cl Chlorine 35.453	18 Ar Argon 39.948
19 K Potassium 39.098	20 Ca Calcium 40.078	21 Sc Scandium 44.956	22 Ti Titanium 47.88	23 V Vanadium 50.942	24 Cr Chromium 51.996	25 Mn Manganese 54.938	26 Fe Iron 55.847	27 Co Cobalt 58.933	28 Ni Nickel 58.71	29 Cu Copper 63.546	30 Zn Zinc 65.38	31 Ga Gallium 69.723	32 Ge Germanium 72.59	33 As Arsenic 74.922	34 Se Selenium 78.96	35 Br Bromine 79.904	36 Kr Krypton 83.80
37 Rb Rubidium 85.467	38 Sr Strontium 87.62	39 Y Yttrium 88.906	40 Zr Zirconium 91.224	41 Nb Niobium 92.906	42 Mo Molybdenum 95.94	43 Tc Technetium 98.906	44 Ru Rutherium 101.07	45 Rh Rhodium 102.906	46 Pd Palladium 106.42	47 Ag Silver 107.868	48 Cd Cadmium 112.411	49 In Indium 114.82	50 Sn Tin 118.69	51 Sb Antimony 121.75	52 Te Tellurium 127.60	53 I Iodine 126.905	54 Xe Xenon 131.30
55 Cs Cesium 132.905	56 Ba Barium 137.327	71 Lu Lutetium 174.967	72 Hf Hafnium 178.49	73 Ta Tantalum 180.947	74 W Tungsten 183.85	75 Re Rhenium 186.207	76 Os Osmium 190.23	77 Ir Iridium 192.22	78 Pt Platinum 195.09	79 Au Gold 196.967	80 Hg Mercury 200.59	81 Tl Thallium 204.37	82 Pb Lead 207.2	83 Bi Bismuth 208.980	84 Po Polonium 209	85 At Astatine 210	86 Rn Radon 222
87 Fr Francium 223	88 Ra Radium 226.025	103 Lr Lawrencium 260	104 Rf Rutherfordium 261	105 Db Dubnium 262	106 Sg Seaborgium 263	107 Bh Bohrium 262	108 Hs Hassium 265	109 Mt Meitnerium 266	110 Ds Darmstadtium 281	111 Rg Roentgenium 281	112 Cn Copernicium 285	113 Uut Ununtrium 286	114 Uuq Ununquadium 289	115 Uup Ununpentium 289	116 Uuh Ununhexium 293	117 Uus Ununseptium 294	118 Uuo Ununoctium 294

57 La Lanthanum 138.906	58 Ce Cerium 140.115	59 Pr Praseodymium 140.908	60 Nd Neodymium 144.24	61 Pm Promethium 145	62 Sm Samarium 150.36	63 Eu Europium 151.964	64 Gd Gadolinium 157.25	65 Tb Terbium 158.925	66 Dy Dysprosium 162.50	67 Ho Holmium 164.930	68 Er Erbium 167.26	69 Tm Thulium 168.934	70 Yb Ytterbium 173.04
89 Ac Actinium 227.028	90 Th Thorium 232.038	91 Pa Protactinium 231.036	92 U Uranium 238.029	93 Np Neptunium 237.048	94 Pu Plutonium 244	95 Am Americium 243	96 Cm Curium 247	97 Bk Berkelium 247	98 Cf Californium 251	99 Es Einsteinium 254	100 Fm Fermium 257	101 Md Mendelevium 258	102 No Nobelium 259

Figure 9-2. The Periodic Table of the Elements.

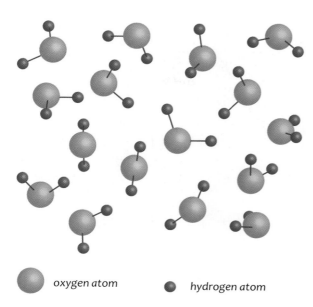

oxygen atom   ● hydrogen atom

Figure 9-3. Water molecules.

When atoms bond together to form a compound the atoms in the compound can be arranged in two different basic types of structures. In many cases the atoms join together in small, individual, identical groups called *molecules*. Water is composed of molecules, each molecule consisting of two hydrogen atoms and one oxygen atom, as depicted in Figure 9-3. Water molecules are known for having a characteristic elbow shape. This shape is responsible for many of water's unusual properties. Other familiar examples of compounds composed of molecules are ammonia (NH_3), carbon dioxide (CO_2), and propane (C_3H_8).

I will mention here in passing that some elements exist in nature in the form of two atoms of the same element bonded together in a so-called *diatomic molecule*. These are not compounds (because the two atoms in the molecule are the same), but they are molecules. Common examples of these are oxygen, hydrogen and nitrogen, symbolized as O_2, H_2 and N_2.

The other common way atoms can combine is to form together in a continuous, geometric arrangement. These compounds are called *crystals*, and the structure the atoms in the compound make when they join together is called a *crystal lattice*. The number of different arrangements atoms can make in a lattice is endless, and these arrangements are responsible for many of the unusual properties crystals possess. But what all lattices have in common is the regular arrangement of the atoms into repeating, geometrical patterns. A sketch of the very simple crystal structure for sodium chloride (NaCl), that is, table salt, is shown in Figure 9-4. The sketch includes some outlines to the crystal to help in visualizing this 3-D depiction.

One last point to note about compounds is that the properties of a compound are completely different from the properties of any of the elements in the compound. Consider the water in Figure 9-3. Oxygen is an invisible gas that we breathe in the air and that supports combustion. Hydrogen is an invisible, flammable gas. Water is composed of oxygen atoms bonded

> The properties of a compound are completely different from the properties of the elements in the compound.

to hydrogen atoms, but one cannot breathe water and water does not combust nor support combustion. Or consider the table salt in Figure 9-4. We all have to have salt in our diets, and we find it tasty. But both sodium and chlorine are deadly in their pure, elemental forms.

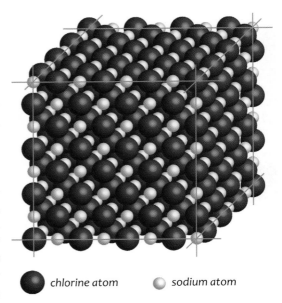

So far we have been discussing one major category of substances, pure substances, which, again, consists of elements and compounds. The other major category is *mixtures*. Any time substances are mixed together without a chemical reaction occurring a mixture is formed. (Remember—if a chemical reaction occurs compounds are formed, not mixtures.) If you toss vegetables in a salad, you've made a mixture. If you put sugar in your tea or milk in your coffee, you've made a mixture. If you mix up a batch of chocolate chip cookie dough, a bowl of party mix, or the batter for a vanilla cake, you've made mixtures.

● chlorine atom　　　　◐ sodium atom

Figure 9-4. The sodium chloride crystal lattice.

There are two basic kinds of mixtures, *heterogeneous mixtures* and *homogeneous mixtures*, illustrated in Figures 9-5 and 9-6. The difference between these is that in a heterogeneous mixture one can visually tell there is more than one substance present in the mixture; the different substances in the mixture are visible to the naked eye. In a homogeneous mixture the substances are mixed together so finely that one cannot see them and the substance appears uniform. Of the example mixtures in the previous paragraph, salads, chocolate chip cookie dough, and party mix are all heterogeneous mixtures. Sweetened tea, coffee with milk, and vanilla cake batter are all homogeneous mixtures.

There are two special types of homogeneous mixtures that are so common that they are worth mentioning. These are *solutions* and *suspensions*. A solution is a liquid mixture formed when one substance, called the *solute, dissolves* into another substance, called the *solvent*, as shown in Figure 9-7. When salt is dissolved in water, the salt is the solute and the water is the solvent. As another example, when a packet of Kool-Aid is dissolved in water, the Kool-Aid is the solute and the water is the solvent. The solute does not necessarily have to be a solid. Mixing cherry syrup (solute) into a Coke (solvent) is a solution, as is vodka (solute) in tomato juice (solvent). When two liquids are mixed into a solution like this the one that

Figure 9-5. The potato soup and rice dish are heterogeneous mixtures.

Figure 9-6. Ketchup and mayonnaise are homogeneous mixtures.

has the most volume is generally called the solvent, although it doesn't really matter. One could just as easily say that the two liquids are dissolving into each other.

There is a special class of *solid* solutions called *alloys*. An alloy is a solid solution of metals. Usually, to make an alloy the metals must be melted first so that they are liquids. But once the metals are melted they can be thoroughly mixed together and allowed to cool and solidify, and then the alloy is formed. There are several very common metal alloys. *Steel* is an alloy made of iron with a small amount of carbon mixed in. There are many different steel alloys, including many different alloys called "stainless" steel because they resist rusting. Steel is one of the most popular building materials in the world, and most alloys of steel include other metals in addition to the iron and carbon.

Other well-known alloys are *brass*, which is an alloy of copper and zinc, and *bronze*, an alloy of copper and tin, which is often used as a sculptural medium. As one more final example of alloys, most cars these days are available with "alloy wheels." These wheels are made mostly of aluminum, but there are small quantities of other metals blended in to give the wheels the desired mechanical properties. There are many different alloys of aluminum, all with slightly different mechanical or electrical properties. This is because aluminum is the material of choice for a great variety of applications (it

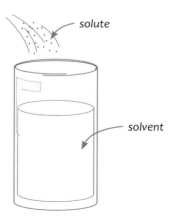

solute

solvent

Figure 9-7. The two components of a solution.

is strong, light-weight and inexpensive), so quite a few different aluminum alloys have been developed for different purposes.

In addition to solutions, the other special type of homogeneous mixture is *suspensions*. A suspension is a homogeneous mixture in which there are two different phases of substances involved. Substances typically exist in three different phases, solid, liquid and gas (or vapor), which we will discuss in the next section.

> A suspension is formed when two different phases of matter are mixed together and remain in their different phases.

If substances in two different phases are mixed together and they remain in their different phases they make a suspension. A common example of a suspension is clouds, which have water droplets (liquid) mixed in air (gas). Shaving cream is another good example, which has tiny air bubbles (gas) mixed into a liquid. Toothpaste has tiny solid particles mixed into a liquid. Other common examples of suspensions are blood and milk.

The relationships between all these different types of substances are summarized in Figure 9-8.

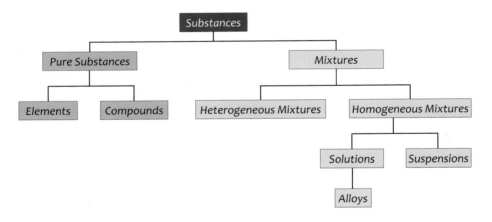

Figure 9-8. The family tree of substances.

Phases of Matter

The three basic phases of substances are *solid, liquid* and *gas* or *vapor*. The third phase may be called gas or vapor, depending on whether the substance normally exists in nature as a gas or not. If a substance normally exists in nature as a gas, we refer to a substance in this phase as a gas. Oxygen and nitrogen are examples of gases. (In fact, air is a mixture made almost entirely of these two gases.) But if a substance is normally a liquid or a solid at room temperature and we boil some of it, we conventionally refer to the substance after it has been converted to the gas phase as a vapor. Steam, for example, is water vapor.

The *internal energy* of a substance is what distinguishes the three phases from one another. We will discuss internal energy in more detail in the next chapter, but for now we can say that the internal energy of a substance is the sum of all the kinetic energies of the atoms or molecules in the substance. Every atom and every molecule is always in motion, and as we have seen in previous chapters, this means each atom or molecule has a certain amount of kinetic energy, equal to $\frac{1}{2}mv^2$.

> The internal energy of a substance—the sum of the kinetic energies of all its atoms or molecules—determines the phase of the substance.

If we add up all of these kinetic energies for a given quantity of a substance we have the internal energy of the substance. As we will discuss more in the next chapter, the internal energy is related strongly to the temperature of the substance. Heating a substance increases the temperature and the internal energy. Cooling a substance decreases the temperature and the internal energy of the substance.

Now let's relate the internal energy and temperature of a substance to its different phases. Refer to the diagrams in Figures 9-9, 9-10 and 9-11 as we go. If a substance has a very low internal energy, this means its temperature is low and the substance is in the solid phase. (For a substance normally in the liquid phase we would say it is now frozen.) Since the atoms have a low internal energy, the atoms' kinetic energy is low and they are moving relatively slowly. This low energy state for the atoms means they will cling strongly to one another by the electrical attraction of their charged particles (protons and electrons), forming a solid. So the atoms are not free to move around. They are stuck in place and can only vibrate where they are. The atoms *do* have kinetic energy, so they are not at rest. But they do not have enough energy to break free of the electrical attractions holding them all together, so their kinetic energy forces them to vibrate in place. This is what is going on with the atoms in any solid. Figure 9-9 depicts the atoms in a solid.

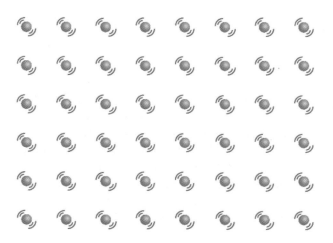

Figure 9-9. Atoms in a solid have low internal energy. They are bound together by electrical attraction and vibrate in place. (The solid depicted here happens to be a crystal.)

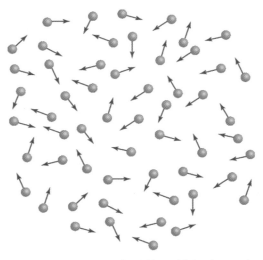

Figure 9-10. Atoms in a liquid have higher internal energy. They are loosely bound together and are free to move around.

Assume now that we heat this substance, raising the internal energy and the temperature of the substance. Every pure substance has a particular temperature at which the higher kinetic energy in the atoms will overcome the electrical attraction between the atoms, allowing the atoms to come apart. This is the *melting point* of the substance. After the substance melts it becomes a liquid. In the liquid phase the atoms are still held together loosely, which is why liquids will stay together in an open container or in puddles if the liquid is spilled. The atoms in a liquid move very fast, and there are a lot of them. The result is that in a liquid the atoms are continuously colliding with each other at very high speeds, encountering an incredible number of collisions every second. Figure 9-10 depicts the atoms in a liquid.

If we heat the substance still further we will raise the temperature to the *boiling point*. At this temperature the internal energy of the atoms is so high that they will no longer stay together, and the substance enters the gas phase. Instead of staying together, if they are not contained, the atoms have so much energy they will fly away at great speed. Because of their higher speeds, the atoms or molecules will spread apart, still colliding with one another, but spreading out as much as they are able. If they are contained in a container of some kind they will still fly around at great speed, but instead of flying off into the atmosphere they will be furiously colliding with each other and with the walls of the container, causing the pressure in the container to go up. We will examine this situation more closely in the next chapter,

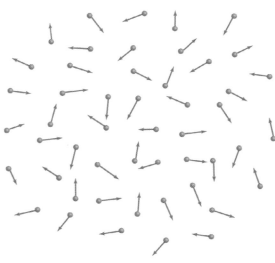

Figure 9-11. Atoms in a gas have high internal energy. They are not bound together at all. They have higher velocities and will spread apart as far as their environment allows them to.

which includes a mind-blowing example showing just how fast these atoms move and how frequently they collide with one another. Figure 9-11 depicts the fast moving atoms in a gas or vapor.

All these phase change processes work the same way in reverse when cooling the substance. If we cool a vapor down to the *condensation point* (the same temperature as the boiling point), the atoms will have low enough energies that they begin clinging to one another in a liquid. The process of a gas cooling and becoming a liquid is called *condensation*. Cool the substance further to the *freezing point* (the same temperature as the melting point), and the energies are low enough that the atoms lock together in a solid where they can only vibrate in place.

Evaporation

Now that we have looked at the connection between internal energy and the different phases of matter, you may be wondering now how substances can evaporate. *Evaporation* is the process of a substance slowly converting to a vapor without first being heated to the boiling point. If substances change phase by being heated or cooled and changing the internal energy, how can a substance evaporate?

We have seen that the sum of the kinetic energies of the molecules in a substance is equal to the internal energy, and the internal energy is related to the temperature. If we look more closely at the molecules in any substance, at any temperature, we will see that the atoms or molecules in the substance are not actually all moving at exactly the same speed. They will be all moving at the same *average* speed. But there will always be a *distribution* of speeds, with many molecules moving at close to the average speed, some molecules moving slower than average, and some molecules moving faster than average. Because of this distribution of kinetic energies in the molecules, there will always be some molecules with a much higher energy than average. These high-energy molecules will sometimes have enough energy to break free from the other molecules in the substance. When this happens, the molecule finds itself zooming around in the vapor state. This is evaporation—molecules leaving the others because of their higher than average energy, rather than because the entire substance has been heated to the boiling point.

Water boils at the relatively low temperature of 100°C, or 373.2 kelvins (K). In a bowl of water at room temperature, 293.2 K, it is not difficult for a few H_2O molecules to have enough energy to place them up at the boiling temperature, allowing evaporation to occur. Water can even do this when it is a solid (ice). This is why ice cubes in the freezer get smaller and smaller as they age. Water molecules on the surface of the ice cubes are evaporating! The boiling point of alcohol is even lower than that of water, so alcohol evaporates even more readily and more quickly than water. Other substances, such as oils, have much higher boiling points. Olive oil, for example, boils at around 300°C, or 573.2 K. It is essentially impossible for a molecule of olive oil in a bowl of oil at room temperature to have enough kinetic energy to put its temperature up almost 300 degrees above average, and so olive oil doesn't evaporate. The same reasoning applies to other oils as well.

Sublimation

The process of a solid converting directly to a gas without going through the liquid phase is called *sublimation*. Dry ice is frozen carbon dioxide (CO_2). It just so happens that at atmospheric pressure the molecules of carbon dioxide go directly from the solid phase to the gas phase as they gain energy by being warmed up. Other substances can do this too, but dry ice is the only common substance that does it at atmospheric pressure.

What is a plasma?

In addition to the three common phases of matter (solid, liquid and gas), there is a fourth phase—plasma. A plasma is an *ionized* gas. An *ion* is an atom that has lost or gained one or more electrons, so that it has a net electrical charge. An ionized gas, or plasma, is formed when the atoms in the gas are ionized. Being full of ions, plasmas are electrically conductive. As a result, the properties of plasmas are so different from the other phases of matter that the plasma is considered to be a separate phase of matter.

Plasmas are formed when the presence of a very strong electric field strips away the electrons from the atoms in a gas. As it happens, such conditions exist throughout the universe, and plasma is actually the most prevalent phase of matter in the universe!

The electric fields that cause plasma to form can also impart energy to the other electrons in the atoms of the gas, causing them to emit photons of visible light as described in Chapter 8. The familiar neon lights work this way, which means we could accurately refer to these lights as "plasma lights." The electric field that produces the neon plasma is provided by a transformer with electric leads inserted into the sealed tube containing the gas.

Essentially the same process occurs during a lightning strike. A high electric field between clouds and the ground causes molecules in the air to ionize, creating an electrically conductive channel between the cloud and the ground. The ionized air molecules emit light the same way the neon lights do. As soon as the electrically conducting channel opens up between the cloud and the ground, the electrical charge in the cloud (which caused the electric field in the first place) instantly flows to ground—a bolt of lightning.

Ideas for Your Classroom

1. Talk about the different elements, how they were discovered and named, and some of their interesting histories in culture. This may sound dull, but read Sam Kean's great book *The Disappearing Spoon* and you will hardly be able to wait to tell some of the stories to your students.

2. Have students perform research to discover ways the different elements are used in technology.

3. Get some dry ice from the grocery store and talk about the phase transition that is happening right before the students' eyes.

4. There are scores of videos on You Tube involving dry ice and/or liquid nitrogen. Many of these videos were prepared by scientists and are both substantive and fun. A few good videos can stimulate a lot of excitement and discussion about the nature of the phase changes that are taking place.

5. Have a competition in which student teams must identify the type of substance named, using the types of substances listed in Figure 9-8.

6. If you are adventurous, you can undertake projects on crystals with your students. Students can learn about some of the different types of crystals and make 3-D models of substances in the basic crystalline arrangements: simple cubic, also called primitive cubic (polonium); body-centered cubic (iron, lithium, sodium) and face-centered cubic (nickel, copper, stainless steel). Warning: The study of crystals can get very complicated, but if you start simple and get the students to do a lot of the research, crystals are fun to study. Helpful pages at wikipedia.org include:

    Periodic table (crystal structure)
    Cubic crystal system
    Crystal structure
    Crystal

Goals for Chapter 10

1. Define and distinguish between heat, internal energy, thermal energy, thermal equilibrium, specific heat capacity, and thermal conductivity.

2. Describe and explain the three processes of heat transfer: conduction, convection and radiation.

3. Describe how temperature relates to the internal energy of a substance and to the kinetic energy of its molecules.

4. Explain the Kinetic Theory of Gases, and use the Kinetic Theory of Gases to explain why the pressure of a gas inside a container is higher when the gas is hotter and lower when the gas is cooler.

5. Apply the concepts of specific heat capacity and thermal conductivity to explain how common materials such as metals, water, and thermal insulators behave.

About This Chapter

The material in this chapter relates closely to our previous study of energy, so you are advised to read Chapter 5 before this chapter. Heat and temperature *are all about energy.*

Chapter 10
Heat and Temperature

Temperature Scales

There are a lot of different temperature scales around because scientists all over the world have been investigating materials at various temperatures for a long time. The three most important are the Fahrenheit scale we have been using all of our lives (those of us who grew up in America), and the two main SI (metric) scales, the Celsius scale (used by nearly everyone outside America) and the Kelvin scale.

The Celsius scale (formerly known to some as the "centigrade" scale) is based on the freezing and boiling temperatures of water (at atmospheric pressure). The scale was specifically designed so that water would freeze at 0°C and boil at 100°C. On this scale, room temperature is around 20-25°C.

For historical reasons, the Celsius and Fahrenheit scales use the strange term "degree." This is odd when you think about it. We don't use a term like this with any other units of measure. The Kelvin scale does not use this term. A temperature of 300 K is read as, "three hundred kelvins."

A degree on the Celsius scale is the same as a "degree" on the Kelvin scale; the degrees are the same size. But the Kelvin scale is an absolute scale, which means there are no negative temperatures on the Kelvin scale. The temperature of 0.0 K is referred to as "absolute zero." According to the laws of physics as we understand them, this temperature cannot be achieved. A region might be refrigerated down to a small fraction of 1.0 K, but nothing can ever reach 0 K. (And nothing can ever be less than 0 K, as will be explained shortly.)

Table 10-1 shows the temperatures for freezing/melting or boiling/condensing of water in these three scales. Since 0°C is the same temperature as 273.2 K, this implies that absolute zero is at −273.2°C.

Phase Change	Degrees Fahrenheit (°F)	Degrees Celsius (°C)	Kelvins (K)
Boiling or Condensing	212	100	373.2
Freezing or Melting	32	0	273.2

Table 10-1. Freezing and boiling points for water in three temperature scales.

Heat and Energy Terminology

In this section we will revisit some of the energy terms we have already en-countered and fill out their definitions just a bit. As we saw in the chapter on energy, *heat* is energy in transit, flowing from one substance to a cooler substance. No substance ever possesses heat. A substance can possess other forms of energy, but heat is the term for energy in the process of flowing from one substance to another because of a difference in temperature.

Thermal energy is a very informal and relative term, so it is only useful when speaking generally. It does not have any real technical use. Basically, thermal energy is energy an object possesses because it has been heated. The term is only really used to compare substances to room temperature. So we might speak of boiling water as having thermal energy because it was heated on a stove. But if an object was taken from a freezer where its temperature was −20 °C and heated up to −15 °C, we probably would not speak of its thermal energy, because even though it was heated it is still very cold relative to room temperature.

Last chapter we saw that the *internal energy* of a substance is the total of all of the kinetic energies possessed by the atoms or molecules of the substance. Atoms or molecules are constantly in motion, vibrating or translating (that is, flying in a straight line) or both. Atoms in solids cannot fly around, so they vibrate in place,

How fast are air molecules moving?

When we say that air molecules are zipping around all the time, how fast are they actually going? The answer is rather shocking. At room temperature an average air molecule is moving at about 1,100 mph, or 500 m/s! This speed is 1.5 times the speed of sound, also called Mach 1.5. Of course, this is just the average speed; half the molecules are moving faster than that! This sounds bizarre.

But it gets weirder, so hold on to your hat. We know there are lots of molecules in the air, so if they are moving this fast, don't they bump into each other a lot? YES! In every cubic centimeter of air there are about 2.7 x 10^{19} molecules. This is a colossal number. If there were this many people on earth there would be over 4,800 people per square foot everywhere on the planet, including the oceans!

With this many molecules all moving so fast, the average distance a molecule travels before colliding with another molecule is much smaller than the wavelength of light, and an average molecule will collide 5 times every nanosecond (billionth of a second). Sprightly little guys, eh? In sum, have a look at a little chunk of air in front of you about the size of a sugar cube. In this little space there are 27,000,000,000,000,000,000 molecules and they each bump into another molecule 5,000,000,000 times per second moving at Mach 1.5 between every hit!

but atoms in gases are free to translate (see the box for an interesting example). Either way, since atoms are always moving they always possess kinetic energy. If one were to add up the kinetic energies of every particle in a certain substance, that would be its internal energy. This term is much more precise than "thermal energy," and can actually be computed. Although it is somewhat complicated to explain, the "temperature" of a substance is very closely related to its internal energy. The higher the temperature, the higher the internal energy.

With this background about internal energy we can elaborate a bit more on *absolute zero*, the zero temperature on the Kelvin temperature scale. The temperature of a substance varies directly with its internal energy. A temperature of 0 kelvins (absolute zero) means no internal energy at all, or in other words, the atoms would be standing still! Atoms can't move any slower than standing still, and thus, there is no temperature lower than absolute zero. As far as we know, there is no place in the universe where the temperature is absolute zero, although physicists in low-temperature research labs have succeeded in achieving temperatures of only a few millionths of a degree above absolute zero. (As one might imagine, very weird things happen at temperatures that low.)

> At absolute zero a substance would have zero internal energy, which means its atoms would have no kinetic energy and thus would be standing still.

Finally, we have the concept of *thermal equilibrium*. The laws of thermodynamics say that if a substance is at a different temperature than its environment, heat will flow from the warmer of the two into the cooler of the two. We are all familiar with this principle, even if we don't know the actual law. In fact it is the Second Law of Thermodynamics that says heat must flow this way. Thermal equilibrium is the state in which an object is at the same temperature as its environment, and when this happens heat flow ceases.

Heat Transfer Processes

There are three processes by which heat can transfer from one place to another. As you read, refer to the illustrations in Figure 10-1 which depict these processes.

The first heat transfer process is *conduction*. This process occurs in solids. In a solid the atoms or molecules of the substance vibrate in place but they are not free to flow around. Imagine a great number of atoms in a substance attached together in a flexible grid, as if they were connected to one another by springs. If one side of the substance was heated, the internal energy of the atoms there goes up, which means they begin vibrating more vigorously because their kinetic energy is increasing. This vibration will be transferred to the other atoms nearby, because the atoms are all linked together, as atoms always are in a solid. The kinetic energy in these vibrations will continue to spread to atoms farther and farther away from the location where the material is being heated. As atoms gain more kinetic energy, their temperature goes up. This is heat flow by conduction.

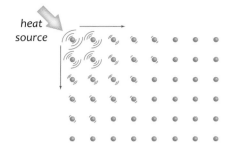

Conduction in Solids
A heat source gives kinetic energy to nearby atoms, which begin vibrating vigorously. These vibrations are passed from one atom to the next within the solid substance. In this figure the blue arrows indicate the direction of the spread of the vibrations, which is the spread of heat, in the substance.

Convection in Fluids
Hot, fast moving molecules (red arrows) from some kind of hot source gradually work their way into a place full of cooler, slower moving molecules (blue arrows). As the molecules repeatedly collide, the hot molecules transfer kinetic energy to the cooler ones. The loss of kinetic energy cools the hot molecules and the gain of kinetic energy warms the cool ones.

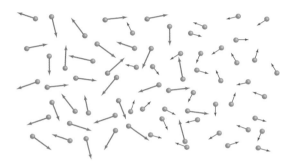

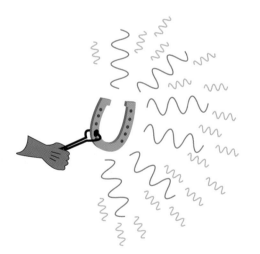

Radiation from Hot Objects
All hot objects radiate infrared electromagnetic waves, which we can feel as heat. The amount of this radiation depends strongly on the temperature of the object—for hotter and hotter objects the amount of infrared radiation given off goes up drastically. The waves are drawn with red and orange lines to indicate the flow of heat, but infrared waves are, of course, invisible.

Figure 10-1. The three heat transfer processes.

A well-known example of conduction is the way heat transfers in the metal of a frying pan. Initially the atoms in the pan are all at room temperature (and are thus at thermal equilibrium with the room). When the center of the pan is heated the atoms there gain internal energy and begin vibrating more vigorously. These vibrations are passed atom to atom and the temperature increases more and more, farther and farther away from the location where the source of heat is. Eventually the vibrations spread all the way out to the handle of the pan and the handle itself gets hot, even though it is nowhere near the heat source.

The second heat transfer process is *convection*. This process occurs in fluids, that is, liquids and gases. The particles of a fluid are free to flow around and mix and mingle and collide with other particles. Particles with high internal energy are hot and will be moving very rapidly, because the internal energy is the kinetic energy of the particles. These particles will mix with cooler particles, and as they do they collide with them and transfer some of their high energy to the lower energy particles. This is just like balls colliding on a pool table. When a fast ball hits a slow one the fast one slows down and the slow one speeds up as kinetic energy is transferred from the ball with more energy to the one with less.

> Atoms transfer energy from one to another by conduction in solids and by convection in fluids.

As we saw in Chapter 7, conservation of momentum applies as well. In fact, colliding gas molecules may be accurately modeled as elastic collisions in which both momentum and kinetic energy are conserved. Unlike pool balls, particles in liquids and gases never stop moving, so over time all the particles share the energy evenly. When this happens, they are all more or less at the same average temperature (thermal equilibrium).

A good example of convection at work is in the old radiators commonly used to heat homes in the days before central heating systems (and still in use in many older homes, particularly up north). Steam is pumped through the inside of the radiator, making the iron radiator hot to the touch. When air molecules collide with the hot surface, they pick up kinetic energy from the rapidly vibrating atoms in the metal. These hot, fast moving molecules then gradually work their way through the room, colliding with the slower, cooler molecules and exchanging energy so the cooler molecules begin moving faster, which means they are hotter.

The third heat transfer process is *radiation*. Radiation is the term for heat energy transferred by electromagnetic waves. As we saw in Chapter 5, electromagnetic waves travel through space and through the atmosphere to carry energy from the sun to the earth. Light, infrared radiation, ultraviolet radiation, microwaves, X-rays—these are all the same thing, electromagnetic radiation (or waves). The only thing that distinguishes these different terms for radiation is the *wavelength* of the waves. In the context of heat transfer, we are mainly talking about *infrared* (IR) radiation, which consists of invisible electromagnetic waves with wavelengths in the range of roughly 750 to 2500 nanometers (billionths of a meter).

In the next chapter we will look at why this electromagnetic heat energy is called "infrared radiation," and we will discuss how infrared radiation relates to other electromagnetic radiation such as radio waves and light. But here it is important to point out that the hotter an object is, the more infrared energy it radiates. The "radiators" used to heat homes radiate IR electromagnetic waves, but they are not actually very hot, so the amount of radiation they emit is low. Thus, despite their name, old-fashioned radiators heat a room more by convection than by radiation. Electric space heaters with glowing red heating coils are so hot that they emit a lot more IR energy, and heat the room primarily by radiation.

When we feel the heat radiating from a hot metal object such as a horse shoe being forged, it is the IR radiation we are feeling. When we hold our hands in front of a fire, it is the IR radiation from the coals we are feeling. Our eyes can't see it the way they can visible light, but our skin can feel it. When we feel warm in the sun even on a cool day, it is the IR radiation from the sun that is warming us. When the inside of a car gets hot it is because of IR radiation from the sun striking the car and then transferring into the car by the radiation passing through the glass and by conduction through the metal. Figure 10-2 depicts all three heat transfer processes as each of them contribute to the warming of the interior of a car in the sun.

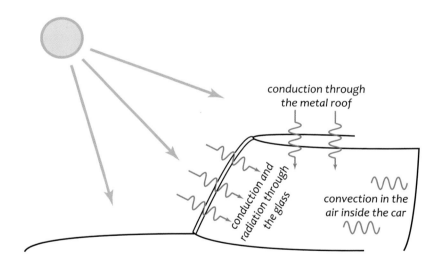

Figure 10-2. Heat transfer processes at work heating the interior of a car.

Kinetic Theory of Gases

With the background we have now in molecular movement and internal energy, we are ready to look at the cause for pressure in gases. This explanation is called the *Kinetic Theory of Gases*.

According to the Kinetic Theory of Gases, the atoms or molecules of a gas in a container are zooming around inside the container all the time at high speed, as depicted in Figure 10-3. The hotter the gas is, the more kinetic energy the particles

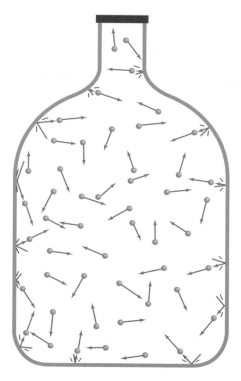

Figure 10-3. Pressure in a container is caused by unimaginable numbers of gas particles continuously striking the walls of the container.

have and the faster they are zooming around. There are an incredible number of particles in even a small container, and as they zoom around, the individual particles in this huge population are constantly striking the walls of the container. These collisions between the particles and the container walls cause the effect we call *pressure*. If the temperature goes up, the particles have higher internal energy, meaning higher kinetic energy, so they are moving faster and striking the container walls harder and more frequently, creating higher pressure. We can summarize this theory of gas behavior this way:

A familiar example of this physics occurs when a person buys a Mylar birthday balloon at the grocery store on a hot day. The balloon vendor fills the balloon with an appropriate amount of helium inside the cool grocery store. When the balloon is carried outside into the blazing heat the balloon swells up so tightly it appears it is ready to burst from the high pressure. Then the balloon is placed inside a car with the air conditioner blasting away. The very cold air from the car A/C is so cold the pressure in the balloon decreases significantly, even way below what it was inside the store. This causes the balloon to shrink and collapse and fall down on the floor of the car. When the buyer arrives home and takes the balloon out of the car, the hot outside air warms up the helium, those atoms pick up speed again and begin colliding once again at high speed on the inside of the balloon causing the pressure to spike back up. All of this is caused by the atoms in the helium gas gaining kinetic energy when they warm up and losing kinetic energy when they cool.

Specific Heat Capacity

The *specific heat capacity* of a substance is a property of the substance that relates to how the material behaves when it is absorbing or releasing heat energy. The specific heat capacity (or simply, heat capacity) of a substance is defined as the amount of heat energy that must transfer into or out of a specific mass of the substance (1 gram) to change its temperature by 1°C.

> The specific heat capacity of a substance indicates the amount of heat energy needed to raise or lower its temperature.

A substance with a low specific heat capacity will change temperature very easily and quickly because very little energy must be added or removed to change its temperature. Metals are like this. A very small amount of heat will raise the temperature of a metal a lot, and removing only a small amount of heat will cause the temperature of a metal to drop a lot.

A substance with a high specific heat capacity will change temperature only very slowly because it must absorb or release a lot of energy to change its temperature. Water is like this. (In fact, water has a great number of very unique properties, and this is one of them.) It takes a lot of heat energy to warm up a pan of water even a little bit. And to cool water down requires removing a lot of heat from it just to cool it down a little bit. For comparison, the specific heat capacity of water is about ten times greater than that of copper, and about five times greater than that of aluminum.

Thermal Conductivity

Like specific heat capacity, *thermal conductivity* is another property of materials that relates to how materials behave when they are absorbing or releasing heat energy. It is common to confuse this term with the specific heat capacity mentioned in the previous section, but these two properties are distinct.

The specific heat capacity of a substance is a measure of how much heat energy is required to change the temperature of the substance. By contrast, the thermal conductivity of a substance is a measure of how well a material transfers heat within its own atomic structure by conduction. Metals have a very high thermal conductivity, so heat conducts readily through a metal. This is because the atoms in a metal are arranged in a crystal lattice, and the geometrical arrangement allows the vibrations to pass easily from atom to atom. On the other hand, building insulation used inside the walls of buildings and houses has a very low thermal conductivity, so heat transfers through it very, very slowly. Materials like this are called *thermal insulators*. Other materials with a low thermal conductivity are glass and plastic. In fact, high thermal conductivity in materials seems typically to accompany high electrical conductivity. We all know that metals conduct electricity the best. Well, they conduct heat the best, too.

The effect of different thermal conductivities in materials is demonstrated dramatically by watching what happens when ice cubes are placed on blocks of plastic and aluminum, as shown in Figure 10-4. The two black blocks are at the same temperature, room temperature. The block on the left is made of some kind of composite wood and plastic material. The block on the right is made of aluminum. The ice cubes were placed on the blocks at the same moment and the photo was taken after about 30 seconds. The ice cube on the right is melting so fast that it baffles those who see this demonstration for the first time. The ice cube on the left is not melting a bit.

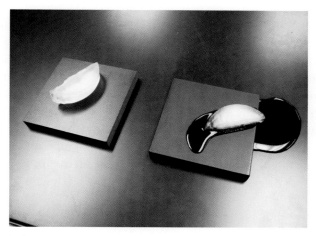

Figure 10-4. High thermal conductivity, illustrated by the block on the right, which is made of aluminum.

When an ice cube is placed on either block, heat flows from the block into the ice cube. However, the thermal conductivity of the wood/plastic block is very low, so even though the spot where the ice cube is sitting is cold, heat flows *very* slowly from the warmer parts of the block to the cold spot. But the high thermal conductivity of aluminum means that heat from the warmer parts of the block can flow very fast to the cold spot, and from there right on into the ice cube to keep warming it up.

From the photo alone, you might think that the block on the right would feel warmer to the touch than the block on the left. The opposite is the case. In fact, the aluminum block feels *cold* to the touch while the left block does not. The reason is that because of aluminum's high thermal conductivity, heat energy is flowing rapidly out of the aluminum into the ice, warming the ice and cooling the aluminum. And even though the aluminum block's temperature drops a lot, its ice cube continues to melt, because the heat just keeps on flowing out of the aluminum and into the ice. For more specific detail on why cold objects *feel* cold to the touch, see the box at the end of this chapter.

Distinguishing Between Specific Heat Capacity and Thermal Conductivity

Specific heat capacity specifies the *quantity* of heat it takes to warm a substance, or the quantity of heat that must be removed from a substance to cool it down. As you can see in Figure 10-5, the heat capacity of water is huge compared to just about everything else. Also notice that the specific heat capacity of metals is quite low compared to water.

The huge heat capacity of water is a major factor in regulating the temperatures on earth. (The atmosphere is another major factor.) About 70% of the earth is covered by water, primarily in the oceans. During the day the radiation from the sun warms the oceans, but a lot of energy must be added to all this water to warm it. At night the thermal energy in the water can escape into the atmosphere, allowing the water to cool. But again, a lot of heat energy has to be removed from water for it to cool down. The result is that the ocean water covering the earth does not change temperature very much. Since there is so much water on the earth, the steady temperature of the water helps regulate the temperature of the atmosphere, and thus of the entire planet. Without the oceans, the temperature swings from day to night on earth would be huge, and complex life on earth could not survive.

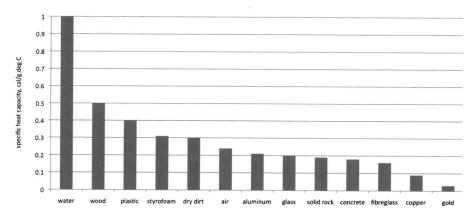

Figure 10-5. Specific heat capacities of various materials.

These considerations (and others) have persuaded astronomers that if complex life exists on other planets those planets probably have a lot of water.

By contrast, thermal conductivity is about how well heat can flow *through* a substance by conduction. As shown in Figure 10-6a, the thermal conductivity of metals completely dominates everything else. Since the thermal conductivities of all other materials are so small compared to metals, a separate chart is shown in Figure 10-6b for the nonmetal substances so that they can be compared. Notice that the thermal conductivities of water and air are miniscule, because heat transfers through fluids mainly by convection, not by conduction, as we discussed previously.[1]

Since the specific heat capacity of water is so much greater than the heat capacity of anything else, the presence of water will be the major factor in questions about how fast things heat up or cool down, or about how much energy must be added to a substance to warm it up or removed from it to cool it down. And since the thermal conductivity of metals is so much greater than the thermal conductivity of anything else, the presence of metal will be the major factor in how rapidly heat will flow through a substance by conduction.

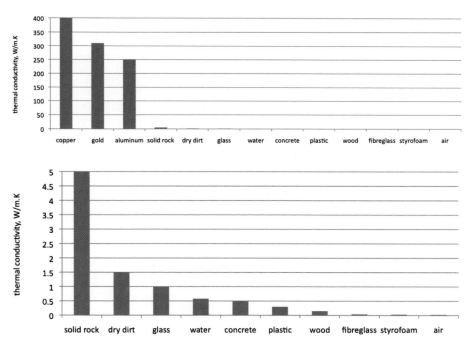

Figures 10-6a (top) and 10-6b (bottom). Thermal conductivities of various materials. The two graphs are nearly the same, but in the lower graph the first three materials are removed and the vertical scale enlarged

---

1   The units of measure on the vertical axis in these charts are watts per meter per kelvin. A watt is one joule of energy per second. So these units give us the rate energy conducts through one meter of the substance for each degree of temperature difference.

Why do the aluminum cases of Apple's MacBook and iPad always feel cold when you pick one up?

The sensation of coldness to the touch is produced when heat in the tissue of our fingers flows out of our fingers and into something else. The faster the heat flows out of our fingertips, the colder the substance feels. This relates very closely to why metal objects out of doors in the cold of winter feel colder than other objects. If you touch a cold piece of wood it will not feel that cold. The thermal conductivity of wood is so low that when you touch the wood the heat flowing from your skin to the wood stays in the place you are touching. As a result, the wood warms up quickly in the one spot. As the temperature of that spot approaches your skin temperature, heat flow from your fingers to the wood slows way down. Since the sensation of coldness is caused by loss of heat, the wood stops feeling cold very quickly. But when you touch a metal object like an iron railing, the heat from your hand flows into the iron and keeps flowing away from the place you are touching, so the place you are touching barely warms up at all.

The high thermal conductivity of aluminum means that when you touch the case of an iPad, heat flows out of your fingers into the iPad and keeps right on flowing through the aluminum case, spreading out throughout the aluminum. Since the heat energy from your fingers does not stay in the spot you are touching, the spot does not warm up much, so the heat from your fingers just continues flowing into the places where you are touching the aluminum case. As long as heat keeps flowing out of your fingers like this, the surface you are touching will feel cold.

Ideas for Your Classroom

1. Purchase a helium-filled Mylar balloon from a grocery store and bring it to your classroom. Push the balloon into an ice chest full of ice water and watch the balloon collapse to a flat pancake. Remove the balloon and watch it puff back up as the air warms the helium inside. Place the balloon in the direct sun, even indoors where the temperature is controlled, and watch the balloon expand almost to the bursting point. Point out to students that no helium is going in or out of the balloon. It's all about how fast the atoms of helium gas are moving around inside the balloon.

2. Place a Pyrex glass container or laboratory beaker on a hot plate. Fill the container with tap water and turn the heat up to high. Students who watch closely as the water warms will see the *convection currents* rippling through the water, as warm water from the bottom of the container floats up and mixes with the cooler water above.

3. Place two thermometers close together in your classroom, one in the direct sunlight and one not. Discuss the specific reasons behind why they read differently.

4. Involve students in projects that explore the effects in nature of the high specific heat capacity of water. Topics to pursue might include the way the oceans help to regulate the temperature of our environment to allow for complex life on earth, the mild temperature of California, and the Gulf Stream's effect on England.

    (The prevailing winds on the west coast are toward the east, so the air blowing on the coast of California has been moving across the Pacific Ocean. Since the temperature of the ocean does not change very much, the temperature of the air arriving in California is nearly always mild.

    Even though London is 8 degrees latitude farther north, the average temperature in London in January is 7 °C; in Toronto it is –2 °C. The Gulf Stream travels right up the east coast of the U.S. and over to England. The Gulf Stream waters arriving at England are still quite warm, and help keep England warm.)

Goals for Chapter 11

1. Define wave, crest, trough, amplitude, wavelength, period and frequency.

2. Describe the following five wave phenomena, giving examples of each:
    a. Reflection
    b. Refraction
    c. Diffraction
    d. Resonance
    e. Interference
        i.   Constructive interference
        ii. Destructive interference

3. Give examples of longitudinal, transverse, and circular waves and the media in which they propagate.

4. Define infrasonic and ultrasonic, and give examples of these types of sounds.

5. Define infrared and ultraviolet, and give examples of these types of radiation.

6. List the major regions in the electromagnetic spectrum, in order from low frequency to high frequency.

7. State the frequency range of human hearing in hertz (Hz), and the wavelength range of visible light in nanometers (nm).

8. State the six main colors in the visible light spectrum in order from longest wavelength to shortest.

9. Explain how sound waves of different frequencies (harmonics) contribute to the timbre of musical instruments.

About This Chapter

There are quite a few vocabulary terms in this chapter. You may find it helpful to make yourself a vocabulary list on an index card as we go.

Chapter 11
Waves, Sound and Light

Because there are so many phenomena in nature that exhibit wave-like characteristics, the study of waves is of central importance in physics. In this chapter we will first look at characteristics common to all waves. Then we will take a closer look at the two wave phenomena we are most familiar with, sound and light.

The Anatomy of Waves

We will begin with a definition:

A *wave* is a disturbance in space and time that carries energy from one place to another.

A wave can be a single pulse, such as a tsunami caused by an earthquake, or a continuous "train" of waves, such as a beam of light or sound waves from a horn. As shown in Figure 11-1, the tops of a wave are called *crests* (or *peaks*), the bottoms are called *troughs*. The height of the wave from the center line to a crest is called the *amplitude*. The amplitude relates to the intensity of the wave, that is, how much energy the wave is carrying, and the units will depend on what kind of wave it is.

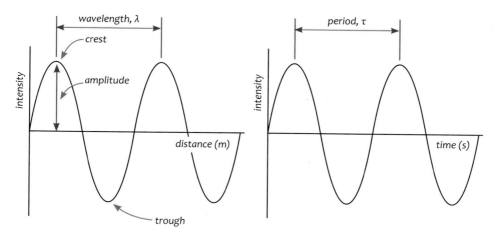

A wave depicted in space at one instant in time. The distance between crests is the wavelength, measured in meters.

A wave depicted in time as it passes one point in space. The distance between crests is the period, measured in seconds.

Figure 11-1. The parts of a wave in graphical representation.

Louder sounds, brighter lights, and more destructive earthquakes are all examples of waves with higher amplitudes. Waves shaped like those shown in Figure 11-1 are often called *sine waves*, and waves possessing this very typical shape are said to be *sinusoidal*.

Waves vary in time, but they also propagate through space, so we can think of the length of a wave in distance (spatial) units or time units. (We usually use the word *propagate* instead of travel or move when we are talking about waves, because waves don't simply travel from place to place. They also spread out as they go and the term propagate connotes this better.) If we consider distance, the length of one cycle of a wave is called the *wavelength*, measured in meters. In time units the length of one cycle of the wave is called the *period*, which is measured in seconds. The period is the amount of time it takes for the wave to complete one cycle. Whether we are speaking of the period or the wavelength, these variables are represented by the length from one crest of the wave to the next crest.

As just mentioned, the MKS unit for the wavelength of a wave is the meter. However, in this chapter many of the examples make use of visible light, which has very short wavelengths, in the range of a few hundred billionths of a meter. It will be helpful in this context to introduce the metric prefix for billionth, *nano-*. Then we can specify wavelengths of visible light using nanometers (nm). For example, a common wavelength for the light emitted by green laser pointers is 532 nm. This value is equivalent to 0.000000532 meters.

> The metric prefix *nano-* means billionth, so a nanometer is a billionth of a meter. Visible light has wavelengths in the range of a few hundred nanometers.

Categorizing Waves

We could divide all people into two categories, American citizens, and people who are not American citizens. A different way to categorize all people would be in the three categories of child, adolescent or adult. Similarly, there are different ways to categorize all waves.

One way to categorize waves is by whether the wave needs a *medium* or not in which to propagate. *Mechanical waves* need a *medium*, that is, *matter* of some kind, in which to propagate. Most waves are like this. Sound does not travel in a vacuum, but it does travel in media such as air and water. Earthquake waves travel in the underground rock; water waves travel on the surface of water.

By contrast, *electromagnetic waves* can travel in the vacuum of empty space without a medium. This is how energy gets here from the sun, as we have seen in previous chapters. Electromagnetic waves can also travel in some media—visible light travels in air and through glass, radio waves travel in air and through wooden walls.

Another way to categorize all waves is according to the relationship between the direction of *oscillation* that is causing the wave and the direction the wave is propagating. The term oscillate means to continuously swing back and forth or up and down between two end points or states. All continuous wave trains are created by something that is oscillating that generates the wave as it oscillates.

There are three basic ways that the oscillation causing the wave can relate to the direction the wave is going. In *transverse waves* the oscillation is perpendicular to the direction of propagation. Light waves and waves on strings are good examples of transverse waves. A wave on a string, like a guitar string, is created by plucking the string, or, as in the case with a piano, by whacking the string with a hammer. Either way, a transverse wave is formed. A transverse wave on a string is depicted in Figure 11-2. This diagram depicts a device that can mechanically vibrate the string to produce a continuous wave train that propagates down the string, just like a person whipping the end of a cord up and down. The red arrows in Figure 8-2 are there to illustrate that the direction of wave propagation is perpendicular to the up and down motion of the device vibrating the string.

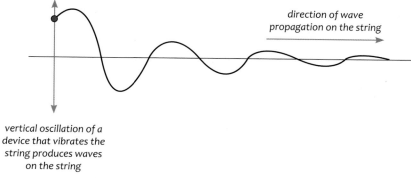

direction of wave
propagation on the string

vertical oscillation of a
device that vibrates the
string produces waves
on the string

Figure 11-2. A depiction of a transverse wave on a string, in which the oscillation and propagation are perpendicular.

With *longitudinal waves* the oscillating motion causing the wave is parallel to the direction of propagation. Sound waves are an example, and considering how sound is produced by a loudspeaker pushing back and forth is a nice way to think about this and remember it. Longitudinal sound waves produced by a loudspeaker are depicted in Figure 11-3. The wave train is actually a succession of pressure fluctuations in the air above and below atmospheric pressure. We will discuss sound waves in more detail, along with other terms in this diagram, later in this chapter.

The third type of relationship between oscillation and direction of propagation is represented by *circular waves*. Waves on water are circular waves. In circular waves the oscillating action is moving in a circular fashion. Because of

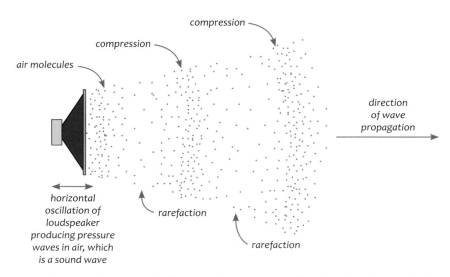

Figure 11-3. An example of a longitudinal sound wave produced by a loudspeaker, in which the oscillation and propagation are parallel.

this, a floating object on water will move in a circular pattern as the waves pass by underneath it, as illustrated in Figure 11-4.

Wave Calculations

There are two common equations we use for working with waves. Both of these equations involve letters from the Greek alphabet. The first equation relates the velocity at which the wave propagates to the frequency and wavelength of the wave:

$$v = \lambda f$$

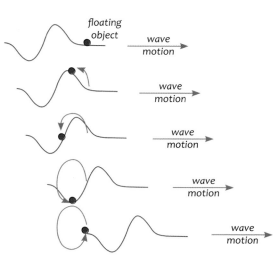

Figure 11-4. A water wave causing a floating object to loop around in a circular fashion as the wave goes by.

where v is the velocity of the wave propagation (m/s), λ ("lambda," the Greek letter l) is the wavelength of the wave (m), and f is the frequency of the wave (Hz).

The *frequency* of a wave is the number of cycles the wave completes in one second. The MKS units for frequency are cycles per second. We have a name for this unit, which is hertz (Hz). So if a wave completes 5,000 cycles per second, its frequency is 5,000 Hz. Using the metric prefix *kilo-*, meaning 1,000, this value can also be written as 5 kilohertz, or 5 kHz. The frequency of a wave is determined by the oscillating device or object producing the wave.

The velocity of a wave depends on the medium in which it is propagating. For example, light moves about 33% slower in glass than in air, but sound travels over 11 times faster in glass than in air. The wavelength of the wave, the third variable in the equation above, is the variable that picks up the slack to make the equation work. For a given medium, the velocity and frequency of a wave are fixed. From the above equation, we can calculate the wavelength as

$$\lambda = \frac{v}{f}$$

From this equation we can see that as frequency goes up, wavelength goes down. In other words, higher frequency waves have shorter wavelengths. Knowing this will be particularly useful when we study light later on in this chapter.

As mentioned near the beginning of this chapter, the length of time it takes for any oscillating system, including a wave of some kind, to complete one full cycle is called the period, measured in seconds. The period of a wave relates directly to the frequency. Since the units for frequency are cycles per second, the reciprocal of the frequency would have units of seconds per cycle. This time value, the number of seconds in one cycle, is the period of the wave, although when we speak of the period or use it in equations we just call the units "seconds." We use the Greek letter τ ("tau," the t in the Greek alphabet) to represent the period of a wave or of

Example Problem

Determine the wavelength of a 1,500 Hz sound wave. (This frequency is right around the pitch people make when they whistle.) Assume that sound travels at 342 m/s in air.

From the given information we have:

$f = 1{,}500 \text{ Hz}$

$v = 342 \ \dfrac{\text{m}}{\text{s}}$

To complete the problem, we write the wave equation in its standard form first, then do the algebra to solve for the wavelength.

$v = \lambda f$

$$\lambda = \frac{v}{f} = \frac{342 \ \frac{\text{m}}{\text{s}}}{1500 \text{ Hz}} = 0.228 \text{ m}$$

any other oscillating system. Since period and frequency are reciprocals, this gives us our second equation,

$$\tau = \frac{1}{f}$$

Wave Phenomena

There are a number of phenomena exhibited by all types of waves. We are going to look at five of them. For some of these descriptions it is helpful to think of the wave as a ray, like the thin line of light we are familiar with in a laser beam. In some of the illustrations below rays are shown as arrows pointing in the direction of propagation.

REFLECTION

It is common knowledge that waves *reflect* off surfaces or objects. This is why we can see ourselves in a mirror, and why we can see the moon from the sunlight reflecting off it back to earth. A wave or ray approaching a surface is called an *incident ray*. After reflecting, the ray that has reflected off the surface is called the *reflected ray*. The *law of reflection* states that the angle of incidence equals the angle of reflection. These two angles are defined with respect to a line perpendicular to the reflecting surface. Figure 11-5 depicts a reflective surface with the perpendicular line shown (the dashed line), and a ray of light striking the surface at the angle of incidence. Using standard notation we designate the angle of incidence as θ_i and the angle of reflection as θ_r. (The Greek letter θ, "theta," is used throughout mathematics and physics to represent measures of angles.) So we can write the law of reflection as $\theta_i = \theta_r$.

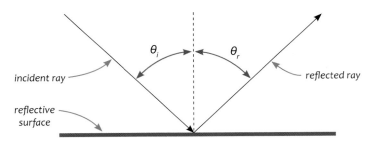

Figure 11-5. Wave reflection.

REFRACTION

All waves can *refract*, but we see it often with light. The speed of light in a plastic prism or glass or water is slower than the speed of light in air. When the light enters the new medium it changes speed instantly. This change of speed

Example Problem

Radio station KUT FM in Austin broadcasts a carrier signal at 90.5 MHz, which is a frequency of 90,500,000 Hz, or 9.05×10^7 Hz. Determine the wavelength and period of this wave.

All radio waves (FM, AM, short wave, etc.) are part of the electromagnetic spectrum and propagate at the speed of light, 300 million meters per second, or 3.00×10^8 m/s. This means the given information for this calculation is:

$$f = 9.05 \times 10^7 \text{ Hz}$$

$$v = 3.00 \times 10^8 \ \frac{\text{m}}{\text{s}}$$

The problem requires us to perform two separate calculations. Let's calculate the wavelength first.

$$v = \lambda f$$

$$\lambda = \frac{v}{f} = \frac{3.00 \times 10^8 \ \frac{\text{m}}{\text{s}}}{9.05 \times 10^7 \text{ Hz}} = 3.31 \text{ m}$$

Next we will compute the period.

$$\tau = \frac{1}{f} = \frac{1}{9.05 \times 10^7 \text{ Hz}} = 0.000000011 \text{ s}$$

This value is 11 billionths of a second, or 11 nanoseconds.

causes the light to change direction, or refract. The photo in Figure 11-6 shows a ray of red laser light coming almost straight down in the air and refracting as it crosses the boundary from air into a plastic prism (the triangle). Some of the light also reflects off the prism, obeying the law of reflection, and heads off to the right in the photograph. When the laser light reaches the other side of the prism (at the bottom of the photo) and comes back out into the air, we can see it refract again, bending sharply to the left at the bottom of the photo. The amount the light bends depends on both of the media in which the wave is propagating. In the case of the photo in Figure 11-6 these media are air and plastic. The amount of refraction or bending also depends slightly on the color of the light, which depends on the wavelength. White light is a combination of all different colors, and when it goes through a prism the different colors refract slightly different amounts, so the white light splits into the different colors, as in a rainbow.

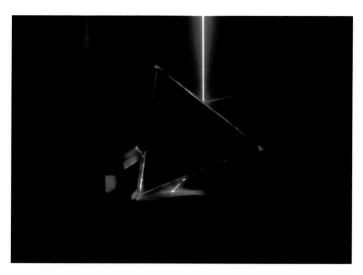

Figure 11-6. Refraction, illustrated by a 633-nanometer laser passing from air into a plastic prism (the triangle), and from the plastic prism into the air at the bottom. Some light can be seen reflecting off the upper side of the prism.

The familiar image of a straw in a glass of water, and the way it appears to be broken, is because of the refraction of light as it passes from air to water, reflects off the straw under the water, and refracts again as it passes from water to air. The light we see reflected from the underwater part of the straw has refracted twice and is propagating in a different direction that the light reflecting from the upper part of the straw. The light we see reflecting from the upper part never went under water and never refracted.

DIFFRACTION

Diffraction occurs when a wave bends around the corner of some obstruction. A familiar example of diffraction is that a person's voice can be heard around the edge of a barrier like the corner of a building because of the sound waves bending around the corner. Without diffraction it would be very difficult to hear what people were saying, because sound waves would travel straight out of our mouths without spreading out, like the beam of a flashlight. And just as the flashlight creates a spot of light, the sound wave would create only a spot of sound. Instead, the sound waves diffract around the edges of our mouths and then begin to spread out as they propagate. Of course, flashlight beams diffract too, but the wavelengths of light are so short that diffraction of light is not usually noticeable unless special equipment is used, as in the next illustration.

A fascinating example of the bending of waves from diffraction occurs when laser light is beamed through a *diffraction grating*, as shown in Figure 11-7. In this figure an orange beam is created by combining the two beams from 633 nm red and 543 nm green lasers. The two laser beams can be seen at the

Figure 11-7. Combined red and green laser beams are split apart and bent by a diffraction grating.

bottom of the image, and are combined in the plastic cube. The combined orange beam exiting the cube hits the diffraction grating in the center of the picture. A diffraction grating is a glass plate with very fine grooves etched

What causes the distant pavement on a highway to appear wet?

Just as the prism refracts a laser beam as the beam passes from air into the plastic prism, air causes light to refract if the light passes from a region of cool air into a region of hot air.

The "wet pavement" phenomenon occurs on hot days as light coming down from the sky passes near the very hot highway pavement. Consider some sky light heading down toward the pavement a few miles in front of a driver on a highway. As this light passes from the cool air high up into the very warm air right above the highway pavement the path of the light refracts (bends). If it bends enough, and the angles of the road are just right, this light can turn from its path heading for the pavement and bend up and hit the driver in the eyes instead. When light hits us in the eyes, our visual processing tells us that the object the light came from lies in the direction the light came from. Since the sky light came to us from near the ground, its source appears to be on the ground.

So what the driver is really seeing is patches of blue sky that appear to be on the ground! Sometimes if one looks carefully, one can even see some clouds in these patches of sky light coming at us from the pavement. This same phenomenon gives rise to mirages in the desert.

into its surface (70 grooves per mm for the grating used to make the image shown, which is actually not very many for a diffraction grating). When the orange beam strikes the grating the grooves in the grating cause the red and green beams to diffract, so they fan out beyond the grating. The grating splits the light into many beams, each of them bending more and more away from the center. You can see also that the two colors are bent different amounts, just as with refraction, so the red and green laser light is separated, except for the very center beam, which still contains both colors. Many of the separated beams are hitting the white screen placed in the beam path, but you can also see distant red and green dots where other beams are hitting the wall in the back of the lab.

RESONANCE

When an original wave and its reflection in a medium consistently line up with each other a *standing wave* is formed. To understand what a standing wave is, consider a wave train continuously propagating in a medium. As the waves reach a boundary such as a wall, they reflect back into the region where the original waves are, so we have the original waves and the reflected waves mingling together in the same space. If the dimensions of the medium are just right, this mixing of original and reflected waves can produce an effect where the crests and troughs of the original and reflected waves line up and stay lined up and the resulting combination of these two waves appears to stand still. Since the wave appears to stand still, it is called a standing wave.

> A standing wave occurs when the peaks and troughs of a wave and its reflection line up and stay lined up. The result is resonance.

When a standing wave occurs the original and reflected waves essentially add together, creating a much stronger wave, that is, one with a much higher amplitude. This is the phenomenon called *resonance*. Most of the time, such as with sound or light waves, we cannot see the waves. But on a vibrating string we can, as shown in Figure 11-8. The wave on the string is not really standing still, it just appears to be. This standing wave was created by attaching the end of the string to a device that oscillates the end of the string up and down

Figure 11-8. A standing wave on a vibrating string strung across a classroom.

60 times per second. When the string is pulled to just the right tension, the standing wave suddenly forms on the string.

For such a standing wave to occur the dimension of the medium in which the wave is propagating (the length of the string in this case) must be equal to a whole number of half-wavelengths. For a standing wave to occur with a sound wave in a room, at least one of the dimensions of the room (height, width or depth) must equal a whole number of half-wavelengths of the sound wave. Resonance is what is happening when someone plays a wind instrument, when a person blows across the top of a bottle, or when you find the sweet notes that resound while you are humming in a tile and glass shower stall.

Another intriguing example of resonance producing standing waves is the pattern formed on the surface of a liquid when the container is vibrating, as in the vibrating coffee in a coffee cup in Figure 11-9. To make this pattern for the photograph, I had to make the table vibrate at just the right frequency so that the coffee cup sitting on the table would vibrate the coffee, producing waves on the surface of the coffee that would turn into standing waves.

Figure 11-9. Standing waves on the surface of coffee in a vibrating coffee cup.

INTERFERENCE

One of the most historically significant wave phenomena is *interference*. It was interference patterns produced by light in 1801 that first gave scientists strong evidence that light was a wave phenomenon. (Before that everyone accepted Isaac Newton's view that light was made of particles.) Interference occurs when two different waves arrive at the same place at the same time. The two waves will always add together, but the result depends on how the two waves are aligned with each other.

As illustrated in Figure 11-10, if two waves arrive at the same place *in phase*, with their crests and troughs lined up, the energies of the waves will add together, producing an effect stronger than either of the individual waves. This effect is called *constructive interference*. Constructive interference with sound waves produces a loud spot. With light waves constructive interference causes a bright spot of light. By contrast, if one wave has to travel farther than the other one it will arrive later and can be *out of phase* with the first one so that the crests of one wave line up with the troughs of the other. This is called *destructive interference*, because when the waves add together they will partially or completely cancel each other out. With sound waves this creates a dead spot where the sound cannot be heard at all. With light waves a dark spot is created where there is no light.

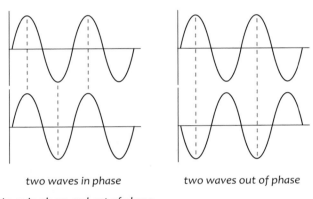

two waves in phase   two waves out of phase

Figure 11-10. Waves in phase and out of phase.

An example of interference is the pattern of alternating light and dark spots called an *interference pattern* that results when laser light diffracts around a very thin obstruction placed in the beam, as shown in Figure 11-11. The obstruction basically splits the beam, creating two beams from one. Then because of diffraction the two beams begin spreading out rapidly as they pass by edges of the obstruction. When the two beams strike the screen, as shown in the photograph in Figure 11-11, interference between the two beams creates a long horizontal region of alternating light and dark spots.

This interference pattern seems so unexpected. Intuitively, if a thin obstruction was placed in the path of a beam of red light, we would expect to see the beam

Figure 11-11. Interference pattern caused by placing a thin obstruction in the beam of a 633-nm red laser.

What is special about laser light and how do lasers work?

The answer to this question combines the idea of phase with the information from Chapter 8 about electrons moving to different energy levels as they absorb or emit energy. We will think of light here as individual photons that carry phase information. If two photons are lined up as they travel, they are in phase.

The phases of photons coming out of ordinary light sources are random. All the photons have different phases. By contrast, laser light is *coherent*, which means all of the photons' phases are lined up with each other so they are all in phase. The coherence of laser light gives it its special properties, such as being able to produce holograms, or 3-D images.

At the heart of a laser is a crystal or gas chamber. The atoms in the crystal or gas are excited by means of the laser's power supply, so they all have electrons "pumped" up to higher energy levels. Normally, the electrons would randomly drop back down to lower energy levels, randomly emitting photons, as we saw in Chapter 8. But the materials in a laser allow the excited electrons to stay for a moment at the higher energy level until they are dislodged by a passing photon. This passing photon stimulates the electron to make its jump to a lower level. When this happens, the electron emits a new photon with the same phase and wavelength as the passing photon. Then these two photons go to two more atoms and trigger the same process in a "chain reaction," resulting in four photons, then eight and so on. All the photons triggered by this process of *stimulated emission* have the same phase, so the laser produces coherent light.

spot with a thin dark line through it, the shadow of the obstruction, as Figure 11-12 suggests. But in the interference pattern, we not only have a bright spot in the center instead of a shadow, the light from the diffracted beam is spread out into a wide strip of light.

As illustrated in Figure 11-13, this interference pattern is caused by waves diffracting around the edges of the obstruction. When the two beams hit the target there are places where the two light beams arrive in phase, producing constructive interference (the bright red spots), and other places where they arrive out of phase, producing destructive interference (the dark gaps between the red spots). This interference pattern is easiest

Figure 11-12. A red light spot on a dark screen with a shadow in the center.

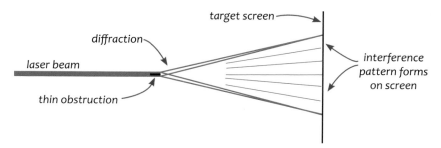

Figure 11-13. Placing a thin obstruction in the path of a laser beam causes diffraction and interference.

to produce with a laser because all the photons in a laser beam are in phase with one another, as explained in the box above.

Sound Waves

As mentioned previously, sound waves are mechanical waves. That is, they must propagate in a medium (matter) of some kind and cannot propagate in an empty vacuum. We most often think of sound waves as propagating in air, but we have all heard sound waves under water, too. Sound waves can also travel in other media, which is why we can hear sounds through closed doors or walls. But sound waves cannot travel in a vacuum where this is no medium. Sadly, this means all the explosions and screeching space fighter planes we see in science fiction movies are absurd, because there is no sound in space.

In air, sound waves are created by causing the pressure in the air to fluctuate slightly above and below atmospheric pressure, as illustrated back in Figure 11-3. The regions of slightly higher pressure are called *compressions*, because in these regions the air molecules are packed more closely together due to the higher pressure. Regions where the pressure is a bit lower than atmospheric pressure are called *rarefactions* (pronounced "RARE-uh-faction"). In a rarefaction the air molecules are more spread apart than at normal atmospheric pressure. A sound wave in air is a continuous train of successive compressions and rarefactions. In air, sound waves travel at a velocity of around 342 m/s, depending on temperature, humidity, and pressure.

Frequencies of Sound Waves

Humans can hear sound waves in the frequency range of about 20 Hz to 20,000 Hz. This means the sources creating the sound waves are themselves oscillating back and forth at rates from 20 Hz to 20,000 Hz.

Frequencies lower than 20 Hz this are called *infrasonic*. (The Latin prefix *infra* means below.) Frequencies higher than 20,000 Hz are called *ultrasonic*. (The Latin prefix *ultra* means above or beyond.) Table 11-1 lists a few reference points for frequencies of common musical notes and sounds.

27.5 Hz	The lowest note (A) on a piano keyboard.
41 Hz	The lowest note (E) on a bass guitar.
82 Hz	The lowest note (E) on a guitar.
440 Hz	The A above middle C on a keyboard, often called "A 440" and used as a reference for tuning pianos and other concert instruments.
100 – 3000 Hz	The frequencies in the human voice lie primarily in this range.
1000 Hz	A low whistle.
4186 Hz	The highest note (C) on a piano keyboard.
6000 Hz – 8000 Hz	This is the range for the "s" sounds we make between our teeth when we say a word like "Susan." This sound is called *sibilance*.

Table 11-1. Reference frequencies of some well-known sounds.

Perfect human hearing extends up to around 20,000 Hz, but by middle age few people can hear sounds above 15,000 Hz. This is natural as our ear drums stiffen up over time and do not respond as well to high frequencies. If a person listens to a lot of loud music over a long period of time the person's hearing will degrade more rapidly than normal. Although human hearing does not extend above 20 kHz, dogs can hear up to nearly 30 kHz. For this reason, dog whistles emit a frequency of around 27 kHz that dogs can hear but humans can't.

Loudness of Sound

We quantify the loudness of sound waves using a scale called the Sound Pressure Level (SPL), which is measured in decibels (dB). Some common reference points for the loudness of sounds are listed in Table 11-2. The decibel values shown are approximate.

Connections Between Scientific and Musical Terms

As is probably evident by now, the terminology scientists use when describing waves relates to the common terminology we all use when speaking of music. When musicians refer to the *pitch* of a musical note they are referring to what scientists, and this chapter, call the frequency. And what we typically refer to as *volume* or *loudness* corresponds to the amplitude of the sound wave.

Electromagnetic Waves and Light

It is difficult to understand what exactly electromagnetic waves are, but don't let this bother you. Scientists have been puzzling over electromagnetic radiation in one way or another for many centuries. We now understand that light, and all other electromagnetic radiation, can be described as a transverse wave made of

0 dB	The level is called the threshold of human hearing, because it is the quietest sound human ears are capable of hearing. You will probably never be in a place this quiet in your entire life, but if you were, you would have the sensation of being completely deaf.
45 dB	This would be about the loudness of faint rustling leaves on a quiet day.
65 dB	Quiet conversation in a quiet room.
85 dB	A moderately noisy environment. Legally, OSHA requires that if the noise level in a workplace (like a factory) is consistently above 85 dB the workers must be supplied with hearing protection. This is because studies have shown that being exposed to noise levels of 85 dB or higher for 8 hours a day over many years can result in permanent hearing loss.
95 dB	Loud music in a movie theater.
110 dB	An excruciatingly loud rock concert.
120 dB	This is usually called the threshold of pain, for obvious reasons.
140 dB	Standing next to a commercial jet when it revs up its engines for take off. This is why the ground crew wear hearing protection.
150 dB	A gun being fired right next to your head. This is why sensible people also use hearing protection when at the rifle range. It is also why movies showing people whispering to one another right after firing a bunch of guns at bad guys are not realistic. Temporary hearing loss after a lot of gun fire would make whispers difficult to hear.

Table 11-2. Approximate loudness of some well-known sounds.

oscillating electric and magnetic fields in space. (This may not sound much more comprehensible, but we will be studying fields again briefly later on when we get to magnetism and maybe that will help. Electromagnetic waves are really tough to visualize!)

When we speak of wavelengths and frequencies of electromagnetic radiation, what we are talking about are the wavelengths and frequencies of the electric and magnetic field waves. These oscillating fields are pretty hard to visualize, but Figure 11-14 is an attempt at a 3-D representation of a propagating electromagnetic wave. The heights of the waves represent the strengths of the electric and magnetic fields at any point in space as the wave train passes by. Each individual arrow in this diagram represents the strength and direction of the field *everywhere* in a plane containing that arrow and perpendicular to the direction of propagation. To help further in visualizing this, the wave is shown again in Figure 11-15. In this second diagram, the electric field wave has been stretched out and shown by itself, and a couple of representative planes of arrows have been added. If you were standing where the wave is drawn, looking in the direction it is propagating, then above you and below you and on both sides of you would stretch out an entire plane of

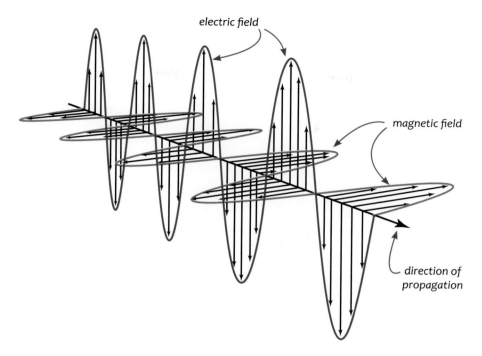

electric field

magnetic field

direction of propagation

Figure 11-14. Three-dimensional depiction of an electromagnetic wave.

the electric field all oriented in the same direction and with the same strength. But as the wave passes by, the strength and direction of this electric field plane is oscillating from its maximum in the upward direction, to the downward direction, and back up again about 500,000,000,000,000 times per second! Using the metric prefix *giga-*, which means billion, this value can be expressed as 500,000 gigahertz, or 500,000 GHz.

Polarization of Light

Just briefly I will mention that when people speak of the *polarization* of light it is the direction of the electric field they are referring to. When light is polarized, the electric field of all the light waves points in the same direction. As it arrives here from the sun, sunlight is non-polarized, meaning the electric fields of all the light waves are pointing randomly in all different directions perpendicular to the direction of propagation.

Polarized sunglasses only let through light waves that are vertically polarized. This is because light that has reflected off the ground or car windshields has become a bit polarized in the horizontal direction due to these reflections, and the sunglasses filter these horizontally polarized waves out. The waves coming at us from car windshields or the concrete pavement (or off the water, if you are at the beach) are the ones that bother us the most with glare. The vertical orientation

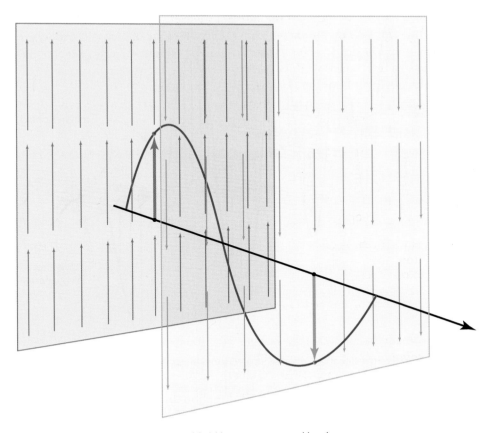

Figure 11-15. Two samples of planes of field lines represented by the wave.

of polarizing sunglasses blocks these particular light waves out, reducing glare considerably.

The Electromagnetic Spectrum

Visible light is only one small piece of the *electromagnetic spectrum*, the entire frequency range of electromagnetic radiation. Different frequencies or wavelengths of visible light are perceived as different colors by our eyes. Red light has the lowest frequency and longest wavelength in the visible spectrum. Violet light has the highest frequency and shortest wavelength in the visible spectrum. The sequence of colors from low frequency to high frequency is red—orange—yellow—green—blue—violet, as depicted in Figure 11-15.

When we speak of electromagnetic radiation sometimes we speak in terms of frequencies, as in the previous paragraph. In other cases we speak in terms of wavelengths. As we saw earlier in this chapter, as frequency increases wavelength decreases, so we could just as easily state the difference between red light and violet light in terms of wavelengths this way: Red light has the longest wavelength in the visible spectrum. Violet light has the shortest wavelength in the visible spectrum. In fact, it is pretty easy to remember the wavelength range of the visible spectrum, which is about 700 nm to 400 nm (red to violet). (Some reference sources have the visible spectrum starting at 750 or 800 nm where the red appears darker and darker.) As suggested from the approximate scale in Figure 11-16, orange light has a wavelength of around 600 to 610 nm, yellow is in the 570 to 580 nm range, green is in the 520 to 550 nm range, and blue light is in the mid to upper 400 nm range.

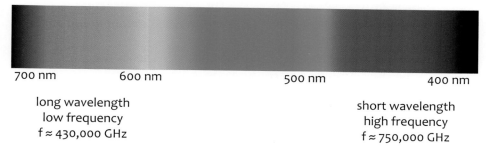

| 700 nm | 600 nm | 500 nm | 400 nm |

long wavelength
low frequency
$f \approx 430{,}000$ GHz

short wavelength
high frequency
$f \approx 750{,}000$ GHz

Figure 11-16. The visible portion of the electromagnetic spectrum.

Electromagnetic radiation with frequencies too low for humans to see is called *infrared radiation*, since *infra* means below and red light has the lowest frequency of the visible light spectrum. Electromagnetic radiation with frequencies too high for us to see is called *ultraviolet radiation*, since *ultra* means above and violet light has the highest frequency in the spectrum of visible light.

The most well-known bands of the electromagnetic spectrum and their approximate frequencies and wavelengths are shown in Table 11-3. As additional examples, the electric and magnetic waves of green light with a wavelength of

Band	Approximate frequency of electromagnetic radiation	Approximate wavelength in a vacuum
AM Radio	1,000 kHz, or 10^6 Hz	300 m
FM Radio	100 MHz, or 10^8 Hz	3 m
Microwaves	10 GHz, or 10^{10} Hz	3 cm
Infrared Radiation	10^{13} Hz	0.003 cm
Visible Light	10^{14} Hz	700 – 400 nm
Ultraviolet Radiation	10^{15} Hz	300 nm
X-Rays	10^{18} Hz	0.3 nm
Gamma Rays	10^{20} Hz	0.003 nm
Cosmic Rays	10^{22} Hz	0.00003 nm

Table 11-3. Regions in the electromagnetic spectrum.

Why is the sky blue and the sunset orange-red?

The oxygen and nitrogen molecules in the air have resonances in the ultraviolet (UV) region of the electromagnetic spectrum. This causes them to absorb many of the most harmful UV wavelengths in sunlight before they get to us. Longer wavelengths, such as the wavelengths of the visible spectrum, will not be absorbed but can be scattered in a process called *elastic scattering*. Elastic scattering will most strongly affect wavelengths that are close to the UV where the molecular resonances are, such as violet and blue, and to a less extent green and longer wavelengths.

In elastic scattering the shorter wavelengths in the visible spectrum hit the air molecules, causing the molecules to oscillate at the frequencies of this short-wavelength light. This, in turn, causes light of the same colors to radiate out in all directions, like radio waves emanating from an antenna. Essentially, the violet and blue photons streaming here from the sun are scattered in all directions by the molecules, while the longer-wavelength orange and red photons mostly continue straight ahead.

Sunlight does not have much violet in it, so the shortest visible wavelength color involved in elastic scattering is blue. As shown in the sketch, with the sun off to the side, blue photons are scattered in all directions, including down to observers on earth, so the sky above appears blue. For the same reason, the sky around the setting sun appears orange and red. The orange and red photons are coming straight through to the observer, while blue and green are scattered in all directions before the light reaches the observer.

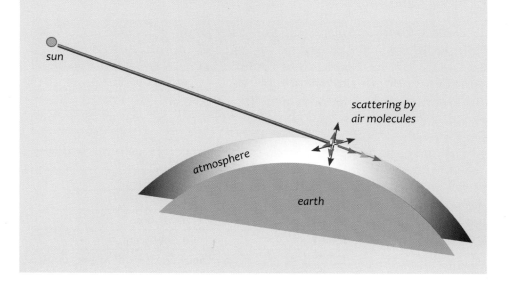

532 nm oscillate 566,000,000,000,000 times each second, or 566,000 GHz. The microwaves in microwave ovens complete 2,450,000,000 cycles each second, or 2.45 GHz.

It is interesting to consider how the wavelengths of these different types of electromagnetic radiation relate to phenomena we are familiar with. Most of us are aware that the reception of an AM radio in a car blanks out when the car passes under a bridge. If we calculate the wavelength of the carrier frequency of an AM radio station we can see why. Radio station KLBJ here in Austin, Texas broadcasts at 590 kHz (590,000 Hz). From the wave equation we can calculate the wavelength of the radio waves propagating out from the KLBJ tower, and it turns out to be 508 meters, which is nearly a third of a mile. Imagine a bunch of waves this long reflecting around every which way in the air. Very few of them will have just the right orientation to fit under a bridge and pass through, so the signal under there is so weak that the car radio loses it. The wavelengths in the FM range are much smaller, only about 3 m (10 feet) or so, so they fit under bridges much more easily and our FM radios don't blank out when we drive under one. The digital radio channels launched about twelve years ago (such as SiriusXM) operate in the much higher range of 2.3 GHz. The wavelengths of these waves are small enough that the signal should be usable just about everywhere within the broadcast region of the satellites.

How small are they? Well, as another example, consider the metal screen with holes in it on the front door of a microwave oven. With a frequency of 2.45 GHz (not far from where the digital radio signals are), the wavelength of this radiation will be 12.2 cm. The holes in the door screen are about forty times smaller than this, at 3 mm or so, so the waves reflect around inside the oven where they can do their job heating up food, instead of escaping out into the room and harming us.

Harmonics and Timbre

Let's say you want to play the note on a flute known as "middle C." To do this the air in the flute must resonate at the frequency of middle C, also called C4, which is 278.4375 Hz. Now let's have a clarinet play this same pitch. To do this the air in the clarinet must also resonate at 278.4375 Hz. How is it that we can tell the difference between the flute and the clarinet if they are both resonating at the same frequency? It's no good saying they sound different. What *is it* about the sound waves these instruments produce that makes them sound different?

Well, one of the reasons they sound different is because while both instruments are resonating at the frequency of middle C, they are also both simultaneously resonating at many other frequencies that are multiples of middle C. All these resonating frequencies are called *harmonics*. The main, lowest resonant frequency is called the *fundamental*

> When an instrument plays a pitch, it is resonating at many frequencies simultaneously. These resonant frequencies are called *harmonics*.

How does a microwave oven heat up food?

Recall from Chapter 9 that water molecules have a characteristic elbow shape. The hydrogen atoms on the ends of the elbow are more positively charged, and the oxygen atom in the middle is more negatively charged, which we describe by saying that the molecule is polar. In the presence of the electric field from electromagnetic radiation, the polar water molecules in food try to twist themselves around to line up with the electric field, much like a magnetic compass trying to line up with the magnetic field of the earth. But whereas the magnetic field of the earth is steady, the direction of the electric field from microwaves is changing direction about 5 billion times per second. This causes a great deal of jostling among the water molecules, which converts the kinetic energy of the molecules' motion into thermal energy in the food, heating it up.

(middle C in this case) or first harmonic. The second harmonic is usually a frequency that is twice the frequency of the fundamental. The third harmonic is three times the fundamental, and so on. In some instruments the harmonics might go up by odd or fractional multiples, but in general the higher harmonics are multiples of the fundamental frequency. When writing about the different harmonic frequencies that are present in a sound wave, the fundamental is denoted as f_1, and the second, third, and higher harmonics are denoted f_2, f_3, and so on.

Figure 11-17 is a sketch of the first three harmonics that would resonate on a string. On a string the harmonics are easy to visualize, exactly like the standing waves shown in the photo of Figure 11-8. But the same basic idea applies to waves resonating in any medium, like air pressure waves in a wind instrument. The horizontal line in the middle of the figure represents the string when it is not vibrating. Since exactly half of the wavelength of the fundamental frequency fits on the string, the string length is equal to one half-wavelength of the fundamental, f_1, shown in blue. Two half-wavelengths, or one full wave, of the second harmonic will fit on the same string. Three half-wavelengths of the third harmonic fit on the string. This continues for the higher harmonics, f_4, f_5, and higher. When the

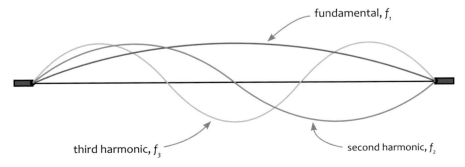

fundamental, f_1

third harmonic, f_3 second harmonic, f_2

Figure 11-17. Wavelengths of the first three harmonics that will resonate on a string.

musician presses the string against the fingerboard or fretboard, the resonating section of the string is shortened, so the resonating wavelengths are shorter and the resonating frequencies (pitches) are higher.

The different harmonic frequencies in an instrument will resonate with different intensities (that is, different amounts of energy) in various instruments. Generally, the fundamental has the greatest amplitude (that is, it is the loudest) and the amplitudes diminish for higher and higher harmonics. The amplitudes of the various harmonics of every violin are similar, which is an important reason every violin sounds like a violin. The harmonic content of every flute is similar, so they all sound like flutes. But even among all of the flutes, there are subtle differences in the harmonic content of the sound resonating in the flute, depending on the materials from which it is made and the details of its construction. So we have a little more energy at this harmonic, a little less energy at that harmonic. This means we can distinguish one flute from another.

A high-quality instrument is one that has a very desirable blend of harmonics, making the instrument sound smooth or mellow. Cheap instruments have a less desirable blend of harmonics, making the instrument sound harsh, muddy or wooden. (The cheapos are probably also more difficult to play, not as loud, and so on, but these are separate issues.) The particular combination of harmonics (and some other factors we will not go into) give each instrument a unique sound quality that makes the instrument identifiable as itself. This unique sound quality is called the instrument's *timbre* (pronounced "tamber").

A graphical representation of the relative loudness (or intensities) of the fundamental and other harmonics in a particular instrument is called the *harmonic spectrum* of the instrument. Figures 11-18 through 11-20 show actual harmonic spectra for three different wind instruments playing the same note, D4, the D right above middle C[1]. The frequency of this pitch is 293.665 Hz.

On the graphs the vertical scale is the loudness in decibels. The horizontal scale is the frequency. The vertical line just to the right of the capital D is 100 Hz, and the lines to the right go up by 100 Hz each until 1000 Hz. They go up by 1000 Hz each to the right of that until 10 kHz, and the right edge of the graph is at 20 kHz.

The peaks in the graph are showing the energy intensity at each resonant frequency (each harmonic). We can easily see the fundamental in each graph, represented by the left-most large peak, right around 300 Hz. The second harmonic at about 600 Hz and the third harmonic at around 900 Hz are clearly visible, as are other higher harmonics at multiples of 300 Hz. The jagged curve across the bottom of all the spectra is simply the background noise in the room where these images were captured. (We were in a very quiet room, but there is always

---

1   These images were captured with an iPad using a fascinating free app called "n-track tuner" while a friend played the different instruments.

100 Hz   1000 Hz   10,000 Hz

Figure 11-18. Harmonic spectrum
of a flute playing 293.665 Hz
(D4).

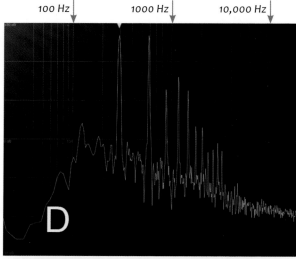

Figure 11-19. Harmonic spectrum
of a clarinet playing 293.665
Hz (D4).

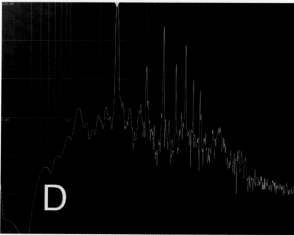

Figure 11-20. Harmonic
spectrum of a saxophone
playing 293.665 Hz (D4).

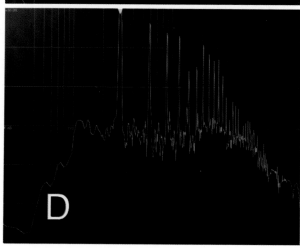

background noise. We don't usually notice it, but sensitive instruments like the built-in microphone in the iPad easily pick it up.)

There are some interesting features to notice in these spectra. First, in the flute spectrum we see that the first and second harmonics (which are the fundamental D pitch and the D one octave up, D5) are at the same intensity. This is unique to the flute spectrum, and is a big reason for the velvety quality of the flute's timbre. Second, the strong harmonics in the clarinet spectrum are the first three odd ones, f_1, f_3, and f_5.

> The unique sound quality of an instrument, its timbre, is attributable to the instrument's particular combination of harmonics and harmonic intensities.

Finally, we notice the very rich complement of higher harmonics in the saxophone spectrum. The higher-order harmonics in the sax are significantly more intense than the comparable harmonics in the other two spectra, including pronounced harmonics at f_8 and higher. There are so many strong harmonics up there that the harmonic spectrum looks like a comb. These strong higher harmonics help to explain the "reedy" sound quality the sax is known for.

How do black lights and black light posters work?

Black lights use excited mercury vapor to emit a lot of energy in the ultraviolet (UV) region of the electromagnetic spectrum. They also emit some light in the visible spectrum, but the tube is made of a special glass that absorbs most of the visible light. This absorption diminishes toward the upper end of the visible spectrum, which is why they look purple.

Black light posters use inks that *fluoresce* in the presence of ultraviolet light. To understand fluorescence, think again of Chapter 8, in which we discussed the process of the electrons in atoms absorbing photons at one wavelength, and then emitting photons at different wavelengths to create atomic spectra. Fluorescence occurs when the electrons absorb high-energy photons in the UV, and emit lower-energy photons in the visible spectrum. This is what the fluorescent paints on the posters do. These paints absorb the UV light coming from the black light, and then emit light in the visible spectrum. The visible wavelengths fluorescent paints give off while fluorescing are usually close to the color the paint gives off by normal reflection in a lighted room. The paints are not reflecting light; the atoms in the paint are the *source* of the light, so the paints exhibit an intense glow the same way other light sources do.

The "whiter-than-white" dye used in T-shirts and white socks also fluoresces, making these items appear brighter, especially in sunlight.

How do fluorescent lights work?

We start with a black light (see previous box). However, instead of the UV light just passing straight out of the lamp tube, there is a coating of phosphorous on the inside of a fluorescent lamp tube. When hit with the UV light produced inside the tube, the phosphorous begins fluorescing (again, see above). So the electrons in the phosphorous coating absorb UV energy and emit energy in a bunch of different wavelengths in the visible spectrum, producing white light. The wavelengths the fluorescent lights emit are stronger on the blue end of the spectrum (nearer to the UV), which tends to make the light from fluorescent lamps look bluish in tint.

What is the difference between fluorescence and phosphorescence?

Both fluorescent and phosphorescent substances can absorb ultraviolet (UV) light and re-emit light in the visible spectrum (see above, and Chapter 8). Fluorescent substances fluoresce as long as they are exposed to the UV light source. Phosphorescent substances can store the UV energy after it has been absorbed and emit it slowly over time. So, the fluorescent paint on a black light poster will extinguish as soon as the black light is switched off. Glow-in-the-dark substances such as the numerals on alarm clocks and watches, or some toys, are phosphorescing. They absorb energy while the light is on, and slowly release it when the light is turned off. Believe it or not, the phosphorous on the inside of a fluorescent lamp does not phosphoresce; it *fluoresces*.

Ideas for Your Classroom

There are hundreds of fun activities related to the material in this chapter. Here are just a few.

1. Have students do projects in which they make their own musical instruments from strings, bottles, tubes, or other materials.

2. Get an inexpensive, low-powered laser (stick to 1 or 2 milliwatts) and explore reflection, refraction and diffraction. (Take precautions so that no one gets hit in the eye, even with the safe power levels mentioned above.)

3. Use an iPad with the free app "n-track tuner" to look at harmonic spectra while students play notes on musical instruments or drums they bring to class. Orchestral instruments work best because of their ability to produce sustained tones. If possible, make this activity even more fun by connecting the iPad to a digital projector so all can see the images on a large screen. Be sure to look at voice spectra, too.

4. Use the iPad and n-track tuner app to listen to specific notes from a musical instrument or a person whistling a single note. While the note is playing, touch the screen at the tip of the peak of the fundamental. The app will display the frequency in the upper right corner. After some practice, have students try to guess the fundamental frequency produced by other musical notes.

5. Refract sunlight with a prism to produce the rainbow of colors in the visible spectrum.

6. Look at black light posters with a black light, and talk about ultraviolet light and visible light. Make sure the room is completely dark.

7. Look at each other in a black light, especially teeth, freckles and white garments (room completely dark).

8. Acquire phosphorescent plants or fish in an aquarium and look at them with a black light. If an aquarium isn't possible, there are some stunning videos on You Tube to try out (worth seeing with or without the aquarium). Search bioluminescence, phosphorescence, and fluorescence.

Goals for Chapter 12

1. Explain the cause of pressure on objects submerged in a fluid.
2. Explain the cause of air pressure.
3. Explain how a barometer works.
4. Distinguish between gauge pressure and absolute pressure.
5. Explain Archimedes' principle of buoyancy, and how it explains why things float.

About This Chapter

A detailed study of pressure can quickly become complicated. In this brief chapter we will just touch on a few basic principles.

Chapter 12
Pressure and Buoyancy

The Cause of Pressure

It is common knowledge that an object will experience pressure underwater, and that the deeper the object is, the greater the pressure will be. In Chapter 10 we saw that the pressure inside a container of gas was caused by the particles of gas colliding with the walls of the container. Now we will examine the cause of air pressure and pressure under the surface of a liquid.

Consider the ordinary glass of water illustrated in Figure 12-1. The water at the top of the glass is being attracted to the earth by the earth's gravity, but it is being supported from underneath by the layer of water just beneath it. The third layer of water down has to support both of the first two layers. Each layer down is supporting all of the layers above it. At a given depth, it is the weight of the liquid above that causes the pressure at that depth. From this simple analysis we see that the pressure at a given depth depends on the earth's gravity, and on the depth.

Clearly, the denser the liquid is, the heavier a given volume of the liquid is, and the harder lower layers will have to push to support the upper layers. So the pressure at a certain depth must also depend on a third factor, the density of the liquid.

In fact, the pressure at a given depth, h, in a liquid is the product of these three factors, or

$$P = \rho g h$$

where P is the pressure in pascals (Pa), ρ (rho) is the density of the liquid (kg/m^3), g is the acceleration due to gravity (9.80 m/s^2), and h is the depth in the liquid (m). An interesting fact about this equation is that the pressure beneath a liquid does not depend on the shape or volume of the container; it depends only on the depth. Imagine a vertical soda straw 30 feet tall full of water. The pressure at the bottom of the straw will be the same as the pressure 30 feet under the surface of a lake.

The pascal is another derived unit, and is the MKS unit for pressure.[1] The pascal is equivalent to the units newtons per square meter (N/m^2), which represents an amount of

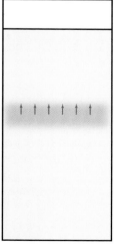

Figure 12-1. A layer of water in a glass must support the weight of the water above it.

---

[1]   The pascal is named for Blaise Pascal, an amazing seventeenth-century French scientist, mathematician and philosopher.

force per unit area. In America, the more familiar USCS units pounds per square inch (psi) are often used for pressure.

Air Pressure and Barometers

The concepts described above for pressure in a liquid work for any fluid, gases as well as liquids. (However, the equation given is only valid for liquids.) This means that the pressure in the atmosphere around us is caused by the weight of the air molecules above us. Of course, we call this pressure *atmospheric pressure*. When our weather forecasters refer to the local value of this pressure they call it *barometric pressure*.

However, there is one big difference between the pressure under the surface of a liquid, and the atmospheric pressure we experience. This difference is due to the fact that gases are *compressible*, and liquids basically aren't. So in a liquid like water, the density of the liquid is the same at any depth. But in a gas such as the atmosphere, the weight of the air above a given altitude compresses the air molecules below, causing the air below to be denser than the air above. As a result, the density of air is greatest at the ground, and gets less dense at higher altitude.

The fact that air density varies with altitude explains why there is less oxygen to breath at high elevations, such as in the mountains. If we lived under water like fish, the pressure would change a lot as we swam up and down (because water is about 830 times denser than air), but the density of the medium we lived in would remain constant. But in air, the density drops as the altitude increases, so there is less air to breathe.

> The fact that air density varies with altitude explains why there is less oxygen to breath at high elevations, such as in the mountains.

At sea level atmospheric pressure is about 101,325 Pa, or in USCS units, 14.7 pounds per square inch (psi). There is also a pressure unit called the *atmosphere* [atm], defined in terms of atmospheric pressure. One atmosphere is defined as the atmospheric pressure at sea level, so 1 atm = 101,325 Pa. We are so used to this pressure that we typically don't notice it, unless we feel it changing during a

---

Example Problem

Determine the pressure at the bottom of a typical swimming pool, 3.0 m in depth. The density of water is approximately 998 kg/m³.

Recalling that the acceleration due to earth's gravity is 9.80 m/s², we can insert this value along with the given depth and density into the equation and compute the pressure:

$$P = \rho g h = 998 \ \frac{\text{kg}}{\text{m}^3} \cdot 9.80 \ \frac{\text{m}}{\text{s}^2} \cdot 3.0 \ \text{m} = 29{,}300 \ \text{Pa}$$

storm front or while flying in an airplane. We even deliberately ignore it in some applications involving pressure, as explained in the next section.

The mercury barometer for measuring air pressure was invented in 1643 by Italian physicist and mathematician Evangelista Torricelli (Figure 12-2). Refer to Figure 12-3 as I explain how the barometer works.

The figure shows how we would make one of these devices today, using a vacuum pump to remove the air from a glass tube set into a bowl of mercury. (Torricelli didn't have a vacuum pump, so he accomplished this a different way, but the result is the same.) As the air is removed from the glass tube, the mercury rises into the tube up to a height of approximately 760 mm. The tube is then capped off and the device will now register changes in atmospheric pressure caused by the weather or by transporting the barometer up to the top of a tall building where the air pressure is a wee bit lower.

Figure 12-2. Italian physicist and mathematician Evangelista Torricelli.

As atmospheric pressure changes, the height of the mercury column in the glass tube rises and falls. At normal atmospheric pressure at sea level the height of the mercury will be 760 mm, which is about 29.9 inches, and sometimes weather reporters will refer to atmospheric pressure as "thirty inches of mercury." Normal barometric pressure variation in the U. S. is from about 725 mm to 775 mm of mercury, which corresponds to a range of 28.5 to 30.5 inches. The higher the atmospheric pressure is, the farther it will push the mercury up into the barometer

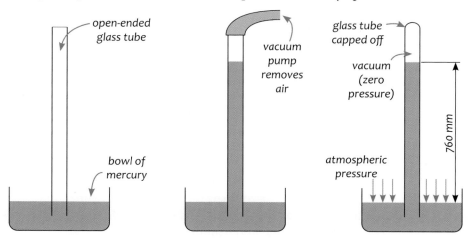

Figure 12-3. Assembly of a mercury barometer.

tube. So if the local barometric pressure was 30.4 inches of mercury, that would be a high-pressure day, and the weather would be clear, sunny and calm. When the barometric pressure falls, it means weather is headed your way as high-pressure regions push wind and moisture toward your now low-pressure region. You might be interested to know that the world record low barometric pressure (other than the pressure inside a tornado, which is extremely low) is 25.7 inches, measured in 1979 during a typhoon in the Pacific Ocean. The pressure unit *torr* is named after Torricelli, and normal atmospheric pressure is equal to 760 torr.

A vacuum is a complete void in space in which there is no matter of any kind. In 1643 scientists did not believe that a vacuum could exist, so at the time the barometer was invented no one could formulate a correct explanation for how it worked. The big question was about the mysterious force that was holding the mercury up in the tube.

French philosopher, mathematician and scientist Blaise Pascal, for whom the MKS unit of pressure is named, explained how the barometer worked in 1647, theorizing that a vacuum did exist in the glass tube above the mercury. On the basis of his own experiments, Pascal explained that there was no air pressure above the mercury column in the tube, and that the pressure of the atmosphere acting on the surface of the mercury in the bowl was *pushing* the mercury up into the tube into the vacuum region. This explanation is correct, but since at the time no one accepted the possibility of a vacuum, scientists did not want to accept Pascal's bold theory. But as we have seen with other theories, a theory gains strength when it repeatedly leads to successful hypotheses, and this one did.

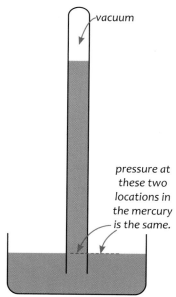

Pascal's explanation is easy to understand if we calculate the pressure in the tube 760 mm below the surface of the mercury. The density of mercury is 13,600 kg/m³. Using our equation $P = \rho g h$, the pressure at a depth of 0.76 m comes out to 101,300 Pa, which agrees with our value for atmospheric pressure to four significant digits. This calculation demonstrates that the pressure at the same height in the mercury inside and outside the tube is the same, as shown in Figure 12-4. On the inside of the tube this pressure is caused solely by the weight of the mercury in the tube. Outside the tube it is cause by atmospheric pressure. These two pressures are the same on the red dashed line in the figure.

Figure 12-4. The barometer illustrates the principle that the pressure at two places that are the same depth in any liquid is the same.

Absolute Pressure and Gauge Pressure

Consider the city water supply, typically distributed to homes at a pressure of around is 80 psi (equal to about 550,000 Pa). This value is the net pressure inside the piping, not including the atmospheric pressure.

To unpack this further, consider a plumber with a pressure gauge to measure the water pressure in the 80 psi water line. When the plumber's gauge is not connected to anything it will read 0 psi, even though it is in the air where the atmospheric pressure is 14.7 psi. This pressure reading is illustrated by the gauge on the left side of Figure 12-5, where atmospheric pressure is labeled 0 psi. When the plumber attaches the gauge to the water line, it reads 80 psi. A pressure scale like this that reads 0 at atmospheric pressure is called a *gauge pressure* scale. A gauge pressure reading reports the pressure above atmospheric pressure. If this pressure gauge were placed in a vacuum it would read −14.7 psi.

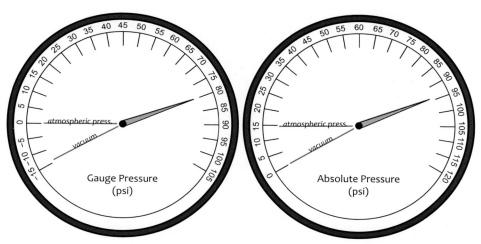

Figure 12-5. Pressure gauges showing a pressure reading of 80 psi (gauge) on a gauge pressure scale (left) and an absolute pressure scale (right). Reference points for atmospheric pressure and vacuum are also shown.

A pressure gauge that reads 0 in a complete vacuum where there is no pressure (such as in a chamber from which all the air molecules were removed) is reporting the *absolute pressure*. Such a gauge will read 14.7 psi in normal air. When attached to a water line with 80 psi pressure, an absolute pressure gauge will read 94.7 psi, which is the sum of the 80 psi water pressure and the 14.7 psi atmospheric pressure.

Although we will not get into any of the calculations here, it should be mentioned in passing that most calculations performed in physics and chemistry involving gases must use absolute pressure. This is simple; one simply adds

> ## Why do our ears pop when descending from high altitude in an airplane?
>
> Up at cruising altitude the pressure in the atmosphere is a lot lower than it is on the ground. To make passengers comfortable, airplanes have pressurized cabins, where the pressure is maintained at about 2/3 of the atmospheric pressure we are accustomed to. When the plane descends quickly for a landing, the plane is coming back down where the air pressure is higher. This causes the pressure in the cabin to begin increasing back to full atmospheric pressure.
>
> For the pressure in our ears to feel normal, the pressure on the inside of the ear drum, the middle ear, needs to be the same as the pressure outside. The Eustachian tube, which is normally closed, connects the middle ear to the nasopharynx, which is at the back of the nasal cavity.
>
> When the pressure outside rises during descent, the pressure on the outside of the ear becomes higher than the pressure in the middle ear. The ear popping we experience is caused by the Eustachian tube opening to let higher pressure air into the middle ear to balance the pressure on both sides of the ear drum. Yawning and swallowing pops open the Eustachian tube to help this equalization process along.
>
> The same process happens when we dive under water. When the diver holds his or her nose and blows, the diver is pressuring up the middle ear to equal the pressure present outside the ear due to the depth of the water.

atmospheric pressure to any gauge pressure measurement to obtain the absolute pressure.

The pressure formula given in the first section of this chapter determines the gauge pressure at a given depth under a liquid. The absolute pressure at any depth will be the pressure from the formula due to the liquid plus atmospheric pressure. A simple calculation shows that in water at a depth of 2.5 meters (8 feet) the absolute pressure is about 125,000 Pa, which is about 125% of atmospheric pressure. This suggests that going four times this deep would put the pressure at about 200,000 Pa, which is about twice atmospheric pressure. In fact, we have here the SCUBA divers' rule of thumb: pressure increases by one atmosphere for every 10 meters (33 feet) of depth.

Archimedes' Principle of Buoyancy

Archimedes of Syracuse, a third-century BC mathematician, inventor and engineer, is regarded as the greatest scientist of antiquity. His principle of buoyancy is the reason huge ships can carry their cargo without sinking. Archimedes' principle is as follows:

An object submerged in any fluid will experience a buoyant force equal to the weight of the fluid it displaces.

A buoyant force is a force pushing up on an object when the object is partially or fully submerged. Anyone who has ever tried to pull a flotation device under water knows that a strong buoyant force is pushing the object toward the surface. Archimedes' principle allows us to calculate the value of this buoyant force.

Applying Archimedes' principle generally involves both the weight equation from Chapter 4,

$$F_w = mg$$

and the density equation from Chapter 9,

$$\rho = \frac{m}{V}$$

In the simple case of a completely submerged object, the volume of the object and the volume of water displaced by the object are the same. Knowing this volume and the density of water ($998 \ kg/m^3$), one can use the density equation to determine the mass of the water displaced by the submerged object. From this mass, the weight of the displaced water may be determined using the weight equation. This weight of water is the buoyant force on the submerged object. The accompanying example shows how the math works.

As long as the weight of an object is less than the buoyant force that would be present if the object were completely submerged, the object will float. If an object is floating, it is only partially submerged, so the object floats deep enough in the water so that the submerged part provides a buoyant force equal to the weight of the entire object. With a buoyant force equal to the object's weight, the object stays at the surface of the water.

The human body is about 3/4 water. Fat tissue is less dense than water, while muscle and bone tends to be denser than water, so overall, the density of the human body is very close to the density of water. This means the buoyant force available from submersion is close to a person's weight. Whether a person can float depends on the person's body fat content. Most people will float, even if just barely. Inhaling helps flotation, because the overall density of the body decreases when the lungs are full of air. Floating is easier in sea water than fresh water, because the dissolved salts make sea water is denser. And we are told that everyone floats easily in the Dead Sea. Submerging oneself in that water (the saltiest on earth) is next to impossible because the water is so dense.

Archimedes' principle applies to objects in the atmosphere as well as objects in water. However, since a volume of air weighs only about 1/830 as much as the same volume of water, the buoyant force due to air is only 1/830 the buoyant force provided by water. Thus, air can provide the buoyant force needed to hold up a helium balloon, but it won't hold up anything much heavier, such as Wile E. Coyote when he runs off a cliff.

Hot air balloons work by filling the huge balloon with hot air, which is less dense than air at normal temperature. The density change caused by the heating of the air is not great, so hot air balloons have to be quite large to provide enough buoyant force to lift the balloon and the gondola with its passengers.

Example Problem

A small boat dock floating on Styrofoam blocks has dimensions 3.0 m wide x 4.0 m long x 0.5 m high. If the density of Styrofoam is 55 kg/m³, how much weight can be piled on the dock before it submerges and sinks?

For simplicity, in this example we will ignore the weight of the boards of the dock, and just consider the Styrofoam blocks.

The volume of the Styrofoam blocks is

$$V = 3.0 \text{ m} \cdot 4.0 \text{ m} \cdot 0.5 \text{ m} = 6.0 \text{ m}^3$$

We solve the density equation for mass, and insert the volume and density values to get the mass of the water that would be displaced if the Styrofoam were completely submerged.

$$\rho = \frac{m}{V}$$

$$m = \rho V = 998 \ \frac{\text{kg}}{\text{m}^3} \cdot 6.0 \text{ m}^3 = 5,988 \text{ kg}$$

The weight of this mass of water is

$$F_w = mg = 5988 \text{ kg} \cdot 9.80 \ \frac{\text{m}}{\text{s}^2} = 58,682 \text{ N}$$

Rounding this off to the correct number of significant figures gives us a weight of 59,000 N. This weight, which is about 13,000 lb, is the buoyant force when the Styrofoam is fully submerged.

The weight of the Styrofoam itself may be found the same way, using the density of Styrofoam.

$$m = \rho V = 55 \ \frac{\text{kg}}{\text{m}^3} \cdot 6.0 \ \text{m}^3 = 330 \ \text{kg}$$

$$F_w = mg = 330 \ \text{kg} \cdot 9.80 \ \frac{\text{m}}{\text{s}^2} = 3{,}234 \ \text{N}$$

The buoyant force has to hold up the Styrofoam itself, which weighs about 3,200 N or 720 lb. But the Styrofoam blocks can hold up approximately 12,300 lb of additional stuff, which is over 6 tons! It should be easy to see that large volumes of air space in the hold of a ship give rise to a huge buoyant force, enough to hold up the heavy steel-hulled ship and all its cargo. It should also be clear that if the ship fills up with water, it will sink.

Ideas for Your Classroom

1. Students old enough to swim on their own can try this experiment when they are at the swimming pool. Use a transparent, plastic floral water tube available from a floral shop or craft store. Invert the tube in the air and submerge it in the water. Near the surface of the water the water will stay even with the bottom of the tube. But if a kid carries the tube to the bottom of the swimming pool (carefully keeping it upside down and vertical) where the depth is 8 feet, the water will be observed to move up into the tube from the bottom about 20% of the way into the tube. At half the depth the water will move into the tube half as far. The effect may be easier to see if the kids are wearing snorkeling goggles.

2. Attach a stone to a length of slender cord. Suspend the stone from a spring scale and measure its weight. Then with the stone still attached to the scale, dip the stone down into a container of water and read the scale again. The difference between the two readings is the buoyant force on the stone, equal to the weight of the water displaced by the stone.

3. A digital luggage scale (available in the luggage section of department stores or online) can be used to perform the same demonstration on larger, heavier objects. Try using a luggage scale and a large bucket to measure the buoyant force on a brick.

Goals for Chapter 13

1. Describe the major milestones in the development of our knowledge of electricity.

2. Define and distinguish between static electricity and electric current.

3. Explain what static electricity and static discharges are.

4. Describe three ways for static electricity to form, and apply them to explain the operation of the Van de Graaff generator and the electroscope.

5. Describe the general way the atoms are arranged in metals.

6. Using the analogy of water being pumped through a filter, give definitions by analogy for voltage, current, resistance, and potential difference.

7. Explain what electric current is and what produces it.

About This Chapter

This is a long chapter, but it really breaks down to just three topics: history, static electricity, and electric circuits. Electricity seems abstract, and tends to be confusing to people. So in this chapter we will take the time to unpack concepts slowly—and introduce helpful analogies—in order to de-mystify the subject.

Chapter 13
Electricity

The Amazing History of Electricity

Being an electrical engineer, I like to tell the story of electricity and magnetism. Included here is a short account of this interesting saga. The earliest recorded observations of electrical phenomena were by the ancient Greeks around 600 BC. They observed that amber rubbed with fur would attract certain materials such as feathers. This is an effect of static electricity, which we will discuss in this chapter.

The modern story of our scientific knowledge about electricity and magnetism begins with William Gilbert, Queen Elizabeth's personal physician, who spent a lot of time investigating static electricity and magnetism (Figure 13-1). In 1600 (the same year Kepler moved to Prague to work with Tycho Brahe) Gilbert proposed that the earth acted like a large magnet. Gilbert's work was the first major scientific work published in England. His new attitude toward science emphasized experiment and scientific observations. (Recall Johannes Kepler's keen interest in comparing theory with *data*.) He was one of the first scientists to embrace this new attitude, which, of course, was to become the very bedrock principle of science. Gilbert discovered many new materials with electrical properties, and coined the word "electric" from the Greek and Latin words for amber. He also invented an early form of a device called an electroscope, described later in the chapter.

Figure 13-1. English scientist William Gilbert.

About 140 years later the Leyden jar was invented, named after the city in the Netherlands where one of the inventors lived. A Leyden jar (Figure 13-2) has a metal lining in it that allows it to hold electric charge. About 10 years after that a new, more sensitive version of the electroscope was invented in England. The Leyden jar and the electroscope are both devices that can store electrical charge, meaning an excess of negatively charged electrons. About this same time, 1752, was when Benjamin Franklin proved that lightning was electrical by charging up a Leyden jar connected to his kite flying in an electrical storm. (Not exactly the safest experiment.) But Franklin also started the convention of denoting the two types of electric charge as positive and negative, and he established the law of conservation

Figure 13-2. Leyden jars.

Figure 13-3. English scientist Joseph Priestly.

of charge. Before Franklin, "positive" and "negative" were called "vitreous" and "resinous," because electricity was believed to consist of two kinds of "fluid." (Back then lots of things were believed to be fluids—fire, electricity, heat, even an "ether" in space that was believed necessary for light to travel in. All of these notions were found to be incorrect, causing the facts to change yet again!)

In 1767 Joseph Priestly (1733-1804, English, Figure 13-3) found that the force of attraction between two electric charges varies inversely as the square of the distance between them, just like the gravitational force between masses in Newton's Law of Universal Gravitation we saw back at the end of Chapter 3. The exact mathematical expression for the electrical attraction between two charges was discovered in 1785 by French physicist Charles-Augustin de Coulomb, and is known as Coulomb's Law. Have a look at the box on the facing page to read about some fascinating parallels between electric forces and gravity.

In 1791 Luigi Galvani (1737-1798), professor of anatomy in Bologna (Italy), was studying muscle contractions in frog legs (Figure 13-4). He noticed that frog legs hanging on copper hooks from an iron balustrade (or railing) twitched as if alive when they touched the iron. He made a fork with iron and copper prongs and reproduced this result in his lab, discovering that electric charge could cause the muscles in a frog's leg to contract. When Galvani's friend, Count Alessandro Volta (also Italian, Figure 13-5) heard about this, he was fascinated. After nine years of thought and experimentation he invented the "Voltaic Pile" in 1800, the predecessor to the modern battery.

A sketch of the Voltaic Pile is shown in Figure 13-6. In Volta's original design the cells were made of metal disks about four inches in diameter and half an inch

Intriguing Similarities between Gravity and Electricity

Even though we will not be looking at Coulomb's Law in any depth, it is still fascinating to consider it, especially because of its similarity to Isaac Newton's Law of Universal Gravitation. Let's look at both laws side by side, Newton's on the left, Coulomb's on the right:

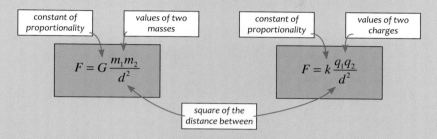

These two equations are both about forces. Newton's equation gives the force of attraction between any two masses. Coulomb's equation gives the force between any two charges, which could be attractive or repulsive, depending on whether the charges are both positive, both negative or one of each. The thing to notice here is that these two equations look just alike. They both have the square of the distance between the objects in the denominator. Newton's law of force between two masses has the two masses multiplied in the numerator, and Coulomb's law of force between charges has the two charges multiplied together in the numerator. The mathematical structure in nature is everywhere we look.

Figure 13-4. Italian anatomy professor Luigi Galvani.

Figure 13-5. Italian scientist Count Alessandro Volta.

thick. The stack of cells was about one and a half feet tall and was encased in a tall, protective glass jar. The pile consisted of a stack of many individual cells. Each cell consisted of a layer of copper, an *electrolyte* layer, and a layer of zinc. An electrolyte is a salt solution that can conduct electricity. In Volta's pile the electrolyte layer consisted of cloth or cardboard soaked in brine (saltwater). The invention of the Voltaic Pile was huge, because for the first time scientists had a reliable source of electricity they could use in the lab so that electricity could be studied further.

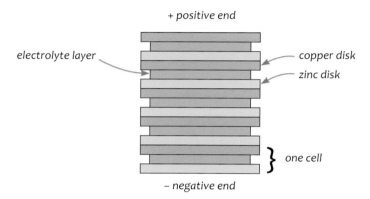

Figure 13-6. The cells in the Voltaic Pile.

By 1820 it was known that electric current and static electricity were different manifestations of the same physical phenomenon. Then a funny thing happened one day in 1820 to Hans Oersted (1777-1851, Denmark), professor at the University of Copenhagen (Figure 13-7). While walking to the college one morning he realized the connection between electricity and magnetism. He went into his lecture hall and right in front of his students he connected a circuit of wire to a Voltaic Pile and placed a magnetic compass near the wire. When he switched on the current the compass needle deflected. This was the first demonstration of the connection between electricity and magnetism. His students did not realize how huge this was and were unimpressed. (Teachers always appreciate the irony of this.) Oersted discovered that a compass near a conductor would deflect and deduced that electric current produces its own magnetic field. He called this effect

Figure 13-7. Danish science professor Hans Oersted.

electromagnetism, and immediately published his results. The physics world went crazy!

When André-Marie Ampère (1775-1836, France, Figure 13-8) heard that news, he began experimenting and within a few weeks showed that two parallel current-carrying wires would attract or repel each other just like magnets. He then figured out the equation for the strength of the magnetic field in relation to the current in the wire, the law now known as Ampère's Law. Ampère's experiments with magnetic fields in coils of current-carrying wire led him to suggest that natural magnetism was the result of tiny circulating currents inside the atoms in magnetic materials. This stunning theoretical leap is now considered to be correct!

Figure 13-8. French scientist André-Marie Ampère.

Next, consider Michael Faraday (1791-1867) in England (Figure 13-9). He had been apprenticed for seven years as a bookbinder and got into physics by reading the books he was binding. He contacted Sir Humphry Davy, one of the most well known and highly respected scientists in London, and asked for a position in his lab. At the advice of one of his cronies, Davy hired Faraday as a bottle washer! So Faraday was given his chance, and he certainly made good on it. In 1831 Faraday demonstrated the opposite effect from Ampère's Law: that a magnetic field can induce an electrical current in a nearby conductor. This is now known as Faraday's Law of Magnetic Induction. This discovery led to the development of generators, motors and transformers. Our lives would be utterly different, and much more difficult, if we did not have these devices. Faraday had almost no mathematical training, yet he brilliantly theorized the existence of "fields" to

Figure 13-9. English scientist Michael Faraday.

explain magnetic phenomena. We will learn some of the details of Ampère's Law and Faraday's Law in the next chapter.

This story reaches its conclusion with the amazing Scotsman James Clerk Maxwell (1831-1879). In 1864 Maxwell (Figure 13-10) published what is perhaps the greatest achievement in theoretical physics of all time, the four equations now known as Maxwell's Equations. These four equations constitute a complete classical description of all known electric and magnetic phenomena in the universe! In addition to his supreme achievement with electromagnetic theory, Maxwell also contributed to the pioneering work on the Kinetic Theory of Gases, which we examined in Chapter 10. Maxwell's theoretical work is ranked at the same level as that of Newton and Einstein.

Maxwell's Equations incorporate some sophisticated mathematics, but they are elegant and simple (at least to those who know vector calculus). It is worth taking a look at them just to consider how so much can be said with so little. The four equations can be written several different ways, but Figure 13-11 shows them in so-called differential form.

Figure 13-10. Scottish theoretical physicist James Clerk Maxwell.

In Chapter 2 we looked with amazement at how a simple equation like Kepler's Third Law of Planetary Motion could model the real physical world so elegantly. Maxwell's equations, universally regarded as one of the greatest and most beautiful discoveries in the history of physics, are even more astonishing. These four short equations first demonstrated that light was an electromagnetic wave. From the study of these equations first came the idea that we could create radio waves and transmit information with them, which is without a doubt one of the most influential ideas in the history of human technology. I never tire of celebrating Maxwell's brilliant achievement.

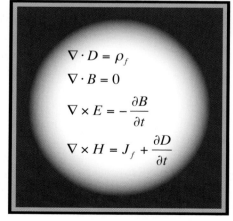

$$\nabla \cdot D = \rho_f$$
$$\nabla \cdot B = 0$$
$$\nabla \times E = -\frac{\partial B}{\partial t}$$
$$\nabla \times H = J_f + \frac{\partial D}{\partial t}$$

Figure 13-11. Maxwell's four beautiful equations.

Charge and Static Electricity

In the context of physics and chemistry, when we refer to *charge* we mean charged subatomic particles. As we have seen, there are two kinds of subatomic particles that have charge, protons with positive charge, and electrons with negative charge. All electrical phenomena are due to these two charged particles. All matter is made of atoms and all atoms have protons and electrons in them, so charged particles—charges for short—are everywhere.

Most of the time the colossal numbers of positive and negative charges that matter is made of are so evenly distributed in a substance or object they essentially cancel each other out, so there is no net electrical charge and we aren't even aware of the charges all around us (and in us). But there are two special circumstances when charges do things that make us notice them. These two special circumstances are when charges are in motion, and when charges are compelled to accumulate somewhere.

> In the context of physics and chemistry, the term *charge* refers to charged particles, protons and electrons.

As we will discuss more later in the chapter, electrons in metals are free to move around, which is why metals conduct electricity so well. The protons in metals are locked in the nuclei (plural of nucleus) of the atoms and are not free to move around. For this reason when we talk about charges in motion or charges accumulating in everyday life, we almost always mean electrons, not protons.

> When speaking of common electrical phenomena such as static electricity or electric current, the charges involved are *electrons*.

When electric charge is moving or flowing it is called an electric current. We'll get to that a bit later. First we will examine charges that have accumulated together and are at rest. The word physicists use to describe something that is not moving is "static," which comes from the Greek word "stasis," meaning "standing still." *Static electricity* is an accumulation of charge that is stationary. An easy way to accumulate static electricity is by combing your hair with a rubber comb. (The Ace Genuine Rubber comb is still available today!) As we will see in the next section, the friction between the comb and the hair can cause static electricity to build up. Then when the comb is held near some small bits of paper the paper will jump onto the comb from the electrical attraction, as shown in Figure 13-12.

It is remarkable how so many of the ideas we have encountered in our tour of physics come in threes. Accordingly, it may not be surprising that there are three ways static electricity can form. In the description that follows we will use a device called an *electroscope* to illustrate each of these three ways. Figure 13-13 on page 209 shows an electroscope when it has no static

> Static electricity is an accumulation of stationary charge.

Figure 13-12. Static electricity causes small bits of paper to be attracted to a rubber comb.

electricity on it (left) and when it is charged with static electricity (right). An electroscope consists of a metal rod with a metal sphere on top and a pair of metal hooks on the bottom. From the hooks are suspended two strips of aluminum foil called "leaves." The glass flask and red rubber stopper aren't part of the action; they are only there to hold the metal parts up. Consider what would happen if an accumulation of electrons, static electricity, were to be placed on the metal sphere. Since the electrons all have the same negative charge, they would repel each other, so they would try to spread themselves out on the metal parts, attempting to push as far away from each other as possible. Electrons can move easily in metals, because metals are good conductors of electricity. So the electrons will spread out up and down the metal parts, including down into the leaves. Since the leaves are free to move, they will swing out due to the electrons on one leaf repelling the electrons on the other leaf. The photograph on the right in Figure 13-13 shows the electroscope with its leaves forced outward due to the static electricity on the metal parts of the electroscope.

How Static Electricity Can Form

The first way static electricity can form is by *friction*. When you walk across a nylon carpet in the winter your feet are actually scraping loose some of the electrons from the atoms in the carpet and they accumulate on and spread out all over your body. There is an accumulation of static charge built up on you! Then when you reach out to touch a door knob the charge that has accumulated on you jumps to the door knob causing the exciting *arc* and snapping sound that we are all familiar with. The same thing happens when you slide your backside into a car with nylon upholstery. The friction causes electrons to get rubbed onto your body and stay there. Then when you are ready to open the door, the static electricity on you will *discharge* when you touch the metal door handle to get out of the car.

As an aside, the term discharge is used to denote the arc or spark that occurs when a large accumulation of static electricity is suddenly released. Electrons are constantly trying to get away from each other, because they all have the same negative charge. This is especially true

> The arc of a static discharge is caused by a stream of charges flowing through the air from a charged object to another (uncharged) object.

Figure 13-13. The electroscope uncharged (left) and charged with static electricity (right).

when many of them have been forced to accumulate. So when an object comes close enough for them to jump to, they do! They literally jump through the air, and their violent path through the air creates a plasma that releases energy in the form of light and sound, as illustrated in Figure 13-14 (see also page 146). The biggest arc any of us will ever see is a lightning bolt, which is a whopping big discharge of the static electricity that builds up in clouds and discharges to the ground.

Figure 13-14. The violet streak of light is an arc from a static discharge as electrons on the large metal sphere jump through the air to the small metal sphere.

Interestingly, the friction involved when gasoline is flowing in a rubber hose can cause quite a bit of static electricity to build up on a car during fueling, which would obviously be quite dangerous. So gasoline hoses have special designs inside to provide a way to "drain off" the charge on the car rather than causing a sparking hazard with gasoline vapors around.

Going back to the electroscope in Figure 13-13, friction comes into the electroscope demonstration in a couple of ways. First, we always begin this demonstration by using friction to create an accumulation of charge which we can then use for the rest of the demonstration. One way to do this is to rub a Styrofoam cup on someone's hair, because the friction causes electrons from the

Why is static electricity worse in the winter?

In warm weather the humidity is usually higher, which means the air contains more moisture. Moisture can conduct electricity just enough so that electrons that accumulate on your person while walking on carpet are able to drain off or escape by attaching to the water molecules in the air.

With the low humidity of the colder months, electrons that accumulate on you *stay* on you, so when you walk across the carpet, slide on a car seat, or comb your hair, the accumulated electrons build up quickly and are ready to discharge with an exciting snap the moment you reach for a door handle.

hair to accumulate on the cup. You may have done this yourself at some point with a balloon, which you can then stick to the wall. Another way to do it is to rub a glass rod with some silk, which will cause electrons to build up on the glass rod. Or one can do it the way the Greeks did by rubbing a piece of amber with some fur. However it is done, the friction from rubbing is what causes the electrical charge to accumulate.

In the electroscope demonstration friction is used again to get the electric charges off the Styrofoam cup and onto the sphere on the top of the electroscope. Just touching the cup to the metal sphere won't do it, because Styrofoam doesn't conduct electricity, so the electrons on the cup cannot make their way to the metal sphere; they are stranded on the cup. (Thus, Styrofoam is an electrical *insulator*.) But if we rub the metal sphere with the cup the electrons on the cup are literally scraped off onto the metal. We cannot see any of this happening, of course. All we see is that the leaves of the electroscope swing out because the charge that is now on the electroscope is trying to spread out as much as it can (because like charges repel).

A second way static electricity can form is by *conduction*. We saw this same term before when we were talking about heat transfer. But in the context of electricity the term has a completely different meaning.

Everyone knows that certain substances, like metals, conduct electricity. This means that electrons flow easily in these substances. More on that a bit later, but for now note that if you create a static build-up by friction, and then touch the object that has the static charge on it to a metal rod, the electric charge will flow, that is *conduct*, in the metal rod and will drain off onto whatever the rod is touching. This effect is demonstrated in the electroscope when the charged object (Styrofoam cup, glass rod, or whatever) touches the metal sphere. When this happens the electric charge conducts down the metal rod in the electroscope and into the metal foil leaves. And now that all of this extra electrical charge is in the leaves, they try to push away from each other. Conduction will occur again if a person touches the metal sphere atop the electroscope with her hand, allowing the extra charge to drain off the electroscope by flowing onto her person and from there into the ground.

The third way static electricity can form is by a process called *induction*. (Warning: This term will also appear in a later chapter in another context which we will have to keep from getting confused with this one. Sorry.) Let's pause for a brief aside on the word induce. This word basically means "force it to happen." If a person is induced to confess a crime, they are put in a position where they figure confession is their only option. When labor is induced in a pregnant woman it is brought about by drugs that force it to happen. So, back to electricity. When static electricity, an accumulation of electric charges, is formed by induction it is somehow forced to happen.

Now, consider a block of metal, as illustrated in Figure 13-15. It is chock full of electrons and they are completely free to move around inside this metal. What will all of those electrons do if an object charged up with excess electrons is brought near to the metal block? As shown in the figure, they will move away from the charged object, because negative charges always try to move away from each other if they can. Even if the charged object never touches the metal block the electrons in the metal block will crowd up together, that is, accumulate, on the opposite side of the block from where the charged object is. This forced accumulation of charge is an accumulation of charge by induction. In the case of induction, the static electricity accumulation is temporary. It will only remain there as long as the charged object which is inducing it is present. Pull the charged object away, and all those electrons in the metal block will relax and spread back out in the block.

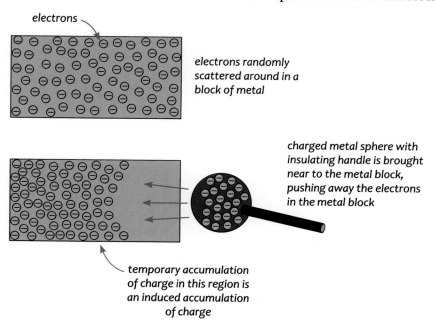

electrons

electrons randomly scattered around in a block of metal

charged metal sphere with insulating handle is brought near to the metal block, pushing away the electrons in the metal block

temporary accumulation of charge in this region is an induced accumulation of charge

Figure 13-15. Charge accumulation by induction.

This effect is demonstrated in the electroscope when the charged Styrofoam cup is brought near the metal sphere, but is not allowed to touch it. The leaves move apart because of the charge induced in them, or forced down into them, by the nearby presence of the charged Styrofoam cup. But the induced accumulation is temporary, and as soon as the cup is pulled away the charges in the metal parts of the electroscope all relax and spread back out again.

Sometimes when I demonstrate induction with the electroscope students get the mistaken notion that electrical charges jump from the cup to the electroscope. Well, they don't. If the cup does not touch the metal sphere no charges actually transfer from the cup to the metal. Induction occurs without any charges transferring from the cup to the metal sphere, and it is a temporary effect that goes away as soon as the cup is withdrawn.

Electric Current

Electric current is flowing or moving charge. In principle, this charge could be positive or negative; flowing positive charges (protons) and flowing negative charges (electrons) would both qualify as electrical currents. But in ordinary circumstances, the protons in a solid substance are locked in the atomic nuclei of atoms that are held in place. So although a current of protons can be created in a laboratory under special circumstances, that is not what usually happens.

> Electric current is flowing or moving charge. In the everyday world, these moving charges are electrons.

On the other hand, electrons in some substances are free to move around, as explained below. We have already seen how electrons can be accumulated to form static electricity. Well in some substances, namely metals, the electrons can be made to flow like water in a pipe. This is what electric current is.

Why Electricity Flows So Easily in Metals

In our study of static electricity I noted that one way for static electricity to accumulate is by conduction, when electrons flow in a metal. We need to look at why metals are such good electrical conductors.

Recall from back in Chapter 9 that there are two basic ways the atoms in solid substances can be arranged. In many solids, the atoms are combined in molecules, tiny clusters of atoms. The other basic form is a crystal structure, in which the atoms in the solid are arranged in an orderly, geometric arrangement called a crystal lattice. As it turns out, metals are like this; they are *crystals*.

In addition to their crystal structure, there is another important thing about the way atoms in metals are arranged. Every

> Metals are crystals—their atoms are arranged in the geometric patterns of a crystal lattice.

atom has a certain number of electrons. In most substances the electrons of an atom are held in a region around the atomic nucleus by the force of electrical attraction between the positive protons in the nucleus and the negative electrons. However, in metal atoms things are a bit different. In metal atoms, some of the electrons stay with the atom they belong to, but others are free to move about within the crystal lattice when an electrical force called a "voltage" is present. The electrons that are free to move around are called *conduction electrons*. We will address the idea of voltage soon. For now, we will just focus on what is going on with these conduction electrons in metals.

In metals the conduction electrons have no idea what atom they came from or belong to, and it doesn't really even matter. What matters is that the conduction electrons can move easily when a voltage is applied to the metal. It also matters that there is a very, very large number of these free electrons. In fact, there are so many free electrons in a metal that scientists actually refer to this ocean of electrons as the *electron sea*.

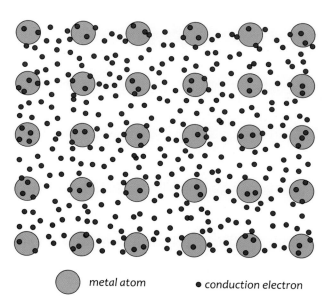

metal atom   • conduction electron

Figure 13-16. Metallic crystal lattice with the "electron sea."

Figure 13-16 depicts the crystal structure in the atoms of a metal, with the electrons in the electron sea scattered throughout the crystal lattice.

The Water Analogy

We are now going to look at how electric circuits work. An electric circuit is just an arrangement of electrical components that forces the electrons to flow in a certain direction so they can do some valuable work for us.

The best way to understand how electricity works is by comparing it to water flowing in a pipe. We cannot see electricity flowing, and for most people electricity is some mysterious force that makes modern life convenient but can cause serious fires or injuries if it gets out of hand. But electricity is just electrons flowing

> The best way to understand how electricity works is by comparing it to water flowing in a pipe.

in wires, and the way they do it is very similar to the way molecules of water flow in a pipe. If we pump water in a closed circuit of piping through, say, a water filter, we have a system that is analogous to an electric circuit in nearly every respect. The sketch in Figure 13-17 shows the water circuit.

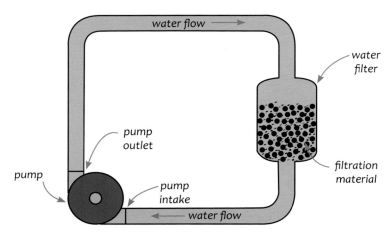

Figure 13-17. A water circuit with a pump circulating water in pipes through a filter.

Imagine that we have a little water pump, like what we would see in an aquarium, and we are pumping the water through the filter to keep it clean.

Let's think for a minute about what causes water to flow in a pipe. Imagine two kids playing a water game with a garden hose. Each of them holds one end of the hose, and the hose is filled to the brim with water. They put the ends of the hose in their mouths and blow hard. Who is going to lose? That is, whose mouth gets full of water? As we can all easily guess, the person who blows with the lowest pressure will get the mouth full of water. The reason is that water always flows from high pressure to low pressure. In fact, it is the *difference* in pressure that makes it flow at all. If the two kids put the hoses in their mouths but did not blow, or blew with the same pressure, the water would not go anywhere. But when a difference in pressure is created, the water will always flow toward the lower pressure.

Now that we have established that water only flows toward lower pressure, let's think more about the water circuit and what the pressures must be like at different points around the circuit in order for it to work. In Figure 13-18 is another sketch of the water circuit. This time we have pressure gauges attached to the pipes at seven places around the pipe. Let's now imagine that we are reading the gauges to determine what the pressure is at various points around the circuit.

If we make a graph of what the "pressure profile" around the circuit would look like based on the pressures all these gauges would be indicating, we would find that the pressures around the circuit would vary as shown in Figure 13-19.

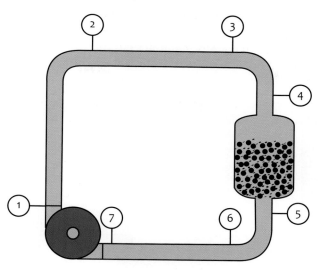

Figure 13-18. Water circuit with numbered pressure gauges added to the pipes.

Notice that the highest pressure in the circuit is at the outlet of the pump, and the lowest pressure in the circuit is at the intake of the pump. It has to be this way, because outside of the pump water always flows toward low pressure. (Inside the pump are blades like those on a fan that are pushing the water toward the discharge, forcing the water to go where the higher pressure is. Outside the pump the water flows by itself, and always toward the lower pressure.)

Notice also that the pressure decreases steadily from place to place around the circuit. Again, this has to be the case, because if the pressure ever went up it would mean the water had to flow the other direction, which we know it does not do. Finally, notice that the largest pressure drop in the system is across the water filter, between gauges 4 and 5. This is because the pipes are unobstructed and only a small difference in pressure between two points will cause the water to flow easily. But the water filter is packed with sand and charcoal and whatnot, so to make the water flow through it the pressure drop across it has to be very large, just as one of those kids would have to blow hard to push water through a clogged hose. In fact, almost all of the pressure drop from the pump outlet to the pump intake

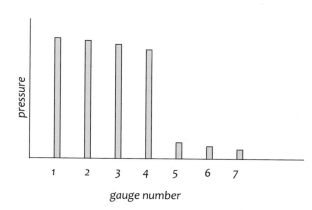

Figure 13-19. The pressure profile around the water circuit.

will occur across the water filter. All of this behavior is exactly analogous to the way electricity flows in wires.

As a last step of analysis about the water circuit before we make the analogy to electricity, Table 13-1 summarizes the different components in the water circuit and the roles they play.

Component	Role
Pump	Makes the water flow. It does this by creating a difference in pressure. Outside the pump water will always and only flow toward lower pressure.
Pipe	Provides a contained pathway in which the water can flow.
Water	Flows in the pipes. Flowing water actually consists of many individual molecules moving along in the pipe.
Filter	Provides resistance to the flow of water. The more material the filter has packed into it the harder it is for the pump to make the water flow. The filter is doing a practical job (cleaning the water) and is the reason we have the water circuit in the first place.

Table 13-1. Components in the water circuit.

The Basic DC Electric Circuit

DC electricity flowing in a wire works exactly the same way as water flowing in a pipe. We have four basic components as before, and the way each of them works is the same as before. Before we proceed let's clarify terms. "DC" means *direct current*. It is a bit of a strange term, but it basically means the currents and voltages in the circuit, which you will understand soon, are constant, steady values. This is what we have with any circuit powered by a battery. The internal electronics inside virtually every electronic gadget are also DC circuits. (The AC from the power outlet is converted to DC right inside the device, or by an adapter built into the plug.) DC circuits will be addressed in this chapter. "AC" means *alternating current*. We are not going to get into AC circuits very much in this book, except for a bit in the next chapter. But in an AC circuit the current and voltage are constantly changing, increasing and decreasing back and forth, going from positive to negative and back again. This kind of electric system is used for the entire electrical power distribution system that carries electricity to all the homes, offices and factories. So the electricity that comes from a wall receptacle is AC.

Now consider a DC electric circuit consisting of a battery, some wire, and a resistor, as shown in Figure 13-20. This type of drawing is called a *schematic diagram*. Schematic diagrams use symbols to show the components in the circuit and how they are connected, but they do not show what the circuit actually looks

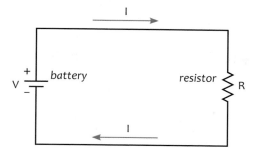

Figure 13-20. The basic DC circuit.

like physically. The wires may be a mile long, bending along on power poles along a roadside, or they may be tiny copper connections inside a computer. The schematic only shows the components and how they connect to each other.

Before we begin analyzing this circuit a few words about the symbols are necessary. The flowing current is indicated by the arrows labeled with a capital I. In physics, the letter I is used as the symbol for electric current. The symbol for the battery in the circuit in Figure 13-20 is actually the symbol for a single cell battery, like a flashlight battery. The long bar on the end of the battery symbol indicates the positive end of the battery. The current comes out of this end of the battery and flows in the wire toward the resistor. As you know, all batteries have a certain voltage, which will be explained further below. But the +/− symbols indicate that the voltage at the (+) end of the battery is higher than the voltage at the (−) end, the difference being the voltage of the battery. Note that the (−) symbol does not mean the voltage is actually *negative*, just as the pressure at intake of a pump is not negative. The +/− symbols simply tell us which end of the battery has the highest voltage (+). Finally, the universal symbol for a resistor is the zigzag line segment.

The small batteries we are familiar with for flashlights and other gadgets are single-cell batteries. The voltage a battery can produce is fixed by its cell chemistry, so if we want a higher voltage we have to stack cells on top of one another, just as Volta's Pile was made out of a stack of individual cells. A car battery has six cells, which would be depicted as shown in Figure 13-21. However, it is common when studying DC circuits to just use the battery symbol for a single-cell battery, regardless of the battery voltage.

Now we are ready to examine the electric circuit the same way we examined the water circuit. Just as in the water analogy, there are four components in the circuit. The battery is analogous to the pump. Its job is to make the current flow. Recall that water flows when a difference in pressure is present, and the water

Figure 13-21. The electrical symbol for a six-cell battery.

always flows toward the lower pressure. The electrical analog to pressure is *voltage*. A battery is a chemical device that produces a difference in voltage, and this difference in voltage forces an electric current to flow in the wire. Electric current always flows from high voltage to low. And just like the water, if there is no voltage drop no current will flow.

> The voltage difference that makes the current flow in an electric circuit is analogous to the pressure difference that makes the water flow in a water circuit.

The pipes of the water circuit are analogous to the wires in the electrical circuit—both are conduits for something that is flowing. In the water pipes, water is flowing, and water consists of many tiny individual molecules. In the electrical wiring, electrical current is flowing, and this current consists of many tiny individual charges.

We will have more to say about resistors later, but here we will note that this electrical device has the same effect on an electrical circuit as the water filter has on the water circuit. It resists the flow of current and causes a large voltage drop. The resistor is the reason we have the circuit in the first place, because the resistor is able to do some kind of work for us, just as the water filter does.

The roles played by the devices in both the water and electrical circuits are arranged for side-by-side comparison in Table 13-2.

Two Important Details

At the risk of introducing a little confusion, there are two little important details from all of this explanation and analogy that need to be added. First, everything stated above about current flowing from positive to negative and all that is valid only within the convention adopted a hundred years ago that we do the math with circuits by assuming the flow of positive charge. (As we have seen, protons have positive charge.) This convention has the advantage of eliminating all the negative signs from our calculations that don't do anything but get in the way, so this is a good convention. But in reality, as explained above, it is not positive charge that flows in the wires of the circuit but negatively charged electrons. So here is the first important detail: We define current as the flow of fictitious positive charges, and we perform circuit calculations under this assumption. (The arrows labeled "I" in Figure 13-20 show the direction of flow for these fictitious positive charges.) This assumption just makes everything easier. In reality though, it is electrons that are actually flowing in the wire—in the opposite direction!

> The convention for circuit diagrams and calculations is to show the direction of flow of fictitious positive charge. In reality, negatively charged electrons are flowing in the opposite direction.

The second important detail relates to the statement above, that for current to flow there must be a voltage difference, just like there must be a pressure difference

Water Circuit Component	Role	Electrical Circuit Component	Role
Pump	Makes the water flow. It does this by creating a difference in pressure. Outside the pump water will always and only flow toward lower pressure.	Battery	Makes the current flow. It does this by creating a difference in voltage. Outside the battery current will always and only flow toward lower voltage.
Pipe	Provides a contained pathway in which the water can flow.	Wire	Provides a contained pathway in which the current can flow.
Water	Flows in the pipes. Flowing water consists of many individual molecules moving along the pipe.	Electric Current	Flows in the wires. Flowing current consists of many individual electrons moving along the wire.
Filter	Provides resistance to the flow of water. The more material the filter has packed into it the harder it is for the pump to make the water flow. The filter is doing a practical job (cleaning the water), and is the reason we have the water circuit in the first place.	Resistor	Provides resistance to the flow of current. The more resistance the resistor has the harder it is for the battery to make the current flow. The resistor is doing a practical job and is the reason we have the electric circuit in the first place. The resistor can be an actual resistor, or some other device represented by a resistor.

Table 13-2. Components in the water and electrical circuits.

for water to flow. Strictly speaking, this is completely correct. However, in practical circuit analysis the voltage difference between the end of the battery and the near end of the resistor in the circuit is typically so small that we can completely ignore it in our circuit calculations. This means we can assume that any two points connected together by solid wire are at the same voltage. To illustrate this, the basic electric circuit with a 9-V battery is shown again in Figure 13-22. In this illustration the voltage at a few places is labeled with this simplification in mind.

Again, there actually is an extremely minute voltage drop along the wire from the end of the battery to the resistor. If there weren't, current would not flow. But this is our second important detail: The voltage difference is so small that for practical purposes in small circuits we can ignore it and pretend that along any continuously connected wire the voltage is the same. Remember again the chart of Figure 13-19. Most of the pressure drop is across the water filter, and very little pressure drop occurs in the pipes.

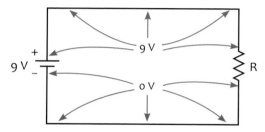

Figure 13-22. Circuit showing voltages (for practical purposes) on the wires.

Electrical Variables and Units

It seems that textbooks rarely point out certain confusing things about the variables and units we use when we are studying circuits. For example, the variable we use to describe the force with which the battery is pushing the current is voltage, with symbol V, and the units we use are volts, symbol V. So we measure voltage with volts. These words kind of look alike and their symbols are the same. But the other variables don't look at all like their units of measure, and their symbols are not the same. The easiest way to lay it out is in another nice table, as in Table 13-3. The symbols are all self-explanatory except the symbol for *ohms*, the unit of electrical resistance, Ω. This symbol is the capital Greek letter omega, the last letter in the Greek alphabet. The unit ohms was named after the German physicist Georg Ohm, who worked in the nineteenth century. Ohm discovered the famous equation relating current, voltage and resistance together—Ohm's Law—that we will discuss in the next section.

Variable	Symbol	Units of Measure	Symbol for Units
voltage	V	volts	V
current	I	amperes, or amps	A
resistance	R	ohms	Ω
power	P	watts	W

Table 13-3. Electric variables and units of measure, and their symbols.

All of the units of measure in Table 13-3 are derived units, except for the ampere. The ampere is one of the seven fundamental units, along with the meter, kilogram and second that we have seen already. The units of measure in the table above are all MKS units and they boil down to combinations of fundamental units. We only really need to explain one of the derived units here, power.

Power is the rate at which energy is delivered or used, and is measured in watts (W). A watt of power is an energy rate of one joule per second, or

$$1\,W = 1\frac{J}{s}$$

For example, a traditional 60-W light bulb, such as we all had in our houses before we replaced the bulbs with compact fluorescents, draws 60 joules of energy every second from the city electrical distribution system. When we pay the electric bill we pay for those joules. (There is a meter on the side of your house that measures how much energy you use, although the units they use aren't the nice joules (J) we use in physics, they are the weird kilowatt-hours [KWH]. It's still just a unit for energy.)

Ohm's Law

The basic equation relating voltage, current, and resistance is called Ohm's Law and is

$$V = IR$$

This is one of the most famous equations in physics. One handy way to remember it is that it spells the word *man* in Latin (*vir*). (At least it's handy if you've studied Latin.) As mentioned above, we may consider the voltage on a single piece of wire to be the same everywhere on it. If we apply this rule and Ohm's Law to a simple circuit with one resistor like the one in Figure 13-20, this would mean that the voltage of the battery is equal to the voltage drop across the resistor.

Example Problem

A battery with a voltage of 2.80 V is connected to a light bulb with a resistance of 9.33 Ω. Determine the amount of current flowing through the wires from the battery to the light bulb. (Note in this example that we are modeling the light bulb as a resistor with a resistance of 9.33 Ω.)

The given information and the unknown are:

$V = 2.80$ V

$R = 9.33$ Ω

$I = ?$

We proceed to write down Ohm's Law, solve the equation for the current, and calculate the result.

$V = IR$

$$I = \frac{V}{R} = \frac{2.80 \text{ V}}{9.33 \text{ Ω}} = 0.300 \text{ A}$$

What Exactly Are Resistors and Why Do We Have Them?

A *resistor* is a little device used in electronic circuits to regulate the voltages and currents throughout the circuit. A complicated electronic gadget like a computer has hundreds of resistors in its circuitry. Figure 13-23 shows an image of some low-power resistors, the way they look just out of the package, and the way they look when installed on a circuit board in an electronic gadget. The gadget pictured is built using technology that is nearly obsolete. Resistors connected in mass-produced electronic devices these days are quite a bit smaller and look somewhat different, as shown in Figure 13-24. The colored bands of the older style

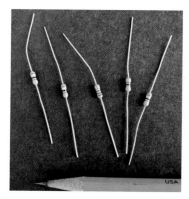

Figure 13-23. Photographs of resistors, new (left) and installed (right).

resistors (still in use, by the way) are coded and represent the resistance, in ohms, of the resistor.

At a basic level, most of the electrical devices we use—electric driers, lighting, hedge trimmers, computers, MP3 player chargers, and on and on—act like resistors in the electric circuits that power everything around us. AC circuits are more complicated than that, but this is an adequate simplification for our purposes here. Light bulbs and electric heaters and toasters are electrically quite

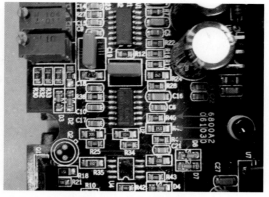

Figure 13-24. Newer technology resistors mounted on a circuit board. Three of the resistors are indicated by the red arrows.

similar to actual resistors, so we can use resistors to model those devices in our circuit calculations. In summary, when we do electric circuit calculations we use the generic symbol for a resistor. But the resistors in our drawing could represent just about any device that needs electric power to operate.

Through? Across? In?

The prepositions and adverbs we use to describe what is going on in an electric circuit are important. Current flows *in* a wire, just like water flows *in* a pipe. The voltage drops *across* a resistor, just like the pressure drops *across* the water filter. What we mean by this is that the voltage "upstream" of the resistor is higher than the voltage "downstream" of the resistor, so the voltage drops *across* it. We never speak of the voltage *through* a resistor because the voltage is not what is going through it. The current is what is going through it. So currents flow *in* wires and through *resistors*. Voltages drop *across* resistors. We speak the same way about any other device in an electric circuit. The current flows through it, the voltage drops across it.

> When speaking of any electrical device, we say the current goes *through* the device (just like flowing water), and the voltage drops *across* the device (just like the pressure dropping across the water filter).

Voltages Are Relative

Consider for a moment our discussion back in Chapter 5 about energy. The gravitational potential energy in an object depends on how high up it is. But how high an object is depends on where the zero reference is for height. Where is zero height? The table top? The floor? The ground outside the building? Sea level? The answer is that it doesn't matter. The only reason we ever calculated the E_G in an object was so we could predict how much work it would take to get it up there or how fast it would be going if it fell down. These calculations do not depend on the absolute height, which is hard to even define. The calculations really depend only on the *difference* in height from some reference point like the floor or the table top to where the object is. It is only the difference that matters.

The same situation holds for voltages. Defining voltage in an absolute sense goes beyond what we can include in our basic treatment here. But that doesn't matter, because in basic circuit calculations the voltage differences (or voltage drops) are all that matters. We simply use the lowest voltage in the circuit as our reference point. Remember where this is? The lowest pressure in the water circuit is at the intake of the pump. Analogously, the lowest voltage in an electric circuit will be at the negative end of the battery. Since the only thing that matters about a voltage is how high it is relative to the reference, we can just say that our reference voltage is the wire connected to the negative end of the battery. Further, we might as well call this voltage zero volts.

In fact, we might as well point out that in the great electrical systems of our noble nation the earth itself is used as the zero voltage reference, and in our power distribution systems we realize this by physically bolting part of the circuit to the ground. This is done by driving a long copper *ground rod* into the ground (at a typical house this rod is about eight feet long) and connecting the power system to it with a hefty copper wire. This is the electrical "ground" that we may sometimes hear mentioned by an electrician. The electrical people call it ground because the reference point for zero volts in the circuit is the ground, and the circuit is connected to the ground, literally.

In an electric circuit diagram an electrical ground connection is indicated by the symbol shown in Figure 13-25. Wherever ground is in an electric circuit, that is where the zero volt reference is. Typically, the ground symbol is not shown for basic circuit problems. This is mainly because a lot of common electric circuits, such as flashlights, MP3 players, cell phones and so on aren't actually connected to the ground unless they are being charged up. So we usually don't show a ground symbol on DC circuits. But just to illustrate, Figure 13-26 shows the one-resistor circuit with the ground symbol shown. Also shown are the voltage, current and resistance using the standard symbols. V_B is a conventional notation used to indicate the voltage of the battery.

Figure 13-25. The symbol for electrical ground.

Power in Electrical Circuits

In an electric circuit the battery, or whatever the power supply actually is, even if it is not a battery, supplies the energy to the devices that need it. The energy is

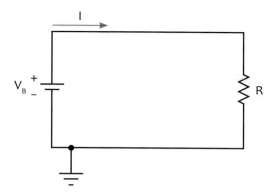

Figure 13-26. An electric circuit with ground connection shown.

supplied at a certain rate, a certain number of joules per second. This energy rate is called the *power* and we measure it in watts (W). The basic equation for power is

$$P = VI$$

where P is the power (W, that is, J/s). So, if a battery has a voltage V and is supplying a current I, it is supplying power to the circuit in the amount $P = VI$.

While we are on the subject of power, let's consider how the conservation of energy works in electrical circuits. The battery supplies energy to the circuit, and this energy is "consumed" (as we say) by the devices in the circuit. If we are talking about the energy supplied by the battery in one second, then this is the power supplied to the circuit, and this power supplied to the circuit must equal the power consumed by all of the devices in the circuit. For resistors, the power is *dissipated* (that is, given off) as heat. For other devices, such as motors, the power is used to do mechanical work ($W = Fd$), as with a fan pushing air or a garage door opener lifting the door.

Two-Resistor Networks

So far we have seen only circuits with one battery and one resistor. We have now covered all of the basics for such circuits and are ready to learn how to handle circuits with more than one resistor. In the real electrical world circuits usually have many resistors, not just one. The bundle of resistors in a circuit, all wired together but not connected to the battery, is called a resistor *network*. We will conclude this chapter by reviewing the basic ways resistors can be connected together in a network.

Resistors in circuits can be connected together in two main ways. The first kind of connection is shown in Figure 13-27. The key feature here is that all of the current that enters resistor R_1 must also enter resistor R_2. There are no other branches or pathways in the circuit, so the current, represented by the red arrows, has no option but to go through both resistors. This kind of connection is called

Example Problem

For the circuit shown in Figure 13-20, assume that the battery voltage is 5.60 V and the resistor value is 7700 Ω. Determine the current flowing in the circuit and the power consumed by the resistor.

The givens and unknowns are:

$V = 5.60$ V

$R = 7700$ Ω

$I = ?$

$P = ?$

To solve for the current flowing in the circuit we use Ohm's Law.

$V = IR$

$$I = \frac{V}{R} = \frac{5.60 \text{ V}}{7,700 \text{ }\Omega} = 0.0007273 \text{ A}$$

(Note that it would be common to describe this circuit using metric prefixes. We would say that the resistance in this circuit is 7.7 k Ω, and the current is 0.7273 mA.)

To compute the power consumed by the resistor we will use the power equation. The voltage drop across the resistor is equal to the battery voltage, and we have just computed the current in the circuit.

$P = VI = 5.60$ V $\cdot 0.0007273$ A $= 0.00407$ W

As mentioned before in the example problems, we need to round these values off to two significant digits, because the resistor value given only has two significant digits. Doing so gives

$I = 0.00073$ A

$P = 0.0041$ W

a *series* connection and we say that the two resistors are connected "in series." We could also wire up three or four resistors in series, or as many as we like. It is important to note that in a series connection there is nothing between the resistors, no other devices, no connections, nothing except the single wire connecting the series resistors together. If there is anything else there the resistors are not connected in series. An important principle to note for series connections

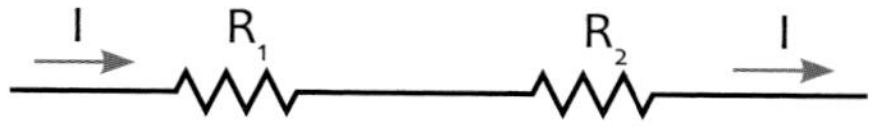

Figure 13-27. Two resistors connected in series.

is this: *When resistors are connected in series, the same current passes through each of them.*

> When resistors are connected in series the same current passes through each of them.

The second way of wiring resistors together is shown in Figure 13-28. Don't freak out at that diagram; the connections shown in the three sketches are the same! It is shown three times simply to show different ways this type of resistor network can be drawn. This kind of connection is called a *parallel* connection, and we say that the two resistors are connected "in parallel."

An important note is critical here. Just because this is called a parallel connection does not mean that when drawn on the paper in a schematic diagram the resistors must appear to be parallel to each other on the page. Recall that a schematic diagram tells us nothing about what the circuit looks like, only how the devices are connected. This is why the three

> Resistors connected in parallel do not have to *look* parallel in the schematic diagram.

networks shown in Figure 13-28 are identical. The way they are drawn on the page is simply for convenience, and the important thing is how they are connected.

The key feature to note about a parallel connection like this is that if two resistors are connected together in parallel, then they are connected together at both ends. If they are not connected together at both ends, or if there is more than one resistor in one of the branches, they are not connected in parallel.

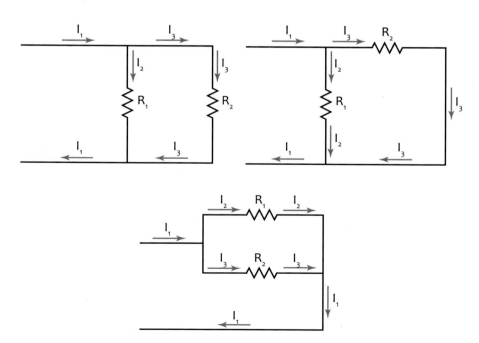

Figure 13-28. Three identical resistor networks showing two resistors connected in parallel.

Notice that in a parallel network the current heading towards the resistors, I_1, will divide at the *junction*, or *node*, in the wires. Some of the current, which is shown as I_2, goes through resistor R_1, and the rest of the current, which is labeled I_3, goes through the other resistor, R_2. The amount of current that will go through each branch depends on the resistance in each branch. Keep thinking about the water analogy. If water is flowing in a pipe and comes to a place where the pipe has two branches the water will divide, some going one way and some the other.

Now let's see what these two basic types of networks look like when they are connected to a battery. The sketches in Figure 13-29 each show circuits with two resistors in series. These two circuits are identical. The sketches in Figure 13-30 each show circuits with two resistors in parallel. As with the series circuits in the previous figure, these two circuits are identical. They may look different, but they are not.

As shown in the series circuit of Figure 13-29, there is only one current and it passes in turn through each of the resistors in the circuit. Referring again to the water circuit, this is analogous to having two filters one after the other in the pipe. The parallel circuit in Figure 13-30 is quite different. In this parallel circuit, at the first junction (or node) the first current I_1 splits into two parts, currents I_2 and I_3. Just like a split or branching in a water pipe, some of the current goes one way and some goes the other way. Downstream of the two resistors the two currents I_2 and I_3 join up again and combine back to the total current they were before the split, namely, I_1.

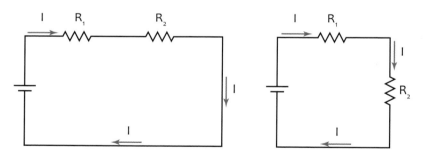

Figure 13-29. Identical DC circuits with two resistors connected in series.

As a further illustration of series and parallel circuits, Figure 13-31 shows each type of connection using a battery and a couple of LEDs. LEDs (light emitting diodes) are small devices that emit light and act like resistors in a DC circuit. The two circuits each use one green LED and one red LED.

Compare the series circuit schematics in Figure 13-29 to the LED series circuit on the left of Figure 13-31. Either of the schematic diagrams could be used to represent the LED circuit when it is wired this way. Notice that the current coming out of the battery (the red wire) must go through the red LED first, then through

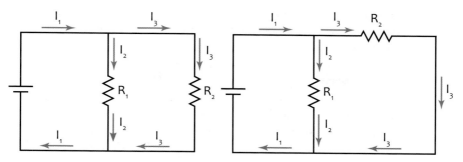

Figure 13-30. Identical DC circuits with two resistors connected in parallel.

the green one, and finally back to the battery through the black wire to complete the circuit.

Now compare the parallel circuit schematics in Figure 13-30 to the LEDs connected in parallel on the right of Figure 13-31. Again, either schematic could be used to represent the LEDs when they are connected together this way. The current exits the battery through the red wire and splits into two parts at the junction of the red wires. Part of the current passes through the green LED, and part passes through the red LED. These two currents come together again at the junction of the black wires and then return to the battery to complete the circuit.

Figure 13-31. Two LEDs connected in a series circuit (left) and a parallel circuit (right).

Why is electricity dangerous?

There are two separate concerns related to the danger of being shocked by electricity. First, all of the signals our bodies use to control heartbeat and respiration are electrical (recall Galvani's discovery of the twitching frog legs). When a person touches a live electrical wire, if the person is standing on the ground the person's body becomes the resistor in a circuit, with the current passing through the person's body to the ground. A current of only 0.010 A or so (10 milliamps) passing through the body like this can fatally disrupt the signals controlling heartbeat and respiration. This is the type of hazard posed by the 120-V and 240-V electrical systems commonly found in homes and commercial buildings.

An electrical system operating at high voltage poses these same hazards, plus more. High currents passing through the body can burn the tissue and damage the victim so badly that revival is impossible. This is why danger signs are posted around high-voltage equipment.

The reason the high voltages from devices like Van de Graaff generators are not harmful is that though they have high voltages, they cannot provide enough current to be harmful. When a student touches the dome of a Van de Graaff generator only a tiny current flows, and that only for an extremely short time. By contrast, an AC power system is *designed* to provide high current to all of the devices that may need it, so touching this high-voltage source will likely be fatal.

Can electricity or lightning hurt a person inside a car?

A bolt of lightning is a very high-voltage, high-current flow of charge. A high current through the body can be fatal, which is why lightning can kill a person standing on the ground. But if a lightning bolt hits a car the current cannot flow to ground because the rubber tires are insulating the car from ground. Moreover, if the car body is metal, the car forms a *Faraday cage*. A Faraday cage is a solid or screened metal enclosure. Because of the way like charges repel each other, electric charge always remains on the *outside* of the cage. So a person inside is safe.

If an accident causes a downed power line to touch a car, it is likely that the people inside will be safe as long as they stay inside. However, anyone who tries to escape while the live wire is still in contact will probably be electrocuted as soon as his foot hit the ground, because he will probably be in contact with both the car body and the ground allowing high current to flow through his body. Best to wait until rescue teams remove the hazard, keeping hands and feet away from metal parts.

Ideas for Your Classroom

As with the wave chapter, there are hundreds of fun activities related to the material in this chapter. Here are just a few.

1. Run a rubber comb through someone's clean hair and watch it pick up small bits of paper. Try rubbing a balloon on the hair and seeing if the balloon will stick to the wall. These effects work better on low-humidity days.

2. A popular experiment for elementary students is to use citrus fruit to light up light bulbs. Instructions are readily available online, but be sure to look for a very specific set of instructions. Not all light bulbs will work.

3. Students can experiment with low-power DC circuits to explore the effects of series and parallel connections. Many kits are available, or one can simply use flashlight batteries and bulbs. An electronics supply shop will have battery and bulb holders to make it easier to connect things together.

4. Older kids love playing with a Van de Graaff generator, if you can acquire one. The Van de Graaff builds up static electricity that can be discharged in many ways for different effects. Standing-up hair is just the start. If a brave person at the end of a daisy-chain of people touches the Van de Graaff, or touches someone who is holding the dome of the Van de Graaff, everyone in the chain will feel his or her muscles twitch. It is a strange but harmless sensation. As with the comb, a Van de Graaff works better on low-humidity days.

5. Enjoy sparking in the dark with Wintergreen Certs breath mints. Crunch them between the molars in a dark room and watch the blue glow! The explanation involves both moving electrons and the absorption/emission of photons discussed in Chapter 8.

NOTE: It is best with students to avoid all projects involving 120-VAC power. Activities using AC electricity are not worth the risk of injury. Stick to projects involving static electricity, or using low-voltage DC power, such as from a flashlight battery.

Goals for Chapter 14

1. Explain what a field is.

2. Describe three major types of fields, the types of objects that cause each one, and the objects or phenomena that are affected by each one.

3. State Ampère's Law.

4. State Faraday's Law of Magnetic Induction.

5. Explain the difference between the theories of gravitational attraction of Einstein and Newton.

6. Apply Ampère's Law and Faraday's Law of Magnetic Induction to given physical situations.

7. Explain the general principles behind the operation of generators and transformers.

About This Chapter

The idea of a field is abstract, and initially difficult for everyone to get a handle on. But magnetic fields from bar magnets are easy to demonstrate and fun to play around with, and playing around with magnetic fields is very helpful for anyone seeking to understand the physics of fields.

Chapter 14
Fields and Magnetism

Types of Fields

In physics the concept of fields is of great importance. Fields also happen to be conceptually difficult to grasp because they are so abstract. So we need to begin this chapter with a two-part definition for fields. Then we will examine three familiar types of fields to see how the definition applies in each case. My definition for a field is as follows:

> First, a *field* is a mathematical abstraction that describes a region in space that will influence specific kinds of matter or radiation. Second, this influence, the result of a field being present, is a force.

Different kinds of fields affect different kinds of things, but the effect is always a force on the thing.

We have heard about fields all our lives. The most familiar is the *gravitational field* around the earth, but *magnetic fields* around magnets and maybe even *electric fields* are also familiar. The gravitational field around the earth is what pulls objects toward the earth's center. The force on an object caused by this field is its weight. One feels the effects of a magnetic field when holding the ends of two magnets near each other. One feels the resulting forces when the magnetic poles attract or repel each other. And you have probably seen the results of the electric field present when static electricity is around. Dry, clean hair that stands up when brushed, synthetic clothes clinging together when removed from the dryer, a balloon that sticks to the wall after being rubbed, the leaves swinging out in the electroscope—these are all evidence of the forces present due to the electric fields caused by static electricity.

The diagrams below help in visualizing what is going on when a field is present. The arrows in these diagrams are called *field lines*, and represent the direction of the force on an object placed in the field, assuming that the object in question is the type of object that could be affected by that type of field.

> Field lines show the direction of the force on an object placed in the field.

The gravitational field caused by an isolated mass is depicted in Figure 14-1. This mass could be a planet or the sun, or actually anything made of atoms. The gravitational field has a spherical shape around a spherical object. Recall that in both Newton's and Einstein's theories

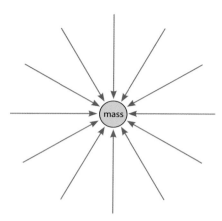

Figure 14-1. Gravitational field around a mass.

of gravity everything with mass causes a gravitational field. But gravity is such a weak force that the force isn't usually noticeable unless the object causing the field is very massive, like the earth, moon, or sun. As far as we know right now, there is only one kind of mass, so there is only one way to draw the gravitational field diagram. (Scientists are now thinking there may be more than one kind of mass. If so, and we confirm it experimentally, that would be yet another fact that changed!)

There is an important difference between the gravitational theories of Einstein and Newton. In Newton's Theory of Universal Gravitation only an object with mass can be affected by the gravitational field that exists around another object with mass. However, you may recall from Chapter 3 that Einstein's general theory of relativity treats gravity as a curvature in "space-time," rather than as a mysterious attraction between objects. As a result, Einstein was able to predict that starlight will bend in its path as it passes near another star such as our sun, even though light does not have mass. As we saw, this prediction was confirmed by Arthur Eddington's photographs during the solar eclipse of 1919. The fact that gravitational fields affect electromagnetic radiation is reflected in the summary table presented below.

Unlike mass, there are two kinds of electric charge. Electric charge is what causes electric fields, depicted in Figure 14-2. In this case, our convention is that the arrows represent the direction of the force on a *positive* "test charge" placed in the field. Since like charges repel, the arrows point away from the positive charge in the diagram on the left. Since opposite charges attract, the arrows point toward the negative charge on the right.

With both gravitational and electric fields, the object causing the field lines to radiate out from it or point in toward it, a particle of mass or charge, can exist by itself. But with the magnetic field, illustrated in Figure 14-3, this is not the case (as far as we know). Magnetic fields are caused by magnets. A magnet always has two poles, which we call north and south. If you cut a magnet in half you won't have a

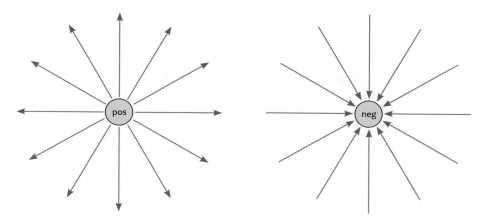

Figure 14-2. Electric fields around two kinds of charge.

north or south pole by itself. You will instead have two magnets, each with north and south poles. Physicists like to express this by saying, "there is no magnetic monopole." The result of this is that the field lines in a magnetic field don't just go off into space. Instead, they start on a north pole and land on a south pole of the same magnet.

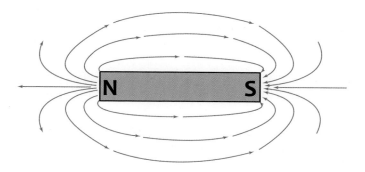

Figure 14-3. Magnetic field around a magnet.

When we consider these three different types of fields it is helpful to think about the kinds of objects that can cause each one and the kinds of things that can be affected by each one. Table 14-1 summarizes this information. This table is not exhaustive, but it covers the basics. (For example, there are some other strange substances affected by magnetism, such as liquid oxygen). The term *ferrous* in the table means "made of iron." This term comes from the Latin word for iron, *ferrum*. This same Latin word gives iron its chemical symbol, Fe.

	Gravitational Field	Electric Field	Magnetic Field
What can cause this type of field?	mass (anything made of atoms or parts of atoms)	unbalanced charge, a changing magnetic field	magnets, current-carrying wires
What can be affected by this type of field?	mass, electromagnetic radiation	charges (anything containing protons or electrons)	magnets, current-carrying wires, ferrous metals

Table 14-1. Causes of fields and what the fields affect.

Laws of Magnetism

There are a number of important magnetic laws commonly studied in physics courses. We will look at two of them. These two laws happen to be intimately related to the operation of the electrical devices that surround us in the modern world, so it is particularly interesting and helpful to know these two laws. They were named after their discoverers, André Ampère and Michael Faraday, whom we met in the previous chapter. We will introduce the two laws in this section, and explore their important applications in later sections.

Ampère's Law is as follows:

> ### Ampère's Law
>
> When current flows in a wire a magnetic field is created around the wire, and the strength of the magnetic field is directly proportional to the current.

An important aspect of this law relates to what happens if the current-carrying wire is wound into a coil. As we will see below, the magnetic field around such a coil of wire is magnified over what it would be with a simple straight wire. In a coil, the magnetic field is proportional not only to the current, but also to the number of loops, or turns (as we say) in the coil.

Before discussing the next law we have to get a grip on a difficult and abstract concept, *magnetic flux*. Recall that graphically we can show the presence of fields in space by drawing field lines indicating the forces that would be present on an object placed in the field. In diagrams of this type, the closer together the field lines are, the stronger the field is. Consider Figure 14-4, which depicts a close-up of the north end of a magnet and the field lines in its vicinity. Near the magnet the

> In a diagram of a magnetic field, the closer the field lines are, the stronger the field is.

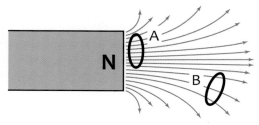

Figure 14-4. Magnetic field lines near the end of a magnet.

field lines are closer together, and as we all know, the magnetic field of a magnet is stronger near the magnet.

Imagine that we place a coil of wire near the end of this magnet at position A and just hold it there. Does it seem reasonable to say that something is passing through this coil of wire? Well, whatever it is that appears to be passing through the coil, our word for it is magnetic flux. In fact, there is nothing physically passing through the coil, and despite the suggestive sound of the word flux, nothing is flowing anywhere. What we do have passing through the coil is part of this mathematically abstract thing called the magnetic field, as indicated by the field lines. Now consider our little coil of wire being at position B instead of A. The difference, as suggested by the figure, is that there is less flux passing through the coil at position B than there is at position A. You can easily imagine that if our little coil of wire were very far away from the magnet there would be essentially no flux passing through it at all, because the magnetic field out there would be so weak.

Now we can state the next law, which is *Faraday's Law of Magnetic Induction*, or Faraday's Law, for short. This law is as follows:

Faraday's Law of Magnetic Induction

If a changing magnetic flux is passing through a coil of wire, an electric current will be induced in the coil.

Recall from our study of static electricity that induction comes from the word induce, which means "force it to happen." Here the magnetic field interacting with this coil of wire is forcing a current to "happen" in the coil. This principle is wonderful—we are able to create electrical current in wires without even touching them or connecting a power supply to them! Because of this principle we can generate electrical power and transport it to our homes and factories. When this became possible it utterly transformed society. As with Ampère's Law, the amount of current induced according to Faraday's Law depends on the number of turns in the coil.

It is critical to notice that current will only be induced in the coil if the amount of flux passing through the coil is *changing*, that is, increasing or decreasing. Holding the coil steady at location A in the figure does nothing, even though a lot of flux is passing through the coil. But if the coil rotates, for example, like a coin spinning on a table top, the flux passing through the coil will be highest when the coil is facing the magnet, and essentially zero when the coil is on edge to the magnet (because the flux will then be passing by the coil without passing through it). Anything else you can imagine that would cause the amount of flux passing through the coil to increase or decrease will also induce current in the coil, but only as long as the change in flux is happening. These possibilities would include moving the coil back and forth, closer to and farther away from the magnet, moving the magnet away from the coil, or even somehow making the diameter of the coil increase or decrease.

The Right-Hand Rule

Our convention for determining the direction of the magnetic field lines around a current-carrying wire is called the *right-hand rule*, illustrated in Figure 14-5. According to the rule, if you grasp the wire with your right hand, with your thumb pointing in the direction of the flowing current, the direction your fingers point as they wrap around the wire is the circular direction the magnetic field lines point around the wire.

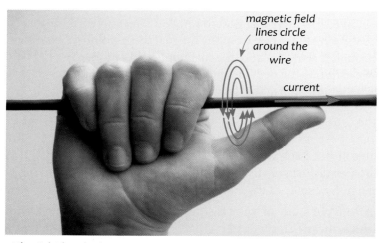

Figure 14-5. The right-hand rule.

An interesting thing happens if we form this wire into a coil as shown in Figure 14-6. If we apply the right-hand rule to the wire at various places we can establish the direction of the magnetic field at different places, as shown in the figure. Now consider two different regions relative to this coil of wire, the region outside the coil (where we are), and the cylindrical region down through the center of the coil (where the green rod in the figure is). Notice, from the little circular arrows surrounding the wire that outside the coil (where we are), both in front of it and

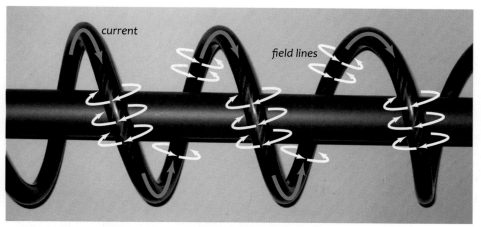

Figure 14-6. *Magnetic field lines around a wire wrapped into coils.*

behind it, the arrowheads point to the left. Inside the coil (where the green rod is), the arrowheads always point to the right.

To get another view of this, imagine that we slice through the coil, cutting through every loop simultaneously. Then imagine we throw away one half and look at the cut ends of the wires in the other half. In Figure 14-7 the black dots represent the cut ends of the wires. Shaded green in the background are shown the remaining pieces of the coils connecting the black dots. (In this diagram I did not include the rod down the center of the coil.) Now examine the shape of the magnetic field going around and through this coil. Down through the center of the loops the field points to the right. The field lines emerge from the coils on the right end and circle around the outside of the coils, heading back to the left, and enter back into the coils from the left end. For the purposes of this sketch the magnetic field lines have been greatly simplified in order to show the primary routes of flux through the coil and back around to the other end. In actuality, if the coils were spaced apart the way they are in the sketch a lot of the flux that could be marching together down the center of the coil would be pointlessly circulating around the individual coil wires.

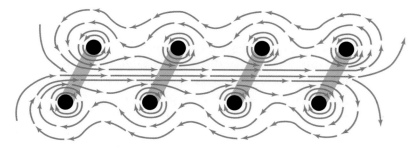

Figure 14-7. *Cross-section of the coils showing the magnetic field lines.*

Electromagnets

What we have done with this coiled wire geometry is create an electric magnet, or *electromagnet*. This electromagnet has its north pole on the right end of the coil where the field lines come out, and its south pole on the left end where the field lines enter the coil. The tighter the coils are wound together, the better the electromagnet will be because no flux can leak out between the coils and circulate around the coil wires. In a tightly wound coil almost all of the flux will stay inside the coil as it travels straight down the center. (Remember, the word "travels" is a metaphor here; nothing is really moving or flowing anywhere, except the current in the wires.) This is shown in Figure 14-8, which depicts another cutaway view, this time of a long, tightly wound coil. A long, tightly wound coil of wire like this is called a *solenoid*. If a solenoid is wound onto a steel rod, called a *core*, the strength of the magnetic flux is increased considerably. So a solenoid is a powerful electromagnetic that can be easily switched on and off.

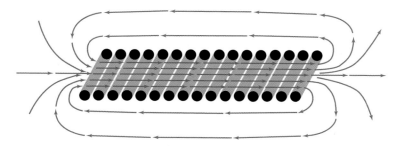

Figure 14-8. Cross-section of a solenoid showing the magnetic field lines.

By placing small moving parts made of ferrous metal near the end of the solenoid, the parts can be made magnetically to move back and forth as the current to the solenoid is turned on and off. Thus, solenoids are devices that can take an on or off electric current and use it to cause mechanical back and forth motion. It turns out that solenoids are hugely practical and hundreds of devices have been invented that use solenoids.

A common example of a solenoid consumers use every day is in the starting circuit in automobiles. When the driver turns the key to start the car, an electric motor begins spinning that turns the car engine just long enough for the ignition system to start up and begin running the car. The starter motor has a gear on it to turn the engine, but once the engine starts the starter motor with its little starter gear needs to get out of the way of the running engine or it will be torn to shreds. This is neatly managed by a solenoid that quickly moves the starter gear in one direction to engage the engine while starting the car and moves in the opposite direction when the key is released to get the starter gear out of the way of the car engine that is now running on its own.

Solenoids are especially useful in the world of industrial electric circuits, because they can function as electrically operated switches in many different applications. These switches are called *relays*, and are used extensively in industrial control systems. A small control relay is shown in Figure 14-9. In the close-up on the right I have indicated the solenoid coil (covered in white tape), the solenoid core, the moving arm that is pulled back and forth as the coil is energized or de-energized, and the electrical contacts at the bottom of the moving arm that are opened and closed as the relay switches on and off.

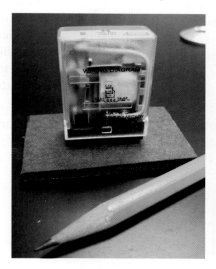 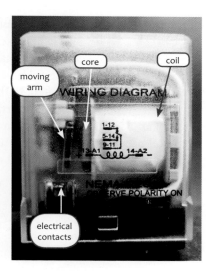

Figure 14-9. A relay (left) and a close-up showing the major internal parts.

A less elegant but still important use for electromagnets is picking up large piles of scrap steel. Used this way, a large electromagnet is attached to the boom of a crane. The operator switches on the magnet and drops it on top of a pile of scrap steel. The crane operator can then pick up several hundred pounds of steel, move it into or out of a train car or some other container, and then switch off the current to the coil when he is ready to drop the steel in the new location. Electromagnets like this are often seen at steel mills that reprocess scrap steel, an important process that keeps waste and costs down by reusing steel that would otherwise be wasted.

Generators and Transformers

Solenoids are gadgets that a lot of people don't even know about. Electric *generators*, by contrast, are devices that everyone knows about. Everyone knows that power stations are located all over the country generating electrical power to run the electrical devices in houses, factories, offices, and industrial plants. Faraday's Law of Magnetic Induction is the simple principle that allows an electric generator to generate hundreds of megawatts of electrical power.

Before we get into how generators work, take note that electric *motors* are basically generators running backwards. Whereas a generator uses mechanical power from an engine to make electric current, a motor uses electric current to run a mechanical machine. Since these two devices are so similar, they are basically the same on the inside. As we look at how a generator works, keep in mind that an electric motor is essentially the same thing.

Consider Figure 14-10, which depicts the poles of a C-shaped magnet with a coil of wire in between them. There is a vertical axle attached to the coil of wire which allows it to rotate. This axle must be connected to an engine that can make the coil rotate. Because the north and south poles of the magnet are close together and facing each other on each side of the coil, there will

> Electric motors are basically generators running backwards.

be a strong magnetic flux passing from the north pole to the south pole, right through the space where the coil is mounted. In the figure the field lines are shown pointing from the north end of the magnet to the south end of the magnet. Faraday's Law of Induction says that when the magnetic flux passing through a coil of wire is changing, a current will be induced in the coil of wire. Also, as mentioned above, the amount of current will depend on the number of

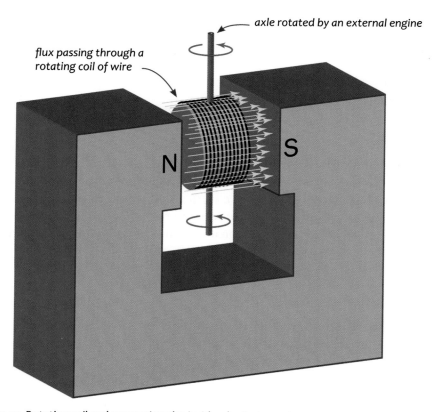

Figure 14-10. Rotating coil and magnetic poles inside a basic generator.

turns of wire there are in the coil, so the coil drawn in the figure has lots of turns. The coil's position in the figure is the position where a maximum amount of flux will pass through the coil. As the coil rotates from here, the flux passing through it will decrease from this maximum value. The flux will fall to zero, rise to maximum again but in the reverse direction (because the coil has rotated half way around), fall to zero again, and so on.

Figure 14-11 is a sketch of what this rising and falling flux looks like. This curve has what we call a "sinusoidal" shape, and this sinusoidal variation of the flux through the coil produces a sinusoidally shaped current in the coil, which is exactly the shape of the voltage and current curves for the AC power distribution system powering our homes. The curves look exactly like the wave curves we explored in Chapter 11 (sine waves), and they can be examined with the same mathematics. In America the frequency of the AC curves is 60 Hz. To produce this frequency in the oscillating flux, the engine must turn the coil so that it completes 60 rotations per second. In Europe the frequency is 50 Hz.

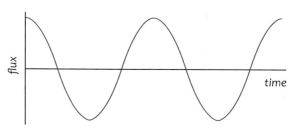

Figure 14-11. Flux through the rotating coil vs. time.

In the generator sketch in Figure 14-10 the magnet is drawn as if it were an ordinary permanent magnet. In practice, this would work for a tiny demonstration generator, but using a permanent magnet large enough for an industrial generator would be very impractical. Instead, large coils of wire operating as electromagnets according to Ampère's Law can be used to create the magnetic field for the generator. These coils are called *field coils*. Part of the generator's own output is used to power these coils. Figure 14-12 is a photograph of a device that is designed in just this way. The photo is actually of a small motor, not of a generator, but as noted earlier, a motor is just a generator running backwards. Both devices depend on coils of wire to produce the stationary magnetic flux, and have rotating coils on a shaft inside the magnetic field. The entire winding system that is fixed in place (the field coils) is called the *stator*. All of the rotating coils and the frames they

> In an industrial generator large electromagnets called *field coils* are used to provide the magnetic field surrounding the rotor.

are wound on is called the *rotor*. In the photograph you can see that on the rotor there is more than just a single coil of wire. In fact, the motor shown has six coils, which is pretty common for a small motor like this one.

Another device that is ubiquitous in our power distribution system is the *transformer*. Transformers make use of both Ampère's Law and Faraday's Law.

Before describing these devices we need to review the background that makes them necessary.

In Chapter 12 we saw that for ordinary electric circuit calculations we could neglect the voltage drops in the wires. But in a large electrical distribution system the miles-long wires will have some significant resistance, and thus there will be a voltage drop in the wires. This voltage drop will mean that power is lost from the system due to heating in the wires caused by the wires' own resistance.

A typical large generator at a power station puts out 100 MW or more of power at a voltage of around 700 or 800 volts. The power station might be located 10 miles from a city and the electricity has to flow through wires to

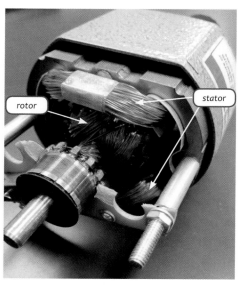

Figure 14-12. Inside look at a small motor showing the stator and rotor coils.

get there. The resistance of such wire might be around 0.05 Ω per 1,000 ft. Without getting tedious with the math, the fact is that even with resistance in the wiring this low we will lose over 2/3 of our total power just heating up the wires as the current flows in the wires to get to the city! Obviously, this is not a practical way to transport electricity.

The problem is the current in the wires. Power losses are proportional to the *square* of the current, and if we have to transport 100 MW at a voltage of 700 V we are going to have high currents. But recall the equation for electrical power, $P = VI$. For a fixed amount of power, if we were able to increase the voltage we would decrease the current by the same factor. If, for example, we increased the voltage by a factor of 300, the current would be reduced by a factor of 300 and the power losses in the wires would drop from 65% of the total power to less than 1%.

This is where Ampère's and Faraday's Laws come in with the nifty invention called the transformer. A transformer is a very simple device that uses these laws to raise or lower an AC voltage while simultaneously lowering or raising the current. In Figure 14-13 we have a square ring, called the core, made of steel plates. Coils are wound around the core on two sides. The coil where the electric current comes in is called the primary coil. Electric current leaves the transformer at the secondary coil. Here is the beautiful part: The ratio of the primary voltage to the secondary voltage will be the same as the "turns ratio" of the transformer. The turns ratio is simply the ratio of the number of turns in the primary coil to the number of turns in the secondary coil. Whatever the ratio is of the number of turns in the secondary to the number of turns in the primary, the voltage will be changed by

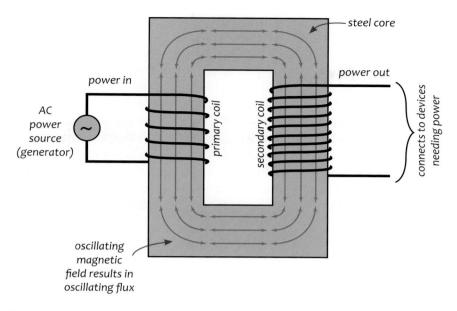

Figure 14-13. Primary and secondary coils in a transformer.

this same ratio. If the voltage goes up, the current will go down, and vice versa. So we can use transformers to boost the voltage way up at the power station, which drops the current way down, since the product stays the same. Then in the city where the electricity will be used, we can use transformers again to drop the voltage down to practical levels for people to use in their homes, offices and factories.

Now let's take a look at the magnetic principles that make transformers work. Referring again to Figure 14-13, we apply an AC voltage to the primary coil. An AC voltage is sinusoidal, just like the sinusoidal flux we saw in Figure 14-11. A sinusoidal voltage like this will cause a sinusoidal AC current to flow in the primary coil. According to Ampère's Law, a magnetic flux will be created inside the coil, just as with the solenoids we studied before. Here, however, the flux is not steady. Since the current in the primary coil is sinusoidal, the flux in the transformer core will also be sinusoidal, reaching a peak, decreasing to zero, reversing direction to a negative peak, back to zero, over and over. The flux in the core will be oscillating at the same frequency as the current in the primary coil.

Now, magnetic flux "flows" very easily inside of iron or steel, like our transformer core. So the flux created by the primary coil goes around the core, passing through the secondary coil. In the figure there are lines in the transformer core representing the magnetic field in the core. The arrows on the field lines indicate that the field is oscillating back and forth, clockwise then counter-clockwise, changing direction 60 times per second. So inside the transformer core the flux is continuously changing. This means that in the secondary coil Faraday's Law of Magnetic Induction kicks in. Since a changing magnetic flux is passing through the secondary coil, a current will be induced in the secondary coil. This secondary current, which is also sinusoidal, flows out of the transformer to whatever electrical devices are connected to it.

Notice what would happen if we connected a battery (DC voltage) instead of an AC voltage source to the transformer primary. Ampère's Law would still operate in the primary coil, and magnetic flux would still be created in the primary coil and in the transformer core. But the flux would be static or steady, that is, not changing. Thus, no current would be induced in the secondary coil at all, because Faraday's Law requires the flux through a coil to be changing to induce current in the coil. As a result, transformers do not work with DC currents and voltages.

Most people have no idea how many transformers they use and depend on every day. There is a transformer at every house that lowers the power distribution voltage from around 10,000 V down to the 240 V that goes to the house. In neighborhoods where the power lines are underground, these house transformers are often inside green metal boxes in the yards of the houses. If the power lines are above ground on poles, the house transformers are on the power poles in gray canisters. An apartment or office building will have a large transformer outside serving the entire building.

Except for devices that do not recharge their batteries, every piece of electronic equipment we use has a transformer in it somewhere. The transformer first drops the voltage down to the 1-10 V range typically used by electronic circuits, and then another device, called a rectifier, converts the AC from the transformer to the DC needed by the electronics. For portable devices such as mobile phones or laptop computers, the devices run on DC batteries. The transformers and rectifiers are in the chargers that recharge the batteries.

> Except devices that do not recharge the batteries, every piece of electronic equipment has a transformer in it somewhere.

Figure 14-14 shows a couple of small transformers of the type used in electronic devices such as a stereo system or computer. In the close-up on the right, the windings of the two coils in the transformer are visible; you can see the windings of copper wire under each of the white plastic plates. Wires are attached to the

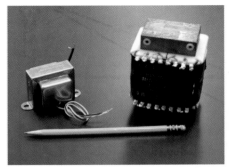

Figure 14-14. Small transformers.

coils in various places and connected to the silver-colored terminals, and from there they would be connected to the rest of the electronics.

Ideas for Your Classroom

1. Play with magnets, and experiment with different materials to see which ones are affected by magnetic fields and which are not. Disk magnets with holes in the center may be placed on an aluminum rod for some fascinating fun that kids will want to play with over and over (see flinnsci.com, cat. no. AP6059).

2. Let students play with different types and strengths of magnets, such a bar magnets and horseshoe magnets.

3. Wrap 30 or 40 turns of insulated wire around a large steel nail. Connect the ends of the wire to a battery and you have an electromagnet that should be strong enough to pick up paper clips and deflect a compass needle. The electromagnet will not pick up a penny and it will not stick to an aluminum window frame, because these are not ferrous metals.

4. Talk about the kinds of things that will be affected by the three commonly known kinds of fields.

5. Build a small AC generator from a kit, and use it to illuminate an LED as the rotor turns (see flinnsci.com, cat. no. AP7276).

6. See how many devices the students can list that use electric motors.

7. Take apart the motor from an electric fan and locate the stator and rotor coils.

8. Observe that Apple uses magnets in many places in their products, including the nifty folding cover for an iPad (both to hold it on and keep it closed), the power cord for recharging a MacBook, and for holding the screen closed when the MacBook is closed.

Goals for Chapter 15

1. Explain the difference between a real image and a virtual image.

2. Define the focal length of a lens.

3. Explain why a real image formed by a biconvex lens will be inverted.

4. Describe, in general, the images formed by convex and concave mirrors and convex and concave lenses.

5. Describe how biconvex lenses are used singly or in combination to form images in common optical devices.

About This Chapter

This chapter has been included because it is common for kids to encounter lenses and mirrors in elementary school science studies. However, geometric optics involves a lot of mathematics, including both geometry and trigonometry. Our first goal in this chapter will be to examine basic optical principles without wading too deeply into mathematical waters. Our second goal will be to look at the optics behind several of the common optical systems we encounter every day.

Chapter 15
Geometric Optics

Ray Optics

In previous chapters we have looked at light as particles called photons (Chapter 8) and as waves of electromagnetic radiation (Chapter 11). But many familiar phenomena lend themselves to the simpler analysis of treating light as rays. The study of geometric optics involves developing the properties of images formed by lenses and mirrors by treating light as thin rays, similar to the laser beam from a laser pointer. This type of analysis is called *ray optics*, or *geometric optics*. The goal is not in understanding the nature of light itself, but in discovering general principles pertaining to the behavior of light as it reflects and refracts in optical systems such as telescopes, microscopes, cameras, and other systems. A ray is simply an arrow pointing in the direction the light is traveling.

Recall from Chapter 11 that when light reflects it obeys the law of reflection. This law states that the angle of incidence equals the angle of reflection. The angles are measured between the light ray (incident or reflected) and an imaginary line perpendicular to the reflecting surface.

Recall also from Chapter 11 that when a ray of light strikes the surface of a transparent material at an angle, the ray that enters the material refracts, that is, it slows down and changes direction at the surface of the new material.

Human Image Perception

We are able to see objects because ambient light reflects off the objects and into our eyes. Rays of light reflecting off an irregularly-shaped object will always diverge, and our visual perception is such that we subconsciously calculate where the rays appear to be diverging *from*. If we trace these diverging rays backward to their source, that's where they come together, or converge. Wherever that is (where the light rays appear to originate) is where our brain places the image we are perceiving, as indicated in Figure 15-1. This is the case whether the object is actually at that location or not.

The conventions and methods of ray optics make use of this fact, that we perceive images to be located where diverging rays of light appear to converge, when following them backwards. In our analysis we refer to objects separately from the images of the objects. And to locate where the image of an object will be, we just follow the rays.

Figure 15-1. Diverging rays will be perceived to originate at the point where they appear to converge.

Flat Mirrors and Ray Diagrams

Figure 15-2 depicts an object and the image it will form in a flat mirror. Rays of light will generally emanate from the object in all directions, but three rays are shown in the figure to give the idea. At the location of the observer the rays are seen to be diverging. But if we trace the rays back, as with the dashed lines in the figure, the place where they appear to converge is the location of the image we see. The distance of the object from the mirror (or lens) has been designated as d_o, and the distance of the image from the mirror as d_i.

In Figure 15-3 we have a *ray diagram* representing the same situation. In a ray diagram it is customary to depict the object and image as vertical arrows located on the center line of the optical component (the mirror or lens). This center line is called the *optical axis*. This graphical arrangement allows us to see the relative sizes

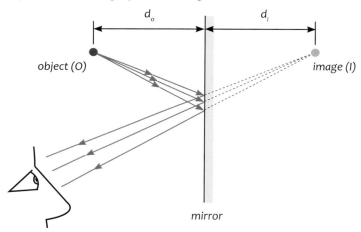

Figure 15-2. Image formation in a flat mirror.

of the object and image, which indicates what, if any, magnification is involved. We can also see if the image is inverted or not relative to the object. The height of the object is y_o, and the height of the image is y_i.

There are a few more features of the ray diagram that we will use repeatedly. Notice that two rays from the object are shown. One of them is parallel to the optical axis. The other ray points toward the center of the optical component,

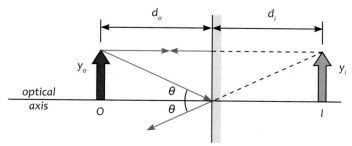

Figure 15-3. *Geometry of object and image in the case of a flat mirror.*

which is where the optical axis passes through. (For a flat mirror, there really isn't a center, but there is for curved mirrors and lenses, so we are describing the general situation here.) When this second ray hits the mirror, it obeys the law of reflection, so the angle this ray and its reflection make with the optical axis are labeled θ (the Greek letter "theta," often used to represent angles in physics). Tracing the reflected ray back and seeing where it would intersect with the horizontal reflection of the horizontal ray allows us to locate the image. From the geometry of the triangles in this diagram, we can say all of the following:

- The image is the same size as the object ($y_i = y_o$).

- The image is upright (not inverted).

- The image is located on the other side of the mirror, the same distance from the mirror as the object ($d_i = d_o$).

- The image is virtual.

    We will explain the last item in the next section.

Real and Virtual Images

Two situations can arise when discussing an optical image. The first is when the light rays forming the image actually pass through the location where the image is. If this is the case, the image is said to be a *real image*. Real images can be seen, and can be projected onto a screen.

The other situation is that the light rays forming the image do not actually pass through the image location. In this case we have a *virtual image*. Virtual images can be seen (by eye and camera), but they cannot be projected onto a screen. This is for the simple reason that the screen would have to be placed at the image location, but the light rays don't actually go there. Referring again to Figure 15-3, we can see that since the light rays from the object reflect off the mirror, they do not pass through the image location. Thus, the image is a virtual image.

An important clarifying point to make here is that to see an image your eye does not have to be at the image location. (In fact, it can't be; see

> A virtual image is formed when the light rays do not actually pass through the image location.

p. 266.) Your eye (or a camera lens) only has to be in the path of the light rays. If the light rays can hit your eye, the image you see will appear to be of a certain size and at a particular location. The size and location can be determined from the ray diagram. Your eyes (or a camera) can see virtual images just as well as real images.

> To see an image one's eye does not have to be at the image location. The eye only has to be positioned so the light rays forming the image will hit it.

Concave and Convex Optics

Many common optical devices such as lenses and mirrors have surfaces that are either flat or spherically shaped. Flat surfaces are called *planar* surfaces. A spherical surface that bulges out into the air is a *convex* surface. A spherical surface that is cupped so it could hold water ("caved in") is a *concave* surface. Lenses that are convex on both sides (the most common type) are called *biconvex* lenses. Examples of several lens configurations are depicted in Figure 15-4.

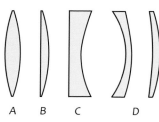

Figure 15-4. Various lenses: A) biconvex, B) plano-convex, C) plano-concave, and D) meniscus lenses.

When light rays traveling parallel to the optical axis of a spherical mirror or lens strike the surface of the optical component they are reflected or refracted to or away from a point on the optical axis called the *focal point*. The location of the focal point in the case of concave and convex mirrors is shown in Figures 15-5 and 15-6. The distance from the focal point to the surface of a mirror or to the center of a lens is called the *focal length*, and is equal to half of the radius of curvature (denoted as *f* in the figures).

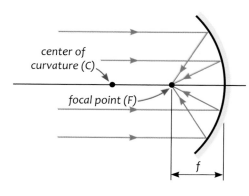

Figure 15-5. Focal point for a concave mirror.

Just as parallel rays striking a spherical surface will be directed to the focal point, rays emanating from a point source of light at the focal point will become parallel after hitting a spherical mirror or lens. For a concave mirror, simply look again at Figure 15-5 and imagine a tiny light source at the focal point. The light rays will emerge in parallel lines from the mirror, just as in the figure with the arrows pointing the opposite direction. The same thing works for lenses, illustrated by the biconvex lens in Figure 15-7.

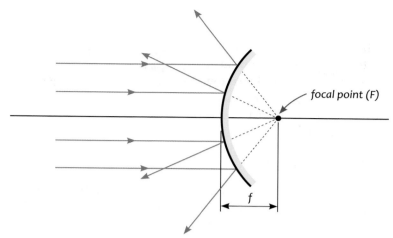

Figure 15-6. Focal point for a convex mirror.

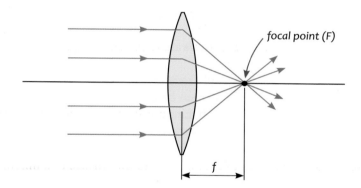

Figure 15-7. Parallel rays passing through a biconvex lens and converging to the focal point.

The focal length is the most important parameter used in the selection of optical components, and we will use it to help describe the behavior of the mirrors and lenses in the balance of this chapter.

Notes on Approximations

There are several important approximations that are widely used in the study of geometric optics. First, the statement above about parallel rays being reflected toward the focal point is only *approximately* correct for spherical mirrors and lenses. It is exactly correct for other shapes, such as concave parabolic mirrors. But spherical shapes are far easier and less expensive to manufacture than parabolic or hyperbolic shapes, so most common optical components are spherical. For optical components with a diameter that is small relative to its radius of curvature, the spherical approximation is very good. Deficiencies in lens or mirror performance due to the approximation inherent in spherical components are called *spherical aberrations*.

For the second approximation, look closely again at figure 15-7 and you will see the rays I've drawn bending in the *center* of the lens. They don't actually do this, of course. Refraction will occur at both of the surfaces, once as the rays pass from air into the glass of the lens, and again as the rays pass from the glass back into the air. However, it is customary in geometric optics to use the so-called *thin lens approximation*, in which all of the refraction is assumed to occur at a single place in the center of the lens. This approximation simplifies the analysis (and figures) a lot and gives very good results for most cases.

And while we are on the subject of approximations, we might as well mention one more. The equations we present in the following sections for lenses and mirrors depend on the assumption that the angles the light rays make with the optical axis are small angles. With small diameter, long focal length lenses this approximation works quite well, and use of this approximation is customary in geometric optics (even though the angles may not look that small in the ray diagrams).

We are now ready to look at the relationships between objects and their images for concave and convex mirrors and lenses.

Spherical Mirrors

We will first consider the image formed by a concave mirror, illustrated by the ray diagrams in Figures 15-8 and 15-9. Looking first at Figure 15-8, three rays are shown originating at the top of the object. As alluded to previously, light rays will of course be emanating from all over the object, in all directions. But with the three rays shown we can locate the top of the image, and thus the location and orientation of the image.

The ray heading toward the center of the lens' curvature, *C*, will reflect straight back because the lens is spherical. This ray is basically traversing the diameter of a circle, hitting the mirror's surface at a right angle, and bouncing right back through the center again. The ray heading toward the focal point, *F*, will reflect parallel to the optical axis, as we saw previously. The ray initially parallel to the optical axis will reflect toward the focal point. All three of these rays will intersect at the location of the top of the image. With the image located, we can see that it is smaller than the object and inverted. If you were to stand in front of this mirror and look at your reflection (your image), this is what you would actually see—a

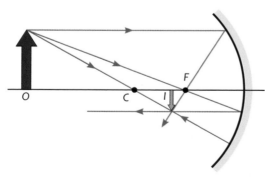

Figure 15-8. Ray diagram for a concave mirror, with the object relatively far away.

smaller, inverted image of yourself. The image also happens to be a real image, because the rays forming the image actually go through it.

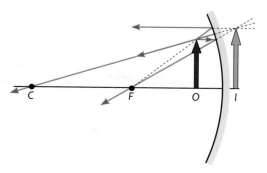

Figure 15-9 shows the same mirror, but with the object close to the mirror, to the right of the focal point. The same three rays are drawn: one in-line with the center, which reflects off the mirror and goes through the center, one in-line with the focal point that reflects parallel to the optical axis, and one parallel to the axis that reflects toward the focal point.

Figure 15-9. Ray diagram for a concave mirror, with the object close to the mirror.

Here the intersection point, shown by the dashed lines, lies to the right of the mirror. Since none of the rays actually pass through this point, this is a virtual image. The image is also upright. And since it is larger than the object, the image is *magnified*.

This arrangement is exactly what is used in those magnifying mirrors people use for applying cosmetics. The mirror has only a very slight curvature, so the center of the mirror is many feet behind the viewer. The person looking in the mirror is quite close, much closer than the focal point. The result is an image that is larger than life and (fortunately) upright.

The convex mirror is shown in Figure 15-10. Again, the same three rays are shown originating at the top of the object: one in-line with the center that reflects off the mirror and bounces straight back, one in-line with the focal point that reflects parallel to the optical axis, and one parallel to the axis that reflects in-line with the focal point. Extending these rays with dashed lines beyond the reflecting

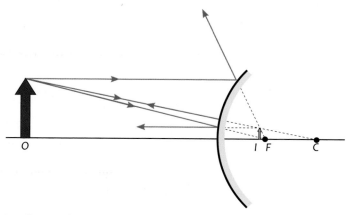

Figure 15-10. Ray diagram for a convex mirror.

> **What's up with the passenger-side mirror on cars, the ones that say "Objects are closer than they appear"?**
>
> The passenger-side mirror is a convex mirror. In Figure 15-10 we see that the light rays from the object reflect in a wide pattern. The same works in reverse to gather light from a wide-angle field of objects and reflect them so the driver can see them. So the convex mirror gives a wide field of view, but as the figure shows, the image is reduced in size, which makes it look farther away. Thus, the warning.

surface we find their intersection point, which is the top of the image. The image is upright, smaller than the object (*minified*), and virtual.

Convex mirrors are frequently seen in parking facilities and retail shops. Images in convex mirrors look small, but the mirror affords a wide-angle view useful for helping to see what's around the corner.

The Mirror Equation

We will not dwell at any length on the mathematics of images for mirrors and lenses. But for those who may be interested, we will look briefly at the basic equations. Recall that the distances from the object and image to the mirror surface are designated d_o and d_i, respectively. The only other parameter involved is focal length, f, which depends on the radius of the mirror's curvature.

Using the approximation referred to previously—that the ray angles relative to the optical axis are small—it can be shown that the following mirror equation describes the location of the image in a spherical mirror:

$$\frac{1}{d_o} + \frac{1}{d_i} = \frac{1}{f}$$

This equation requires a convention for the algebraic signs used on the values for d_i, and f. For real images d_i is positive, and for virtual images d_i is negative. The value of f is positive when the focal point and center are in front of the mirror (concave). The value of f is negative when the focal point and center are behind the mirror (convex).

The magnification of a mirror, M, is given by

$$M = -\frac{d_i}{d_o}$$

This equation says that the ratio of image and object *distances* is the same as the ratio of image and object *sizes*. The sign convention for M is that if M is positive the image is upright.

Example Problem

A convex mirror with a focal length of 12 inches is used to monitor the aisles in a grocery store. If a person 65 inches tall stands 10 feet (120 inches) from this mirror, what kind of image will be produced?

We must first solve the mirror equation to find the image distance, d_i. This involves a good bit of algebra:

$$\frac{1}{d_o} + \frac{1}{d_i} = \frac{1}{f}$$

$$\frac{d_o d_i}{d_o} + \frac{d_o d_i}{d_i} = \frac{d_o d_i}{f}$$

$$d_i + d_o = d_i \cdot \frac{d_o}{f}$$

$$d_i - d_i \cdot \frac{d_o}{f} = -d_o$$

$$d_i \left(1 - \frac{d_o}{f} \right) = -d_o$$

$$d_i = \frac{-d_o}{1 - \frac{d_o}{f}} = \frac{d_o}{\frac{d_o}{f} - 1}$$

Inserting values (with a negative focal length for a convex mirror), we find the image distance to be

$$d_i = \frac{d_o}{\frac{d_o}{f} - 1} = \frac{120 \text{ in}}{\frac{120 \text{ in}}{-12 \text{ in}} - 1} = \frac{120 \text{ in}}{-11} = -10.9 \text{ in}$$

This negative distance indicates the image is virtual. The magnification is

$$M = -\frac{d_i}{d_o} = -\frac{(-10.9)}{120} = 0.091$$

The positive magnification indicates the image is upright. The size of the image is just under 1/10 the size of the object. The actual value is obtained by multiplying the object height by the magnification, or 65 in·0.091 = 5.9 in.

Light Through a Lens

The analysis of lenses will go quickly now that we have all the basic concepts down from our study of mirrors. We will begin by looking at the biconvex lens depicted in back in Figure 15-7. Because parallel rays converge at the focal point after passing through a biconvex lens, this lens is called a *converging lens*. The lens in a basic magnifying glass is a simple biconvex lens, as is the objective lens in a microscope.

Figure 15-11 depicts a biconvex lens with an object in front of it. Since light passes through the lens we identify the focal point on both sides of the lens. Again, for rays parallel to the optical axis, the focal point is the place where they converge after passing through the lens. Three rays originating from the top of the object are drawn in the figure to help us locate the image. One ray is parallel to the optical axis. As with the reflections in spherical mirrors, this ray will refract and head toward the focal point of the lens. A second ray is drawn heading straight for the lens' center, and which passes straight through. The third ray heads toward the focal point on the object side of the lens. When this ray hits the lens it will refract and continue parallel to the optical axis.

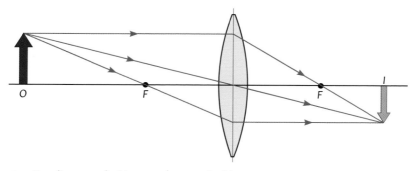

Figure 15-11. Ray diagram of a biconvex (converging) lens.

Now let's consider this question: How does this ray diagram of the biconvex lens help us understand how lenses work when combined with an observer? In considering this question, consider the two observer viewing positions shown in Figure 15-12. In the upper part of the figure, the observer position is between the lens and the image position. Here the rays approaching the observer's eye are not diverging from a common point as they are in the lower part of the figure. But these three rays are all originating from the same point, namely, the top of the object of the other side of the lens. This situation makes the object appear *out of focus*. When rays that should be arriving at the eye from the same point appear to be coming from different points, the object will appear out of focus.

In the lower part of the figure, the observer is farther away from the lens than the image location. Notice that now it doesn't matter how far the observer is away from the lens. At any position to the right of the image, the rays arriving at the eye are all emerging from the same point, so the observer will see a focused image at any location.

The image formed is real and inverted. The size and location of the image depends on the focal length of the lens and the distance of the object from the lens. We will briefly look at the mathematics of this in the next section.

Next consider the ray diagram of a biconcave lens, depicted in Figure 15-13. This lens is called a *diverging lens*, because rays parallel to the optical axis will be refracted away from the axis. This is the case with the upper ray in the figure. Again, to help us locate the image we follow three specific rays from the

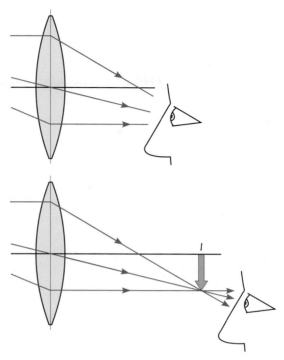

Figure 15-12. Seeing a focused image requires being farther away from the lens than the image distance.

top of the object. The first ray is parallel to the optical axis, and is refracted to be in-line with the focal point. The second ray is directed at the focus on the other side of the lens, and will be refracted to be parallel to the optical axis. The third one goes straight through the center of the lens and is unaffected.

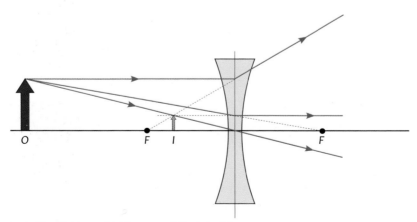

Figure 15-13. Ray diagram of a biconcave (diverging) lens.

As with all the optics we have seen so far, these three rays will intersect at the top of the image. The image is virtual and upright.

Once again let's consider what this diagram tells us about how the lens will behave with an observer. As shown in Figure 15-14, no matter where the observer is, the rays coming through the lens all appear to be originating from the top of the image. This means the image will be in focus no matter where the observer is.

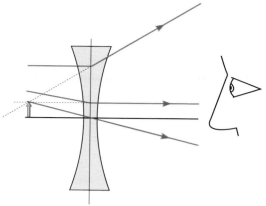

Figure 15-14. Any viewing position results in a focused image, because the rays always appear to originate at the top of the image.

Single-Lens Applications

We will now look at the ray diagrams for several common single-lens applications. We will begin with a brief look at the eye. The following four applications describes how a single biconvex lens works with the object in four distinct locations, from far to near.

THE EYE

Refraction of light rays entering the eye occurs both at the cornea and in the lens. Together they act like a biconvex lens with a focal length of 15.6 mm in front of the eye, and 24.3 mm inside the eye. As shown in the upper part of Figure 15-15, the rays from objects viewed at a distance enter the eye essential parallel to the optical axis and are focused on the retina at the back of the eye. When viewing distant objects like this the lens is relaxed. As you would expect from our discussion of the biconvex lens, the image on the retina is inverted. (But don't worry—your brain is built to correct for that!)

To view near objects, as in the lower part of the figure, the muscles at the edges of the lens cause the lens to change shape in order to direct the light rays to a point at the retina. This ac- tion of the lens, referred to as

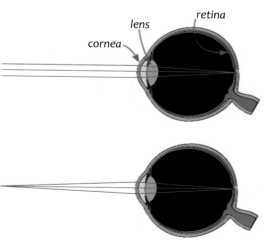

Figure 15-15. The eye focusing light on the retina from a distant spot (top) and a near spot (bottom).

accommodation, changes the location of the focal point. The farthest point on which the eye can focus is called the far point, and the nearest point on which the eye can focus is called the near point. With age the lens becomes less flexible and cannot provide the accommodation necessary to focus on objects outside of a narrower range of distances. This is where corrective lenses (glasses or contacts) come in.

THE CAMERA

Objects far away from a lens, as shown in Figure 15-16, will produce a minified, inverted image. This is the arrangement used by a basic camera, and the ray diagram is the one shown back in Figure 15-11. The image location is at the film or CCD (charge-coupled device) sensor where the image is to be recorded. To focus the camera so that the image is at the film or CCD sensor, the lens is moved in or out by adjusting the camera focus. This changes both the

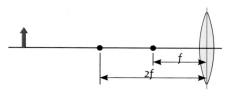

Figure 15-16. The camera records small images of large objects, requiring the object to be much farther away than 2f from the lens.

object and image distances until the image is focused at the proper location.

THE PHOTOCOPIER

The job of a photocopier is to make a life-sized copy. The paper placed on the machine is the object, and the paper the copy is being made on is where the image must fall. To make a life-sized copy the object and the image must be the same height. This will happen when both the object and the image are a distance 2f from the lens, as shown in Figure 15-17. This is the symmetry point for a biconvex lens, where the object and the image are the same size. The ray diagram is similar to Figure 15-11, but with the object and image each at a distance 2f from the lens.

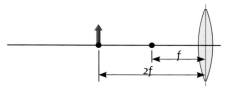

Figure 15-17. The photocopier records life-sized images of objects, requiring the object to be a distance 2f from the lens.

THE PROJECTOR

If the object distance is in between 2f and f (Figure 15-18), the inverted image will be larger than the object. This is how a projector works, and the

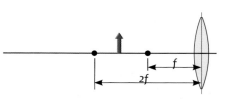

Figure 15-18. A projector works by placing the object in between the 2f and f positions to create a large image of a small object.

ray diagram is shown in Figure 15-19. The object is the film, or slide, or with digital projectors, a transparent LCD (liquid crystal display) device that acts as a pixelated color filter that forms an image generated by a computer. As with the previous applications, the image will be inverted. This is accommodated by making the film, slide, or LCD device upside down in the projector so that the

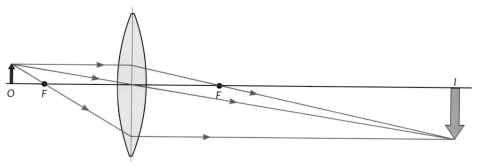

Figure 15-19. In a projector the object is in between the 2f and f points on the optical axis, producing a magnified image.

projected image comes out right side up. The light source itself is placed to the left of the object, and the light shines through the object and the lens to create the projected image. The display screen is placed at the image location. As with a camera, the lens position is moved back and forth to adjust the focus.

THE MAGNIFYING GLASS

To use a biconvex lens as a magnifying glass, the object distance is less than the focal length of the lens, as shown in Figure 15-20. The purpose of a magnifying glass is to magnify small objects, and to produce an image that is upright. (Unlike cameras and photocopiers, it's hard for us to think straight about what we are looking at if the image is inverted.) Figure 15-21 shows the ray diagram that demonstrates how this is accomplished. When the small object is placed in between the focal point and the lens, we get a

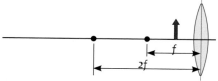

Figure 15-20. An upright, magnified image occurs when the object distance is less than f.

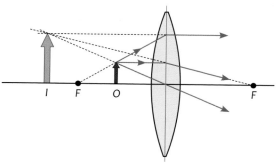

Figure 15-21. The magnifying glass creates an upright, magnified image when the object is between the focus and the lens.

magnified, upright image, as the dashed lines indicate. Notice that on the right side of the lens (where the viewer would be) the three rays from the top of the object all appear to converge at the top of the image. The image is virtual, which means you can take a picture of what you see in a magnifying glass, but you can't project it on to a screen because the light rays do not actually go to where the image is.

The Lens Equation

As we did with mirrors, we will take a brief look at the math for these lenses. As before, we use d_o, d_i, and f to represent the object and image distances and the focal length. Here however, distances are measured to the center of the lens, rather than to the surface. You may be amazed to know that *the lens equation is exactly the same as the mirror equation,*

$$\frac{1}{d_o} + \frac{1}{d_i} = \frac{1}{f}$$

You may also be amazed that the magnification equation for lenses is also the same as for mirrors,

$$M = -\frac{d_i}{d_o}$$

The sign convention used for these equations is that d_i and f will both be negative for the case when a diverging lens produces a virtual image.

Multiple-Lens Systems

Systems making use of more than one lens are used in many different types of optical systems today. You may know that Galileo's telescope made use of two lenses. We will look at his arrangement shortly. A camera with a zoom lens is another example of a multiple-lens system.

In this section we will look at a few applications of two-lens systems. The basic idea for designing a two-lens system is that *the image produced by the first lens becomes the object for the second lens.* Moreover, the total magnification of the system, M_T, is the product of the magnifications of the individual lens magnifications M_1 and M_2, or

$$M_T = M_1 \cdot M_2$$

Multiple-lens calculations can get quite complicated, so we will not really get much into the math. Our goal in this last section will be limited to reviewing the ray diagrams for a few well-known applications just so you can have a feel for how the optical systems work.

CORRECTIVE LENSES (GLASSES)

When people suffer from nearsightedness, the image produced by the eye falls in front of the retina, as shown in the upper part of Figure 15-22. The lenses in glasses use meniscus lenses, as shown in Figure 15-4 (D). To correct nearsightedness, a lens is used that is thicker at the edges than in the center (a diverging lens). As shown in the lower part of Figure 15-22, when the lens is placed in front of the eye a virtual image is formed that is close enough to the eye so that the eye can focus on it.

To correct farsightedness requires a meniscus lens that is thicker in the middle than at the edges, as shown on the far right of Figure 15-4. Farsightedness causes the image to be placed behind the retina (outside the eyeball). The corrective lens again produces a virtual image that is far enough away from the eye for the eye to focus on it.

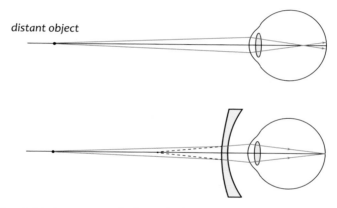

Figure 15-22. Nearsightedness causes the image in the eye to be focused in front of the retina. Correction of the image distance is enabled by placing a meniscus lens in front of the eye.

THE REFRACTING TELESCOPE

In Figure 15-23 we have the ray diagram for a refracting telescope using two biconvex lenses. This arrangement is equivalent to placing a camera and a magnifying glass back to back. The two lenses in the telescope are called the objective and the eyepiece. The objective works like a camera lens. It produces an intermediate image that is minified and inverted. The intermediate image is located in between the focal point for the eyepiece and the eyepiece itself, which means the eyepiece works as a magnifying glass, or magnifier. As we saw before, the magnifier produces an image that is upright (meaning, in this case, that the final image remains inverted, since it was already inverted when the magnifier took over), virtual and magnified. The viewer focuses the image by moving the eyepiece. To make the telescope work effectively, the objective must have a long focal length, and the eyepiece will have a short focal length.

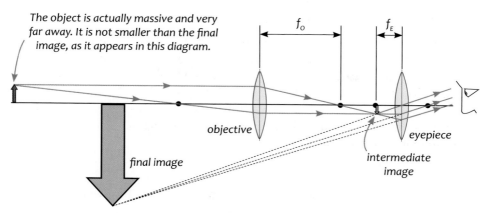

The object is actually massive and very far away. It is not smaller than the final image, as it appears in this diagram.

f_o

f_E

objective

eyepiece

final image

intermediate image

Figure 15-23. Ray diagram for a refracting telescope.

One could say that the role of the objective is simply to create an image that can be viewed up close with the magnifier. This intermediate image must fit inside the telescope tube, which makes it obvious that the image must be greatly minified. (An image of the moon or a star that was not greatly minified would not fit in there.)

This lens arrangement is called a *Keplerian* telescope, since Johannes Kepler used two biconvex lenses this way in his own telescope. This type of magnification system works well for looking at distant stars, because the inverted image does not bother us. The *Galilean* telescope, so-named for the obvious reason that Galileo used one, uses a concave lens in place of one of the convex lenses in an arrangement similar to the laser beam expander discussed next.

A LASER BEAM EXPANDER AND COLLIMATOR

Our final application will be a two-lens system for expanding and collimating a laser beam. We need to begin by explaining *collimation*.

The light in a laser is very close to being collimated, which means that the diameter of the beam remains constant as the beam propagates. In fact, a perfectly collimated beam of light is impossible; any beam of light will always spread out, or diverge, as it propagates. But with a laser the angle of divergence, shown as θ in Figure 15-24, is very small (about 0.05 degrees is typical). But even though all lasers do have an angle of divergence, for lab work the beam diameter is essentially constant over a short distance, so we speak of lasers as collimated.

In many applications, a laser beam needs to be expanded to a larger diameter, and then re-collimated after the expansion. This can be done with a Keplerian telescope, allowing the light to move through the telescope in the reverse direction, and placing the focal points of the two lenses at the same place.

Figure 15-24. The angle of divergence in a laser beam.

Another way to do it is with a Galilean telescope. This arrangement is shown in Figure 15-25.

In a beam expander, the laser beam enters through a concave lens, L_1 (or, usually, a plano-concave lens, as shown). Since the incoming light rays are collimated, they are parallel, and thus the concave lens refracts all the rays so they diverge in a direction in line with the L_1 focal point. This point becomes the object for the biconvex lens, L_2, which has its focal point in the same location as the concave lens focal point. Since all the rays are diverging from the same point (the focal point for L_2), the biconvex lens collimates them, refracting them so they are parallel to the optical axis.

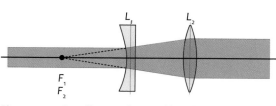

Figure 15-25. Ray diagram for a Galilean beam expander.

For this arrangement to work, the two lenses must obviously have different focal lengths, since the focal points are in the same place. As long as the focal lengths are long so that we are dealing with small angles, the math of this arrangement works out to give a magnification for the expander equal to the ratio of the focal lengths. Designating the focal lengths for lenses L_1 and L_2 as f_1 and f_2, respectively, the magnification will be

$$M = \frac{f_2}{f_1}$$

As mentioned before, the lens arrangement in Figure 15-25 was also used by Galileo in his telescope. When used as a telescope, the lens arrangement shown in Figure 15-25 would be reversed so that the light from a distant object enters through the biconvex lens. Just as with the Keplerian telescope, the objective biconvex lens forms a greatly minified intermediate image, which is then magnified by the plano-concave eyepiece for viewing.

IMAGING WITH THE EYE

Early in the chapter I mentioned that to see an image your eye needs to be in the path of the rays, but that it cannot be at the location of the image formed by a lens. The reason is that the eye itself is a lens. As with all of the multiple-lens systems we have reviewed, when two lenses are used together, the image of the first lens becomes the object for the second lens. So for the eye to focus on the image from a lens and produce its own image on the retina, the image from the first lens needs to be between the eye's near point and far point (see page 261). The distance from this image to the eye becomes the object distance for the cornea/lens lens system in the front of the eye.

Ideas for Your Classroom

1. Obtain a set of inexpensive concave and convex mirrors from an online science supplier such as Flinn Scientific (flinnsci.com). Experiment with looking at the images formed by objects in various locations.

2. Obtain several hand-held magnifying glasses, preferably circular with a diameter of about 2 inches. Let students play with these, and help them to notice that held up at arm's length, the image of an object a few feet away is inverted. Have them also play with the positioning of the lens relative to their eye and observe the range of lens positions that provides a focused image. Third, help them see that if the lens is held very close to the eye (where the image is out of focus) the image is not inverted.

3. Take a magnifying glass outside in the direct sunlight. Focus the rays from the sun onto a leaf or piece of paper and observe that the parallel rays from the sun will converge at the focal point with enough energy to make the leaf or paper burn. Caution: Never focus the sun's rays into a person's eye or onto a person's skin!

4. Obtain some inexpensive plastic convex and concave lenses and lens holders from an online science supplier such as Flinn Scientific (flinnsci.com). Using a small illuminated object such as a glow-in-the-dark figurine or a small Christmas tree light as the object, look at the real image formed on a screen by the convex lens in a dark room. In a lighted room, look through the concave lens to see the virtual image it forms. With both configurations, experiment with different positions of the object, lens, screen and observer.

5. Use a low-power (5 mW or less) laser pointer and two plastic biconvex lenses to set up a Keplerian beam expander/collimator. I suggest focal lengths of 100 mm for L_1 and 1000 mm for L_2. Using an index card as a screen, place the screen at different distances from L_2 to verify that the beam is collimated by observing that the expanded diameter stays the same as the screen is moved to different positions. Caution: Even though low-power laser pointers are safe, never allow the laser to hit anyone in the eye.

Thanks for reading *Science for Every Teacher, Volume 1: Physics*. We hope you enjoyed the journey and will find it worth coming back to in the future. See you in *Science for Every Teacher, Volume 2: Chemistry!*

Appendix A
Converting Units of Measure

One of the most basic skills scientists and engineers use is re-expressing quantities into equivalent quantities with different units of measure. These calculations are called unit conversions.

Before we begin, a note is in order about measurements with units. To those who deal with units of measure all the time this seems obvious. But to those without such experience, it may help to spell this out.

The units of measure with a measurement are treated mathematically exactly like a multiplied factor. They can be multiplied, cancelled, and so on just like a number or a variable. For example, we can write

$$\frac{3xy}{5by} = \frac{3x}{5b}$$

We can do this because the y in the numerator cancels the y in the denominator (because $\frac{y}{y} = 1$). For exactly the same reason can also write

$$\frac{15 \text{ ft} \cdot \text{lb}}{3 \text{ ft}} = 5 \text{ lb}$$

The feet (ft) appear as a multiplied factor in both the numerator and denominator, so they cancel out (because $\frac{\text{ft}}{\text{ft}} = 1$).

Now to the process of performing unit conversions. We begin with the basic mathematical principle behind the execution of unit conversions. First, we all know that multiplying any value by unity (one) leaves its value unchanged. Second, as we have just seen, in any fraction if the numerator and denominator are equivalent, the value of the fraction is *unity*, which means *one*. A "conversion factor" is simply a fractional expression in which the numerator and denominator are equivalent ways of writing the same quantity. This means a conversion factor is just a special way of writing unity (one). Third, as we have also just seen, we know that when multiplying fractions, factors that appear in both the numerator and denominator may be cancelled out. So when performing common unit conversions, what we are doing is repeatedly multiplying our given quantity by unity until cancellations alter the units of measure so they are expressed the way we wish. Since all we are doing is multiplying by one, the value of our original quantity is unchanged; it simply looks different because it is expressed with different units of measure.

To elaborate a bit more on the idea of unity mentioned above, here is an example using a common conversion factor. School kids all learn that there are 5,280 feet in one mile, which means 5,280 ft = 1 mi. One mile and 5,280 feet are equivalent ways of writing the same length. If we place these two expressions into a fraction, the numerator and denominator are equivalent, so the value of the fraction is unity, regardless of the way we write it. The equation 5,280 ft = 1 mi can be written in a conversion factor two different ways, and the fraction equals unity either way:

$$\frac{5,280 \text{ ft}}{1 \text{ mi}} = \frac{1 \text{ mi}}{5,280 \text{ ft}} = 1$$

So if we have a measurement such as 43,000 feet that we wish to re-express in miles, the conversion calculation would be written this way:

$$43,000 \text{ ft} \cdot \frac{1 \text{ mi}}{5,280 \text{ ft}} = 8.1 \text{ mi}$$

There are two comments to make here. First, conversion factors are fractions, so they can all be written two ways, depending on which quantity is placed in the numerator. So we need a way to know how to write the conversion factor. The rule is that we write the conversion factor in a way that allows the units we are trying to eliminate to cancel out. In the example above, we desire that the "feet" in the given quantity (which is in the numerator) will cancel out and get replaced with miles, so the conversion factor needs to be written with feet in the denominator and miles in the numerator.

Second, if you perform the calculation above, the result written on your calculator screen will be 8.143939394. So why didn't I write down all of those digits in my result? Why did I round my answer off to simply 8.1 miles? The answer to that question has to do with the significant digits in the value 43,000 ft that we started with. The topic of significant digits is taken up in Appendix B.

There are several important techniques students need to use to help them perform unit conversions correctly. I will illustrate them below with examples.

1.   Never use slant bars in unit fractions. Use only horizontal bars.

     In printed materials one often sees a value written with a slant fraction bar in the units, as in the value 35 m/s. Although writing the units this way is fine for a printed document, students should not write values this way when they are performing unit conversions. This is because students often get confused and do not realize that one of the units is in the denominator in such an expression, as with the s (seconds) in 35 m/s, and the conversion factors used must take this into account.

     Example: Convert 57.66 mi/hr into m/s.

Writing the given quantity with a horizontal bar makes it clear that the "hours" unit is in the denominator. This will help in writing the hours-to-seconds factor correctly.

$$57.66 \; \frac{\text{mi}}{\text{hr}} \cdot \frac{1609 \text{ m}}{\text{mi}} \cdot \frac{1 \text{ hr}}{3600 \text{ s}} = 25.77 \; \frac{\text{m}}{\text{s}}$$

Now that we have the result, writing it as 25.77 m/s is fine.

By the way, you may be wondering where the 1609 m/mi factor came from. Some conversion factors are things most people learned back in school, such as 3 feet = 1 yard and 365 days = 1 year. But there are scores of conversion factors that we may be less familiar with or may not know at all. There are many scientific references in books and online containing tables listing these conversion factors. So when we need one, say for converting Btu into joules (J), we just look it up. It is easy to look this example up and find that 1 Btu = 1055 J.

2. The term "per" implies a fraction.

   Some units of measure are often written with a "p" for "per," such as mph for miles per hour, or gps for gallons per second. Students should change these expressions to fractions with horizontal bars when they work out the unit conversion.

   Example: Convert 472.15 gps to L/hr.

   Write down the given quantity with the gps changed to gal/s, and write these units with a horizontal bar:

   $$472.15 \; \frac{\text{g}}{\text{s}} \cdot \frac{3.786 \text{ L}}{1 \text{ g}} \cdot \frac{3600 \text{ s}}{1 \text{ h}} = 6,435,000 \; \frac{\text{L}}{\text{h}}$$

3. Use the $\boxed{\times}$ and $\boxed{\div}$ keys correctly when entering values into the calculator.

   When dealing with several numerator terms and several denominator terms in a long chain of conversion factors, multiply all the numerator terms together first, hitting the $\boxed{\times}$ key between each, then hit the $\boxed{\div}$ key and enter all of the denominator terms, hitting the $\boxed{\div}$ key between each. This will eliminate the need to use any parentheses or write down intermediate results.

   Example: Convert 43.17 mm/hr into km/yr.

   The set-up with all of the conversion factors is as follows:

$$43.17 \, \frac{mm}{h} \cdot \frac{1 \, m}{1000 \, mm} \cdot \frac{1 \, km}{1000 \, m} \cdot \frac{24 \, h}{1 \, d} \cdot \frac{365 \, d}{1 \, y} = 0.378 \, \frac{km}{y}$$

To execute this calculation in a calculator one should enter the values and operations in this sequence:

$$43.17 \times 24 \times 365 \div 1000 \div 1000 =$$

4. When converting units for area and volume such as cm² or m³, one must use the appropriate length conversion factor twice for areas or three times for volumes.

The units "cm²" for an area means the same thing as "cm · cm." Likewise, "m³" means "m · m · m." So when using a length conversion factor such as 100 cm = 1 m or 1 in = 2.54 cm, one needs to use it twice to get squared units (areas) or three times to get cubed units (volumes).

Example: Convert 3,550 cm³ to m³.

$$3{,}550 \, cm^3 \cdot \frac{1 \, m}{100 \, cm} \cdot \frac{1 \, m}{100 \, cm} \cdot \frac{1 \, m}{100 \, cm} = 0.00355 \, m^3$$

Notice in this example that the unit cm occurs three times in the denominator, giving us cm³ when they are all multiplied together. This cm³ term in the denominator will cancel with the cm³ term in the numerator. And since the m unit occurs three times in the numerator, they multiply together to give us m³ for the units in our result.

This issue only arises when we have a unit raised to a power, such as when using a length unit to represent an area or a volume. When using a conversion factor such as 3.786 L = 1 g, the units of measure are written using units that are strictly volumetric (liters and gallons), and are not obtained from lengths the way in², ft², cm³, and m³ are. Another common unit that uses a power is acceleration, which has units of m/s² in the MKS unit system.

Example: Convert 5.85 mi/h² into MKS units.

$$5.85 \, \frac{mi}{h^2} \cdot \frac{1609 \, m}{1 \, mi} \cdot \frac{1 \, h}{3600 \, s} \cdot \frac{1 \, h}{3600 \, s} = 0.000726 \, \frac{m}{s^2}$$

With this example we see that since the "hours" unit is squared in the given quantity, the conversion factor converting the hours to seconds must appear twice in the conversion calculation.

Appendix B
Significant Digits

The notion of the precision of a numerical value enters into the physical sciences in several instances. First, we routinely deal with measurements, and every measurement has an inherent precision that depends on the instrument used to make the measurement. Second, we often use physical constants such as the acceleration due to gravity or the speed of light. Seldom do we use *exact* values for such quantities (if such can even been said to exist); generally we use an approximate value that has adequate precision for the task at hand. Third, we must constantly deal with units of measure and with conversions of values from one set of units to another. Often the conversion factors we use for unit conversions are not exact, and again we tend to rely on values that are precise enough for the task at hand.

The precision in a numerical value is indicated by the number of so-called *significant digits* (also called significant figures) it contains. Thus, the number of digits we write in any value we deal with in science is very important. In the case of a measurement, the number of digits in the value of the physical quantity is meaningful, because it shows the precision that was present in the instrument used to make the measurement. The same thing applies to physical constants (many of which are themselves measurements) and conversion factors. To express these numerical values correctly, and to use them correctly in subsequent calculations, we must correctly manage the significant digits in several cases:

- interpreting a value someone has already recorded
- reading and recording a new value from a measurement instrument, and
- using values from measurements or reference tables in computations.

Let's begin by reviewing the rules for determining the precision in a value already recorded, such as a value stated in a text or experimental result. Since the precision is indicated by the number of significant digits, identifying the precision inherent in the numerical value is equivalent to determining how many significant digits there are in the value. The rule for determining how many significant digits there are in a given value is as follows:

The number of significant digits (or figures) in a number is found by counting all the digits from left to right beginning with the first nonzero digit on the left. When no decimal is present, trailing zeros are not considered significant.[1]

Let's apply this rule to the following values to see how it works.

---

1 This definition is quoted from *Trigonometry*, Charles McKeague and Mark Turner, 6th ed.

15,679   This value has 5 significant digits.

21.0005   This value has 6 significant digits.

37,000   This value has only 2 significant digits, because when there is no decimal trailing zeros are not significant. Notice that the word *significant* here is a reference to the *precision* of the measurement, which in this case is rounded to the nearest thousand. The zeros in this value are certainly *important*, but they are not *significant* in the context of precision.

0.0105   This value has 3 significant digits, because we start counting with the first nonzero digit on the left.

0.001350   This value has 4 significant digits. Trailing zeros count when there is a decimal.

The significant digit rule enables us to distinguish between two measurements like 13.05 m and 13.0500 m. Mathematically, of course, these values are equivalent. But they are different in what they tell us about the process of how the measurements were made. The first measurement has 4 significant digits. The second measurement is more precise. It has 6 significant digits, and was made with a more precise instrument.

Consider again the zeros at the end of 37,000 that were not significant. Here is one more way to think about significant digits that is helpful when teaching students about significant digits. The precision in a measurement depends on the instrument used to make the measurement. If we express the measurement in different units, this has no effect on the precision inherent in the measurement. A measurement of 37,000 grams is equivalent to 37 kilograms. Whether we express this value in grams or kilograms, the value still has 2 significant digits.

Now that we have defined significant digits and have seen how to identify them in a numerical value, we will next address how to apply the idea of significant digits when making new measurements.

The issue of which digits are significant with a digital instrument can get very tricky, and depends in a complex way on the design of the sensors, the electronics, and the software or firmware used in the instrument to generate the display. But for the digital instruments commonly found in high school science labs a basic working rule of thumb is to assume all of the digits are significant except the leading zeros.

For analog instruments, here is the rule for determining how many significant digits there are in a measurement one is making:

The significant digits in a measurement are all of the digits known with certainty, plus one digit at the end that must be estimated between the finest marks on the scale of the instrument.

The photos in Figure B-1 illustrate this point with two different types of measurements. The photograph on the left side of this figure shows a rule being used to measure the length of a brass block in millimeters (mm). We know the first two digits of the length with certainty; the block is clearly between 31 mm and 32 mm long. We have to estimate the third significant digit. The marks on the rule are in 0.5 mm increments. Comparing the edge of the block with these marks I would estimate the next digit to be a 6, giving a measurement of 31.6 mm. Two digits of this measurement are known with certainty, the third one was estimated, and the measurement has three significant digits.

The photograph on the right side of the figure shows a liquid volume measurement in milliliters (mL) being made with a graduated cylinder. You can see the curvature of the meniscus, which appears reddish in color. (Taking measurements with a graduated cylinder is explained in Appendix D.) Reading the level at the bottom of the meniscus, we know the first two digits of the volume measurement with certainty, because the volume is clearly between 82 mL and 83 mL. We have to estimate the third digit, and I would estimate the line to be at 40% of the distance between 82 and 83, giving a reading of 82.4 mL.

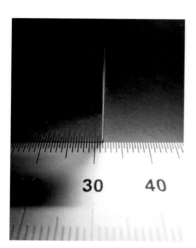

Figure B-1. Reading the significant digits on a rule and graduated cylinder.

Finally, we will consider the rules for using significant digits in computations, which include any unit conversions that must be performed. First I will list the two rules students must attend to for multiplication and division. These two rules are not difficult to understand, and it is appropriate for most students to learn to use these rules as freshmen in high school.

Rule 1 Count the significant digits in each of the values you will use in a calculation, including the conversion factors you will need to use. (Conversion factors that are exact, such as 12 in = 1 ft, are not considered.) Determine how many significant digits there are in the least precise of all of these values. The result of your calculation must have this same number of significant digits.

Rule 2 When performing a multi-step calculation keep at least one extra digit during intermediate calculations, and round off to the final number of significant digits needed at the very end. This practice will make sure that small round-off errors don't add up during the calculation. This extra digit rule also applies to unit conversions performed as part of the computation.

For computations involving addition and subtraction a separate rule applies. This rule is a bit more difficult for students to grasp, and I usually recommend that the appropriate place for students to learn to use it is in their first full chemistry course. The rule is rather cumbersome to put into words, but the example that follows will clarify.

Rule 3 Observe the right-most digit in each value to be added and identify the one that has the highest place value. This place value will be the place value of the right-most digit in the sum.

For example, consider the following sum:

$$
\begin{array}{r}
56.55 \\
2.3626 \\
+14.0 \\
\hline
72.9
\end{array}
$$

The place values of the right-most digits are hundredths, ten-thousandths, and tenths. The highest of these place values is the tenths. Thus, the place value of the sum must be tenths, giving the result shown. The justification for this rule is that the third value (14.0) is only known to the nearest tenth, so it is not possible to state the sum more precisely than to the nearest tenth.

One final note about significant digits I have found helpful is this: When a measurement is written in scientific notation, the digits written down in front of the power of 10 (the stem) *are* the significant digits. Sometimes, the only way to write a value with the correct precision is to write it in scientific notation. For example, given a value such as 100 m/s that was precise to the nearest one m/s, the value would need to be written to indicate that it had three significant digits. The only way to do this is to write 1.00×10^2 m/s.

Appendix C
Scientific Notation

Mathematical Principles

Scientific notation is a way of expressing very large or very small numbers without all the zeros. This is of enormous benefit when one is dealing with a value such as 0.0000000000001 cm (the approximate diameter of an atomic nucleus). The basic idea will be clear from a few examples. Let's say we have the value 3,750,000. This number is the same as 3.75 million, which can be written as 3.75 x 1,000,000. Now, 1,000,000 itself can be written as 10^6 (which means one followed by six zeros), so our original number can be expressed equivalently as 3.75 x 10^6. This expression is in scientific notation. The number in front, the stem, is always written with one digit followed by the decimal and the other digits. The multiplied 10 raised to a power has the effect of moving the decimal over as many places as necessary to recreate our original number.

As a second example, the current population of earth is about 6,974,000,000, or 6.974 billion. One billion has nine zeros, so it can be written as 10^9. So we can express the population of earth in scientific notation as 6.974 x 10^9.

When dealing with extremely small numbers such as 0.000000016 the process is the same, except the power on the 10 will be negative. The easiest way to think of it is to visually count how many places the decimal in the value would have to be moved over to get 1.6. To get 1.6, the decimal has to be moved over 8 places, so we can write our original value in scientific notation as 1.6 x 10^{-8}.

Using Scientific Notation in a Scientific Calculator

All scientific calculators have a key for entering values in scientific notation. This key is labeled EE or EXP on most calculators, but others use a different label[1]. It is common for those new to scientific calculators to use this key incorrectly and obtain incorrect results. I will outline the general procedure here.

The whole point of using the EE key is to make keying in the value as quick and painless as possible. When using the scientific notation key to enter a value, you do not press the × key, nor do you enter the 10. The scientific calculator is designed to reduce all of this key entry, and the potential for error, by use of the scientific notation key. You only enter the stem of the value and the power on the ten and let the calculator do the rest.

---

1   One infuriating model uses the extremely unfortunate label x10ˣ which looks a *lot* like 10ˣ, a different key with a completely different function.

Here's how. To enter a value simply enter the digits and decimal in the stem of the number, then hit the $\boxed{\text{EE}}$ key, then enter the power on the ten. The value will then be entered and you may do with it whatever you need to. As an example, to multiply the value 6.974 x 10⁹ by 25 using a standard scientific calculator, the sequence of key strokes will be as follows:

6.974 $\boxed{\text{EE}}$ 9 $\boxed{\times}$ 25 $\boxed{=}$

When entering values in scientific notation with negative powers on the 10, the $\boxed{+/-}$ key is used before the power to make the power negative. Thus, to divide 1.6 x 10⁻⁸ by 36.17, the sequence of key strokes will be:

1.6 $\boxed{\text{EE}}$ $\boxed{+/-}$ 8 $\boxed{\div}$ 36.17 $\boxed{=}$

Again, neither the "10" nor the "x" sign that comes before it should be keyed in. The $\boxed{\text{EE}}$ key has these built in.

Students sometimes wonder why it is incorrect to use the $\boxed{10^x}$ key for scientific notation. To execute 6.974 x 10⁹ times 25, they are tempted to enter the following:

6.974 $\boxed{\times}$ $\boxed{10^x}$ 9 $\boxed{\times}$ 25 $\boxed{=}$

The answer is that sometimes this works, and sometimes it doesn't, and calculator users need to learn to use key entries that *always* work. The scientific notation key ($\boxed{\text{EE}}$) will keep a value in scientific notation all together as one number. That is, when the $\boxed{\text{EE}}$ key is used, then to the calculator 6.794 x 10⁹ is not two numbers, it is a single numerical value. But when the $\boxed{\times}$ key is manually inserted, the calculator treats the numbers separated by the $\boxed{\times}$ key as two separate values. This will cause the calculator to render an *incorrect* answer for a calculation such as

$$\frac{3.0 \times 10^6}{1.5 \times 10^6}$$

The denominator of this expression is exactly half of the numerator, so the value of this fraction is obviously 2. But when using the $\boxed{10^x}$ key the 1.5 and the 10^6 in the denominator will be separated and treated as separate values. The calculator will then perform the following calculation:

$$\frac{3.0 \times 10^6}{1.5} \times 10^6$$

This comes out to 2,000,000,000,000 (2 x 10¹²), which is not the same as 2! The bottom line is that the $\boxed{\text{EE}}$ key, however it may be labeled, is the correct key to use for scientific notation.

Appendix D
Measurement Basics

This appendix is a brief primer on measurement and error. To the novice, making a measurement seems like a straightforward task, and for a rough approximation of a measurement, it is. But in fact, accurate measurement constitutes an entire field of study in itself, the field of metrology. Making measurements is a complex undertaking.

Experimental science deals in measurements. Most of the raw data associated with or resulting from an experiment are measurements of some kind. For this reason, it is essential that students studying science learn how to make proper measurements, and learn the limitations of measurements with respect to accuracy and precision. (Accuracy and precision are discussed in Chapter 3.)

For the present, our goal is simply to present the basic issues surrounding measurement and error that students should learn prior to entering college. Learning these skills should begin in upper elementary grades and continue into high school. Teachers in all grades should always use and demonstrate proper measurement procedures in class.

Types of Error

There is no such thing as a perfect or exact measurement. All measurements entail limitations that cause the measured value of a physical quantity to differ from the true value of that quantity. The limitations in a measurement can derive from inaccuracy (error), imprecision, or both.

The error present in scientific measurements can be divided into two main categories, random error and systematic error. Random errors are caused by unknown and unpredictable fluctuations in the experimental set-up. These fluctuations influence measurements in a random fashion. Here are some examples of factors contributing to random error:

- Changes in the apparatus or instrumentation due to temperature fluctuations that cause materials to expand and contract.

- Vibrations or air currents that influence the measurements.

- Slight fluctuations in a measured value due to minute variations in equipment or instrumentation alignment.

- The presence of dust or contaminants that influence a measurement.

- Electronic noise that influences the readings in electronic instruments.

When a scientist calculates and analyzes the uncertainty in a measurement, it is for the most part the random error that is under consideration. Random error causes a series of measurements to fluctuate randomly around the mean value of the measurements. Whether or not the random error is noticeable or detectable depends on the resolution of the instrument used to make the measurement. If numerous measurements of a particular variable are performed with an instrument sensitive enough to detect the fluctuations in the measurement due to random error, the measured values will generally form a Gaussian (bell curve) distribution about the mean of the measurements, as depicted in Figure D-1. While not universally accepted, it is common practice to use the sample standard deviation of the measurements as an estimate of the *uncertainty* in the measurements. The precision of a measurement will be determined either by the uncertainty in the measurement or by the resolution in the measurement instrument.

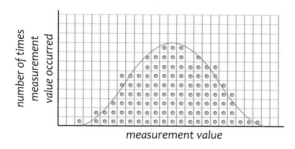

number of times measurement value occurred

measurement value

⊚ = one occurrence of a particular
measurement value

Figure D-1. A Gaussian distribution forms from the data when a specific measurement is made repeatedly with an instrument precise enough to show the variation.

Systematic errors are errors that bias the experimental results in one direction. Systematic error can be caused by equipment defects, miscalibration of measurement instruments, or an experimenter who consistently misreads or misuses the instruments in the same way. Usually when discussing systematic error we are talking about problems that could be eliminated by proper use, calibration and operation of the equipment.

Systematic error can also occur if there is a lurking variable affecting all of the measurements, such as gravity or magnetism. Such factors can bias all of an experimenter's measurements in the same way. Yet another way systematic error can creep into an experiment is by factors that are left out of the theoretical predictions, and that result in "experimental error" biased in a certain direction. A common example of this for high school physics is when analysis of experiments in mechanics do not take friction into account. This is another type of systematic error, although this time it is not an error with operating the equipment, it is an error built-in to all of the experimenter's predicted values.

Parallax Error and Liquid Meniscus

Two common measurement issues involving special technical terms are avoiding *parallax error* and working correctly with the *meniscus* on liquids. These terms both have to do with using analog instruments with measurement scales that must be correctly aligned for an accurate measurement.

Parallax error occurs when the line of sight of a person taking a measurement is at an incorrect angle relative to the instrument scale and the object being measured. As shown in Figure D-2, the viewer's line of sight must be parallel to the lines on the scale, and perpendicular to the scale itself. Misalignment of the viewer's line of sight will result in a faulty measurement due to parallax error.

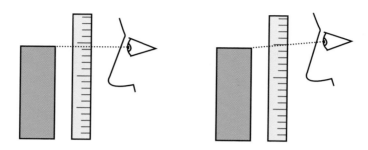

Figure D-2. In the sketch on the left the measured object, measurement instrument and viewer line of sight are correctly aligned. In the sketch on the right the misalignment of the viewer is causing parallax error in the measurement.

When a liquid is placed in a container, the surface tension of the liquid causes the liquid to curve up or down at the walls of the container. In most liquids the surface of the liquid curves up at the container wall, but a well-known example of downward curvature occurs when liquid mercury is placed in a glass container. In this case the surface of the liquid metal curves down at the container wall. We will concentrate here on the common upward curvature exhibited by water.

If the container is tall and narrow, as with a graduated cylinder, then the curving liquid at the edges gives the liquid surface an overall bowl shape. This bowl-shaped surface is called a meniscus. The correct way to read a volume of liquid is to read the liquid at the bottom of the meniscus. Figure D-3 illustrates the correct way to read a volume of liquid in a graduated cylinder by reading the liquid level at the bottom of the meniscus and avoiding parallax error.

Proper Measurement Procedures

There are, of course, numerous procedures associated with taking different types of measurements with different types of instruments. In this section we will limit our discussion to a few additional techniques associated with common measurements students make using standard apparatus in a typical school science program.

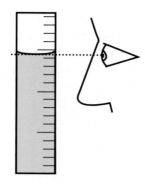

Figure D-3. Correctly reading a liquid volume in a graduated cylinder. The viewer's line of sight is at the bottom of the meniscus, and is perpendicular to the scale to avoid parallax error.

Measurements with a Meter Stick or Rule

1. For maximum accuracy, avoid using the end of a wooden rule. The end is usually subject to a lot of pounding and abrasion, which can wear off or compress the wood on the end.

2. As indicated in Figure D-4, arrange the rule against the object to be measured so the marks on the scale come in contact with the object being measured. This will help minimize parallax error.

3. As indicated in Figure D-5, use a straight-edge to assure the end of a metal rule is accurately aligned with the edge of an object being measured.

        incorrect   *correct*

Figure D-4. Proper placement of a rule or meter stick.

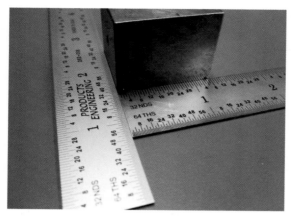

Figure D-5. Use of a straightedge for proper alignment of the end of the rule with the object being measured.

Measurements with a Triple-Beam Balance

1. Calibrate the balance before making measurements. This is accomplished by turning the calibration weight under the pan until the scale's alignment marks are perfectly aligned.

2. Make sure the 10-g and 100-g weights are locked into a notch on the beam. Otherwise, the measurement will not be correct.

3. As shown in Figure D-6, when adjusting the position of the gram weight, it is good practice to slide this weight with the tip of a pencil held below the beam instead of with one's finger. If done carefully, this technique will allow the gram weight to be manipulated into position without disturbing the balance of the beam as the balance point is approached.

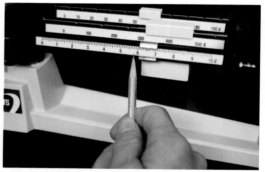

Figure D-6. Move the gram slider with a pencil to prevent disturbing the beam as the balance point is approached.

Measurements with a Thermometer

1. Mercury thermometers are more accurate than spirit thermometers. However, if a mercury thermometer breaks you have a real problem cleaning up and disposing of the spilled mercury. Thus, for student use I recommend using only spirit thermometers.

2. When measuring temperatures be sure to notice that the thermometers have a mark indicating the proper degree of immersion for the most accurate reading.

3. Thermometer accuracy can be severely compromised if gaps get into the red liquid. Always store spirit thermometers vertically in an appropriate rack to help prevent gaps from getting into the liquid.

Units of Measure

Fundamental and Derived Units

In the SI system there are seven fundamental units of measure, shown in Table D-1. All other units of measure are derived from combinations of these seven fundamental units.

Physical Quantity	Unit of Measure	Symbol
length	meter	m
mass	kilogram	kg
time	second	s
electric current	ampere	A
temperature	kelvin	K
luminous intensity	candela	cd
amount of substance	mole	mol

Table D-1. The seven fundamental units in the SI unit system.

SI Unit Prefixes

Unit prefixes are used in the SI system to simplify references to very large and very small quantities. There are twenty standard prefixes listed in readily accessible references. Students should begin learning the common centi-, milli-, and kilo- in elementary school. By the time students are freshman in high school, they should also know micro-, nano-, mega-, and giga-. High school juniors and seniors should also know pico- and tera-. These prefixes are listed in Table D-2.

My personal justification for the prefixes teachers should require students to learn is based on the ubiquitousness of their use in technology. We live in the era of nanotechnology, when references to prefixes for fractions down to the nano- level are common in technical literature and news. Likewise, improvements in data storage and communications technologies have made the prefix giga- very common, with tera- not far behind. For these reasons basic technical literacy requires that students know these prefixes.

Prefix	Definition	Symbol	Illustration
centi-	10^{-2}	c	There are 10^2 (100) centimeters (cm) in one meter (m).
milli-	10^{-3}	m	There are 10^3 (1,000) millimeters (mm) in one meter (m).
micro-	10^{-6}	μ	There are 10^6 (1,000,000) micrometers (μm) in one meter (m).
nano-	10^{-9}	n	There are 10^9 (1,000,000,000) nanometers (nm) in one meter (m).
pico-	10^{-12}	p	There are 10^{12} (1,000,000,000,000) picometers (nm) in one meter (m).
kilo-	10^3	k	There are 10^3 (1,000) meters (m) in one kilometer (km).
mega-	10^6	M	There are 10^6 (1,000,000) meters (m) in one megameter (Mm).
giga-	10^9	G	There are 10^9 (1,000,000,000) meters (m) in one gigameter (Gm).
tera-	10^{12}	T	There are 10^{12} (1,000,000,000,000) meters (m) in one terameter (Tm).

Table D-2. Common metric prefixes.

SI Derived Units

Within the SI system there are many different units of measure derived from combinations of the seven fundamental units. I don't propose to try to treat all of these derived units here, but in Table D-3 I have listed the derived units that are likely to come up in a physical science or physics class.

Physical Quantity	Unit Name	Unit Symbol	MKS Derivation
force	newton	N	$kg·m/s^2$
energy	joule	J	$kg·m^2/s^2$
power	watt	W	$kg·m^2/s^3$
pressure	pascal	Pa	$kg/(m·s^2)$
frequency	hertz	Hz	s^{-1}
voltage	volt	V	$k·m^2/(A·s^3)$
electric resistance	ohm	Ω	$k·m^2/(A^2·s^3)$
electric charge	coulomb	C	$A·s$
capacitance	farad	F	$A^2·s^4/(kg·m^2)$
inductance	henry	H	$kg·m^2/(A^2·s^2)$
magnetic field	tesla	T	$kg/A·s^2)$
magnetic flux	weber	Wb	$kg·m^2/(A·s^2)$

Table D-3. Common derived units in the SI system.

Interesting Unit Facts

I will end this appendix with a few facts about units of measure that I have found to be interesting. I enjoy mentioning these from time to time to my students.

1. In the old days the primary standard for the SI unit of length was a 1-m long platinum bar kept in a vault at the International Bureau for Weights and Measures in Sèvres, France. However, since 1983 the standard has been that one meter is equal to the distance traveled by light in a vacuum in 1/299,792,458 of a second.

2. The reference standard for the kilogram is a one-kilogram platinum mass kept in a vault at the International Bureau for Weights and Measures. Officials are discussing a new way of defining the kilogram that may be adopted in the near future. A new standard will make calibration to the primary standard more accessible worldwide, and will make the primary standard fixed and permanent. (The platinum mass is not permanent; it loses a few atoms each year and slowly gets lighter and lighter.)

3. The definition above for the meter immediately raises the question of how the second is defined. Since 1967 it has been defined in atomic terms, specifically, 9,192,631,770 periods of a certain wavelength of light emitted by cesium atoms. By defining the meter and the second in terms of light and atoms the primary reference standards are available to anyone anywhere who has the technology, and it is no longer necessary to use the length of a metal bar in France as a standard that other lengths have to be compared to.

4. The historical length of 1 inch was so close to being 2.54 cm that back in 1959 the powers that be decided to redefine the inch to be equal to *exactly* 2.54 cm. This gave us an exact and easy-to-remember conversion factor to use for converting units between the SI and USCS systems, 1 in = 2.54 cm.

Appendix E
Photo Credits

32 Claudius Ptolemäus, picture of 16th century book frontispiece, public domain. 37, Copernicus: Unknown, public domain. 37, Tycho: Eduard Ender († 1883), public domain. 38 Tycho, *Astronomiae instauratae mechanica* (1598), public domain. 39 Unknown, public domain. 42 Justus Sustermans, public domain. 43 Sir Godfer Kneller, public domain. 44 Ferdinand Schmutzer, 1921, public domain. 46 NASA, public domain. 83 Unknown, public domain. 86 John D. Mays. 87, Fig. 6-5: John D. Mays. 87, Fig. 6-6: Matteo, licensed under CC 2.0. 87 Fig. 6-8: John D. Mays. 88 Fig. 6-9: Joshua Garcia, U.S. Air Force, public domain. 88 Fig. 6-11: John D. Mays. 91 John D. Mays. 92 Fig. 6-15: Georges Jansoone on 11 September 2005, licensed under CC-BY-SA 3.0. 92 Fig. 6-16: John D. Mays. 93 George Payn Quackenbos, from *A natural philosophy: embracing the most recent discoveries in the various branches of physics, and exhibiting the application of scientific principles in every-day life*, 1860, public domain. 94-97 John D. Mays. 111 Giovanni Battista Piranesi, "Interno del Colosseo con edicole per la Via Crucis," circa 1750. 113 Fig. 8-2: Hendrick Bloemaert, public domain. 113 Fig. 8-3: Arthur Shuster & Arthur E. Shipley: *Britain's Heritage of Science*. London, 1917, based on a painting by R.R. Faulkner; public domain. 114 Nikolai Yaroshenko, public domain. 115 *The Great War: The Standard History of the All Europe Conflict* (volume four), H. W. Wilson and J. A. Hammerton. Amalgamated Press, London, 1915; public domain. 117 *The Electron: Its Isolation and Measurements and the Determination of Some of its Properties*, Robert Andrews Millikan, 1917; public domain. 118 Unknown, public domain. 120 Bortzells Esselte, Nobel Foundation, public domain. 121 AB Lagrelius & Westphal, public domain. 123 Eggs: TacoDeposit, licensed under CC-BY-SA 3.0. 123 m&m's: Tiia Monto, licensed under CC-BY-SA 3.0. 125 Unknown, public domain. 126 Chemicalinterest, public domain. 127 John D. Mays. 131 John D. Mays. 135 John D. Mays. 140 John D. Mays. 146 Pslawinski, licensed under CC-BY-SA 2.5. 157 John D. Mays. 170-174 John D. Mays. 186 John D. Mays. 193 S. L. Pelaco, public domain. 201 Granger, public domain. 202, Leyden Jars: Daderot, public domain. 202, Priestly: Unknown, public domain. 203, Galvani: Source: http://neurolab.jsc.nasa.gov/timeline.htm; public domain. 203, Volta: Source: http://www.anthroposophie.net/bibliothek/nawi/physik/volta/bib_volta.htm; public domain. 204 Andrew Gray, licensed under CC-BY-SA 3.0. 205, Ampère: Ambrose Tardieu, public domain. 205, Faraday: Mathew Brady studio, public domain. 206 Source: *Practical Physics*, Millikan and Gale, 1920; public domain. 208-209 John D. Mays. 222-223 John D. Mays. 229 John D. Mays. 238-239 John D. Mays. 241 John D. Mays. 244 John D. Mays. 246 John D. Mays. 260 Eliashc, licensed under CC-BY-SA 3.0, public domain. 274 John D. Mays. 281-282 John D. Mays.

Appendix F
References

Chapter 3
Some of the historical information about Copernicus is from *A More Perfect Heaven*, Dava Sobel, Walker, 2011.
Some of the historical information about Tycho and Kepler is from *Kepler*, Max Caspar, Dover, 1993.

Chapter 4
Statements about Newton's wording of the Laws of Motion are based on the revised Motte translation, *Sir Isaac Newton's Mathematical Principles*, University of California Press, 1947.

Chapter 5
The nuclear decay problem was adapted from *College Physics*, 5e, Raymond Serway and Jerry Vaughn, Saunders, 1999.

Chapter 8
My history of atomic models owes a lot to *Conceptual Chemistry*, John Suchoki, Benjamin Cummings/Adison Wesley, 2001.
Rutherford's comment about the artillery shell bouncing back is found on wikipedia.org, among other places.

Chapter 10
Most of the data in the box about the speed of air molecules are from Penn State College of Earth and Mineral Sciences website, http://www.ems.psu.edu/~bannon/moledyn.html. Specific Heat Capacity and thermal conductivity values were obtained from engineering-toolbox.com.

Chapter 11
The harmonic spectrum images were captured on an iPad with an app called "n-track tuner."

Chapter 12
Information about Torricelli and Pascal was obtained from wikipedia.org.

Chapter 13
Much of the historical information about the history of electricity was adapted from *The Great Physicists from Galileo to Einstein*, George Gamow, Dover, 1988.

Chapter 15
A significant resource for this chapter was *Physics: Algebra/Trig*, 2e, Eugene Hecht, Brooks/Cole, 1998.

Index